Student Solutions Manual

John Garlow
Laurel Technical Services

BASIC
COLLEGE
MATHEMATICS

THIRD EDITION

Jeffrey Slater   John Tobey

PRENTICE HALL Upper Saddle River, NJ 07458

Senior Editor: *Karin Wagner*
Production Editor: *Dawn Blayer*
Assistant Editor: *Audra Walsh*
Manufacturing Buyer: *Alan Fischer*
Special Projects Manager: *Barbara A. Murray*
Supplement Cover Manager: *Paul Gourhan*

Printed in the United States of America

10 9 8 7 6 5 4 3

ISBN 0-13-660515-X

Prentice-Hall International (UK) Limited, *London*
Prentice-Hall of Australia Pty. Limited, *Sydney*
Prentice-Hall Canada, Inc., *Toronto*
Prentice-Hall Hispanoamericana, S.A., *Mexico*
Prentice-Hall of India Private Limited, *New Delhi*
Prentice-Hall of Japan, Inc., *Tokyo*
Simon & Schuster Asia Pte. Ltd., *Singapore*
Editora Prentice-Hall do Brasil, Ltda., *Rio de Janeiro*

CONTENTS

Chapter 1

Pretest Chapter 1

1. 78,310,436
= Seventy-eight million, three hundred ten
thousand, four hundred thirty-six

3. 5,064,122

5. 2,237,000

7. $\begin{array}{r} 28,318 \\ 5,039 \\ +17,213 \\ \hline 50,570 \end{array}$

9. $\begin{array}{r} 6439 \\ -4328 \\ \hline 2111 \end{array}$

11. $\begin{array}{r} 45,861,413 \\ -43,879,761 \\ \hline 1,981,652 \end{array}$

13. $\begin{array}{r} 2658 \\ \times 7 \\ \hline 18,606 \end{array}$

15. $\begin{array}{r} 365 \\ \times 908 \\ \hline 2\,920 \\ 0 \\ 328\,5 \\ \hline 331,420 \end{array}$

17. $\begin{array}{r} 7376 \text{ R1} \\ 7\overline{)51,633} \\ \underline{49} \\ 26 \\ \underline{21} \\ 53 \\ \underline{49} \\ 43 \\ \underline{42} \\ 1 \end{array}$

19. $6 \times 6 \times 6 \times 6 = 6^4$

21. $2 \times 3^3 - (4+1)^2$
$= 2 \times 3^3 - 5^2$
$= 2 \times 27 - 25$
$= 54 - 25$
$= 29$

23. $6 \times 7 - 2 \times 6 - 2^3 + 17 \div 17$
$= 6 \times 7 - 2 \times 6 - 8 + 17 \div 17$
$= 42 - 12 - 8 + 17 \div 17$
$= 42 - 12 - 8 + 1$
$= 30 - 8 + 1$
$= 22 + 1$
$= 23$

25. 26,539 rounds to 26,500 since 3 is less
than 3.

27. $\begin{array}{r} 200 \\ 500 \\ 400 \\ 800 \\ +700 \\ \hline 2600 \end{array}$

29. $\begin{array}{r} 1483 \\ -317 \\ \hline 1166 \text{ miles} \end{array}$

31. $\begin{array}{ll} 3 \times \$46 = \$138 & 138 \\ 3 \times \$29 = \$87 & 87 \\ 2 \times \$37 = \$74 & +74 \\ & \hline \$299 \end{array}$

1.1 Exercises

1. $6731 = 6000 + 700 + 30 + 1$

3. $108,276 = 100,000 + 8,000 + 200 + 70 + 6$

5. 23,761,345
$= 20,000,000 + 3,000,000 + 700,000$
$+ 60,000 + 1,000 + 300 + 40 + 5$

7. 103,260,768
$= 100,000,000 + 3,000,000 + 200,000$
$+ 60,000 + 700 + 60 + 8$

9. $600 + 70 + 1 = 671$

11. $9000 + 800 + 60 + 3 = 9863$

13. $70,000 + 6,000 + 30 + 6 = 76,036$

15. $700,000 + 6000 + 200 = 706,200$

17. a. 7

   b. 50,000

19. a. 8

   b. 80,000

21. 53 = Fifty-three

23. 8936
= Eight thousand, nine hundred thirty-six.

25. 36,118
= Thirty-six thousand, one hundred eighteen.

27. 105,261
= One hundred five thousand, two hundred sixty-one.

29. 23,561,248
= Twenty-three million, five hundred sixty-one thousand, two hundred forty-eight.

31. 4,302,156,200
= Four billion, three hundred two million, one hundred fifty-six thousand, two hundred.

33. Three hundred seventy-five = 375.

35. Fifty-six thousand, two hundred eighty-one = 56,281.

37. One hundred million, seventy-nine thousand, eight hundred twenty-six = 100,079,826.

39. $1965
= One thousand, nine hundred sixty-five.

41. 9 million or 9,000,000

43. 16 million or 16,000,000

45. $201 billion or $201,000,000,000

47. $380 billion or $380,000,000,000

49. a. 5

   b. 2

51. a. 3

   b. 4

53. 613,001,033,208,003

1.2 Exercises

1. Answers may vary. Samples are below.

   a. The order of the addends can be changed without changing the sum.

   b. The addends can be grouped together in any way without changing the sum.

3.

+	3	5	4	8	0	6	7	2	9	1
2	5	7	6	10	2	8	9	4	11	3
7	10	12	11	15	7	13	14	9	16	8
5	8	10	9	13	5	11	12	7	14	6
3	6	8	7	11	3	9	10	5	12	4
0	3	5	4	8	0	6	7	2	9	1
4	7	9	8	12	4	10	11	6	13	5
1	4	6	5	9	1	7	8	3	10	2
8	11	13	12	16	8	14	15	10	17	9
6	9	11	10	14	6	12	13	8	15	7
9	12	14	13	17	9	15	16	11	18	10

5.
$$\begin{array}{r} 4 \\ 2 \\ 8 \\ +\,9 \\ \hline 23 \end{array}$$

7.
```
    3
    8
    9
 +  6
 ───
   26
```

9.
```
   12
   45
 +  3
 ───
   60
```

11.
```
   63
   24
 + 12
 ───
   99
```

13.
```
  2847
  1634
 +  98
 ─────
  4579
```

15.
```
  6908
  2173
 + 4255
 ──────
 13,336
```

17.
```
  8235
 + 5626
 ──────
 13,861
```

19.
```
  18,718
 + 24,021
 ────────
  42,739
```

21.
```
   36
   41
   25
    6
 + 13
 ────
  121
```

23.
```
   106
    13
     4
    28
 + 981
 ─────
  1132
```

25.
```
    126
   8142
     37
 + 9604
 ──────
 17,909
```

27.
```
  1,362,214
  7,002,316
 + 3,214,896
 ───────────
 11,579,426
```

29.
```
   837,241,000
 + 298,039,240
 ─────────────
 1,135,280,240
```

31.
```
     516,208
      24,317
 + 1,763,295
 ───────────
   2,303,820
```

33. $12 + 8 + 156 + 72 = 20 + 156 + 72$
$= 176 + 72 = 248$

35. $15{,}216 + 485 + 5208 = 15{,}701 + 5208$
$= 20{,}909$

37.
```
   224
   387
 + 183
 ─────
   794
```
She spent $794 on gifts.

39.
```
  2311
  2502
 + 3173
 ──────
  7986
```
The vacations have cost him $7986.

41.
```
   204
   196
   324
 + 131
 ─────
   855
```
855 feet of fencing are needed.

43.
```
   64,000,000
   31,800,000
 + 25,300,000
 ────────────
  121,100,000 square miles
```

45.   2,144,856
    307,244
+ 470,239
2,922,339 votes

47. a.   415
    364
    159
+ 196
1134 students

   b.   1134
     27
     68
   102
+ 61
1392 students

49. a.   Out-of-state
   5276
   2437
+1840
$9553

   b.   In-state
   3640
   1926
+1753
$7319

   c.   Foreign
   8352
   2855
+ 1840
$13,047

51. $89 + 166 + 23 + 45 + 72 + 190 + 203 + 77$
$+ 18 + 93 + 46 + 73 + 66 = 1161$

53.   Answers may vary. You could not group the
addends in groups that sum to 10s to make
column addition easier.

Cumulative Review Problems

55.   121,000,374 = One hundred twenty-one
million, three hundred seventy-four.

57.   Nine million, fifty-one thousand, seven
hundred nineteen = 9,051,719.

1.3 Exercises

1.   8
-2
  6

3.   13
-5
  8

5.   6
-5
  1

7.   15
-6
  9

9.   16
-0
16

11.   18
-9
  9

13.   11
-4
  7

15.   13
-7
  6

17.   11
-8
  3

19.   15
-6
  9

21.   98   37
-37 $+61$
 61   98

23.   85   73
-73 $+12$
 12   85

25. $\begin{array}{r} 126 \\ -\ 95 \\ \hline 31 \end{array}$ $\begin{array}{r} 95 \\ +\ 31 \\ \hline 126 \end{array}$

27. $\begin{array}{r} 768 \\ -143 \\ \hline 625 \end{array}$ $\begin{array}{r} 143 \\ +625 \\ \hline 768 \end{array}$

29. $\begin{array}{r} 1763 \\ -\ 422 \\ \hline 1341 \end{array}$ $\begin{array}{r} 422 \\ +1341 \\ \hline 1763 \end{array}$

31. $\begin{array}{r} 24{,}396 \\ -13{,}205 \\ \hline 11{,}191 \end{array}$ $\begin{array}{r} 13{,}205 \\ +11{,}191 \\ \hline 24{,}396 \end{array}$

33. $\begin{array}{r} 986{,}302 \\ -433{,}201 \\ \hline 553{,}101 \end{array}$ $\begin{array}{r} 433{,}201 \\ +553{,}101 \\ \hline 986{,}302 \end{array}$

35. $\begin{array}{r} 19 \\ +110 \\ \hline 129 \end{array}$ Correct

37. $\begin{array}{r} 1113 \\ +5067 \\ \hline 6180 \end{array}$ Correct

39. $\begin{array}{r} 5020 \\ +\ 1020 \\ \hline 6040 \end{array}$ Incorrect $\begin{array}{r} 6030 \\ -5020 \\ \hline 1010 \end{array}$

41. $\begin{array}{r} 42{,}531 \\ +\ 55{,}232 \\ \hline 97{,}763 \end{array}$ Incorrect $\begin{array}{r} 98{,}763 \\ -42{,}531 \\ \hline 56{,}232 \end{array}$

43. $\begin{array}{r} {}^{8\ 13} \\ 9\cancel{3} \\ -47 \\ \hline 46 \end{array}$

45. $\begin{array}{r} {}^{1\ 15} \\ 12\cancel{5} \\ -88 \\ \hline 37 \end{array}$

47. $\begin{array}{r} {}^{14} \\ {}^{3\ 4\ 11} \\ 4\cancel{5}\cancel{1} \\ -376 \\ \hline 75 \end{array}$

49. $\begin{array}{r} {}^{8\ 10} \\ 9\cancel{0}5 \\ -324 \\ \hline 581 \end{array}$

51. $\begin{array}{r} {}^{0\ 9\ 9\ 9\ 10} \\ 10{,}000 \\ -\ 6{,}704 \\ \hline 3{,}296 \end{array}$

53. $\begin{array}{r} {}^{11} \\ {}^{4\ 1\ 9\ 9\ 10} \\ 1\cancel{5}2{,}000 \\ -117{,}908 \\ \hline 34{,}092 \end{array}$

55. $\begin{array}{r} {}^{11\ 12\ 10} \\ {}^{3\ 1\ 2\ 0\ 12} \\ 42{,}312 \\ -39{,}998 \\ \hline 2{,}314 \end{array}$

57. $\begin{array}{r} {}^{9\ 10} \\ {}^{5\ 10\ 0\ 10} \\ 760{,}108 \\ -536{,}992 \\ \hline 223{,}116 \end{array}$

59. $x + 14 = 19$
$5 + 14 = 19$
$x = 5$

61. $34 = x + 13$
$34 = 21 + 13$
$x = 21$

63. $100 + x = 127$
$100 + 27 = 127$
$x = 27$

65. $\begin{array}{r} 960 \\ -778 \\ \hline 182 \end{array}$ votes

67. $\begin{array}{r} 10{,}524{,}210 \\ -\ 3{,}539{,}296 \\ \hline 6{,}984{,}914 \end{array}$

69.   Total earned = \$475
Total paid out = \$142 + \$85 = \$227
$475 - 227 = 248$
He received \$248.

71. $\begin{array}{r} 4,375,099 \\ -3,413,864 \\ \hline 961,235 \end{array}$ people

73. $\begin{array}{r} 8,881,826 \\ -5,195,392 \\ \hline 3,686,434 \end{array}$ people

75. $\begin{array}{r} 11,430,602 \\ -11,110,285 \\ \hline 320,317 \end{array}$ people

77. $\begin{array}{r} 125 \\ -96 \\ \hline 29 \end{array}$ homes

79. $\begin{array}{r} 219 \\ -139 \\ \hline 80 \end{array}$ homes

81. $\begin{array}{r} 63 \\ -45 \\ \hline 18 \end{array}$ $\begin{array}{r} 63 \\ -55 \\ \hline 8 \end{array}$

The greatest change was between 1994 and 1995.

83. She should choose Willow Creek and Irving because the smallest difference was 9 homes.

85. $a - b = b - a$ if a and b represent the same number.

87. $\begin{array}{r} 28,007,653,121,863 \\ - 27,986,430,705,999 \\ \hline 21,222,415,864 \end{array}$

Cumulative Review Problems

89. Eight million, four hundred sixty-six thousand, eighty-four = 8,466,084

91. $16 + 27 + 82 + 34 + 9 = 168$

1.4 Exercises

1. Answers may vary. Samples are below.

   a. You can change the order of the factors without changing the product.

   b. You can group the factors in any way without changing the product.

3.

$\times$	6	2	3	8	0	5	7	9	1	4
5	30	10	15	40	0	25	35	45	5	20
7	42	14	21	56	0	35	49	63	7	28
1	6	2	3	8	0	5	7	9	1	4
0	0	0	0	0	0	0	0	0	0	0
6	36	12	18	48	0	30	42	54	6	24
2	12	4	6	16	0	10	14	18	2	8
3	18	6	9	24	0	15	21	27	3	12
8	48	16	24	64	0	40	56	72	8	32
4	24	8	12	32	0	20	28	36	4	16
9	54	18	27	72	0	45	63	81	9	36

5. $\begin{array}{r} 32 \\ \times 3 \\ \hline 96 \end{array}$

7. $\begin{array}{r} 104 \\ \times 2 \\ \hline 208 \end{array}$

9. $\begin{array}{r} 6102 \\ \times \ \ 3 \\ \hline 18,306 \end{array}$

11. $\begin{array}{r} 101,204 \\ \times \ \ \ \ 3 \\ \hline 303,612 \end{array}$

13. $\begin{array}{r} 14 \\ \times 5 \\ \hline 70 \end{array}$

15. $\begin{array}{r} 87 \\ \times 6 \\ \hline 522 \end{array}$

17.
$$\begin{array}{r} 326 \\ \times\ \ 5 \\ \hline 1630 \end{array}$$

19.
$$\begin{array}{r} 1087 \\ \times\ \ 7 \\ \hline 7609 \end{array}$$

21.
$$\begin{array}{r} 12,526 \\ \times\ \ \ \ \ 8 \\ \hline 100,208 \end{array}$$

23.
$$\begin{array}{r} 235,702 \\ \times\ \ \ \ \ \ 4 \\ \hline 942,808 \end{array}$$

25.
$$\begin{array}{r} 156 \\ \times\ 10 \\ \hline 1560 \end{array}$$

27.
$$\begin{array}{r} 27,158 \\ \times\ \ \ \ \ 100 \\ \hline 2,715,800 \end{array}$$

29.
$$\begin{array}{r} 482 \\ \times\ \ 1000 \\ \hline 482,000 \end{array}$$

31.
$$\begin{array}{r} 316,250 \\ \times\ \ \ \ \ 10,000 \\ \hline 3,162,500,000 \end{array}$$

33.
$$\begin{array}{r} 423 \\ \times\ 20 \\ \hline 8460 \end{array}$$

35.
$$\begin{array}{r} 2120 \\ \times\ \ \ 30 \\ \hline 63,600 \end{array}$$

37.
$$\begin{array}{r} 14,000 \\ \times\ \ \ \ 4,000 \\ \hline 56,000,000 \end{array}$$

39.
$$\begin{array}{r} 1022 \\ \times\ \ \ 31 \\ \hline 1\ 022 \\ 30\ 66 \\ \hline 31,682 \end{array}$$

41.
$$\begin{array}{r} 146 \\ \times\ 54 \\ \hline 584 \\ 730 \\ \hline 7884 \end{array}$$

43.
$$\begin{array}{r} 89 \\ \times\ 64 \\ \hline 356 \\ 534 \\ \hline 5696 \end{array}$$

45.
$$\begin{array}{r} 607 \\ \times\ \ 25 \\ \hline 3035 \\ 1214 \\ \hline 15,175 \end{array}$$

47.
$$\begin{array}{r} 569 \\ \times\ \ \ 73 \\ \hline 1\ 707 \\ 39\ 83 \\ \hline 41,537 \end{array}$$

49.
$$\begin{array}{r} 912 \\ \times\ \ \ 76 \\ \hline 5\ 472 \\ 63\ 84 \\ \hline 69,312 \end{array}$$

51.
$$\begin{array}{r} 5123 \\ \times\ \ \ \ 29 \\ \hline 46\ 107 \\ 102\ 46 \\ \hline 148,567 \end{array}$$

53.
$$\begin{array}{r} 9053 \\ \times\ \ \ \ 91 \\ \hline 9\ 053 \\ 814\ 77 \\ \hline 823,823 \end{array}$$

55.
$$\begin{array}{r} 178 \\ \times\ 235 \\ \hline 890 \\ 5\ 34 \\ 35\ 6 \\ \hline 41,830 \end{array}$$

57.
$$
\begin{array}{r}
678 \\
\times \ 132 \\
\hline
1\ 356 \\
20\ 34 \\
67\ 8 \\
\hline
89,496
\end{array}
$$

59.
$$
\begin{array}{r}
2076 \\
\times \ \ 105 \\
\hline
10\ 380 \\
00\ 00 \\
207\ 6 \\
\hline
217,980
\end{array}
$$

61.
$$
\begin{array}{r}
3561 \\
\times \ \ \ \ 403 \\
\hline
10\ 683 \\
00\ 00 \\
1\ 424\ 4 \\
\hline
1,435,083
\end{array}
$$

63.
$$
\begin{array}{r}
1023 \\
\times \ \ \ 4005 \\
\hline
5\ 115 \\
4\ 092 \\
\hline
4,097,115
\end{array}
$$

65.
$$
\begin{array}{r}
260 \\
\times \ \ \ 40 \\
\hline
10,400
\end{array}
$$

67.
$$
\begin{array}{r}
307 \\
\times \ 30 \\
\hline
9210
\end{array}
$$

69. $7 \cdot 2 \cdot 5 = 7 \cdot 10 = 70$

71. $11 \cdot 7 \cdot 4 = 77 \cdot 4 = 308$

73. $10 \cdot 7 \cdot 10 = 700$

75. $12 \cdot 3 \cdot 5 \cdot 2 = 12 \cdot 3 \cdot 10 = 36 \cdot 10 = 360$

77. $x = 8 \cdot 7 \cdot 6 \cdot 0$
$x = 0$

79.
$$
\begin{array}{r}
48 \\
\times \ 67 \\
\hline
336 \\
288 \\
\hline
3216
\end{array}
$$
3216 square feet

81.
$$
\begin{array}{r}
345 \\
\times \ \ 35 \\
\hline
1\ 725 \\
10\ 35 \\
\hline
12,075
\end{array}
$$
$12,075

83.
$$
\begin{array}{r}
240 \\
\times \ \ 5 \\
\hline
1200
\end{array}
$$
$1200

85.
$$
\begin{array}{r}
266 \\
\times 12 \\
\hline
532 \\
266 \\
\hline
3192
\end{array}
$$
$3192

87.
$$
\begin{array}{r}
34 \\
\times 18 \\
\hline
272 \\
34 \\
\hline
612
\end{array}
$$
612 miles

89.
$$
\begin{array}{r}
85 \\
\times 12 \\
\hline
170 \\
85 \\
\hline
1020
\end{array}
$$
1020 hamburgers

91.
$$
\begin{array}{r}
6,530,000 \\
\times \ \ \ \ \ \ \ \ 800 \\
\hline
5,224,000,000
\end{array}
$$

93. $4 \times 9 \times 25 \times 12 \times 5 = 4 \times 25 \times 9 \times 12 \times 5$
$= 100 \times 9 \times 12 \times 5$
$= 900 \times 12 \times 5$
$= 900 \times 60 = 54,000$

95. $7(x) = 56$
$7(8) = 56$
$x = 8$

97. $63 = 9(x)$
$63 = 9(7)$
$x = 7$

99. Yes. $5 \times (8-3) = 5 \times 8 - 5 \times 3$

$a \times (b-c) = (a \times b) - (a \times c)$

Cumulative Review Problems

101.
$$
\begin{array}{r}
263 \\
27 \\
891 \\
5 \\
+\,63 \\
\hline
1249
\end{array}
$$

103.
$$
\begin{array}{r}
802 \\
-\,743 \\
\hline
\$\ 59
\end{array}
$$

1.5 Exercises

1. a. When you divide a nonzero number by itself, the result is 1.

   b. When you divide a number by 1, the result is that number.

   c. When you divide zero by a nonzero number, the result is zero.

   d. You cannot divide a number by 0.

3. $6\overline{)42}$ with quotient 7

5. $8\overline{)24}$ with quotient 3

7. $8\overline{)40}$ with quotient 5

9. $9\overline{)36}$ with quotient 4

11. $7\overline{)21}$ with quotient 3

13. $8\overline{)56}$ with quotient 7

15. $7\overline{)63}$ with quotient 9

17. $8\overline{)72}$ with quotient 9

19. $9\overline{)63}$ with quotient 7

21. $9\overline{)63}$ with quotient 7

23. $1\overline{)7}$ with quotient 7

25. $6\overline{)0}$ with quotient 0

27. $54 \div 6 = 9$

29. $6 \div 6 = 1$

31. $32 \div 6$

$$
\begin{array}{r}
5\,\text{R}2 \\
6\overline{)32} \\
30 \\
\hline
2
\end{array}
\qquad
\begin{array}{r}
\text{Check} \\
5 \\
\times\,6 \\
\hline
30 \\
+\,2 \\
\hline
32
\end{array}
$$

33. $76 \div 8$

$$
\begin{array}{r}
9\ \text{R}4 \\
8\overline{)76} \\
72 \\
\hline
4
\end{array}
$$

$$
\begin{array}{r}
\text{Check} \\
9 \\
\times\,8 \\
\hline
72 \\
+\,4 \\
\hline
76
\end{array}
$$

35. $128 \div 5$

$$
\begin{array}{r}
25 \text{ R3} \\
5\overline{)128} \\
\underline{10} \\
28 \\
\underline{25} \\
3
\end{array}
$$

Check
$$
\begin{array}{r}
25 \\
\times 5 \\
\hline
125 \\
+ 3 \\
\hline
128
\end{array}
$$

37.
$$
\begin{array}{r}
23 \text{ R4} \\
7\overline{)165} \\
\underline{14} \\
25 \\
\underline{21} \\
4
\end{array}
$$

Check
$$
\begin{array}{r}
23 \\
\times 7 \\
\hline
161 \\
+ 4 \\
\hline
165
\end{array}
$$

39.
$$
\begin{array}{r}
32 \\
9\overline{)288} \\
\underline{27} \\
18 \\
\underline{18} \\
0
\end{array}
$$

Check
$$
\begin{array}{r}
32 \\
\times 9 \\
\hline
288
\end{array}
$$

41.
$$
\begin{array}{r}
37 \\
5\overline{)185} \\
\underline{15} \\
35 \\
\underline{35} \\
0
\end{array}
$$

Check
$$
\begin{array}{r}
37 \\
\times 5 \\
\hline
185
\end{array}
$$

43.
$$
\begin{array}{r}
322 \text{ R1} \\
4\overline{)1289} \\
\underline{12} \\
8 \\
\underline{8} \\
9 \\
\underline{8} \\
1
\end{array}
$$

Check
$$
\begin{array}{r}
322 \\
\times 4 \\
\hline
1288 \\
+ 1 \\
\hline
1289
\end{array}
$$

45.
$$
\begin{array}{r}
127 \text{ R1} \\
6\overline{)763} \\
\underline{6} \\
16 \\
\underline{12} \\
43 \\
\underline{42} \\
1
\end{array}
$$

Check
$$
\begin{array}{r}
127 \\
\times 6 \\
\hline
762 \\
+ 1 \\
\hline
763
\end{array}
$$

47.
$$
\begin{array}{r}
753 \\
8\overline{)6024} \\
\underline{56} \\
42 \\
\underline{40} \\
24 \\
\underline{24} \\
0
\end{array}
$$

Check
$$
\begin{array}{r}
753 \\
\times 8 \\
\hline
6024
\end{array}
$$

49.
$$
\begin{array}{r}
1357 \text{ R4} \\
5\overline{)6789} \\
\underline{5} \\
17 \\
\underline{15} \\
28 \\
\underline{25} \\
39 \\
\underline{35} \\
4
\end{array}
$$

Check
$$
\begin{array}{r}
1357 \\
\times 5 \\
\hline
6785 \\
+ 4 \\
\hline
6789
\end{array}
$$

51.
$$
\begin{array}{r}
1757 \text{ R5} \\
7\overline{)12304} \\
\underline{7} \\
53 \\
\underline{49} \\
40 \\
\underline{35} \\
54 \\
\underline{49} \\
5
\end{array}
$$

Check
$$
\begin{array}{r}
1757 \\
\times 7 \\
\hline
12{,}299 \\
+ 5 \\
\hline
12{,}304
\end{array}
$$

53.
$$
\begin{array}{r}
2478 \text{ R3} \\
9\overline{)22305} \\
\underline{18} \\
43 \\
\underline{36} \\
70 \\
\underline{63} \\
75 \\
\underline{72} \\
3
\end{array}
$$

Check
$$
\begin{array}{r}
2478 \\
\times 9 \\
\hline
22{,}302 \\
+ 3 \\
\hline
22{,}305
\end{array}
$$

55. $185 \div 36$

$$
\begin{array}{r}
5\text{ R}5 \\
36\overline{)185} \\
\underline{180} \\
5
\end{array}
$$

57. $267 \div 52$

$$
\begin{array}{r}
5\text{ R}7 \\
52\overline{)267} \\
\underline{260} \\
7
\end{array}
$$

59. $427 \div 61$

$$
\begin{array}{r}
7 \\
61\overline{)427} \\
\underline{427} \\
0
\end{array}
$$

61.
$$
\begin{array}{r}
160\text{ R}10 \\
12\overline{)1930} \\
\underline{12} \\
73 \\
\underline{72} \\
10 \\
\underline{0} \\
10
\end{array}
$$

63.
$$
\begin{array}{r}
48\text{ R}12 \\
30\overline{)1452} \\
\underline{120} \\
252 \\
\underline{240} \\
12
\end{array}
$$

65.
$$
\begin{array}{r}
615\text{ R}11 \\
15\overline{)9236} \\
\underline{90} \\
23 \\
\underline{15} \\
86 \\
\underline{75} \\
11
\end{array}
$$

67.
$$
\begin{array}{r}
210\text{ R}8 \\
36\overline{)7568} \\
\underline{72} \\
36 \\
\underline{36} \\
8 \\
\underline{0} \\
8
\end{array}
$$

69.
$$
\begin{array}{r}
202\text{ R}7 \\
18\overline{)3643} \\
\underline{36} \\
43 \\
\underline{36} \\
7
\end{array}
$$

71.
$$
\begin{array}{r}
4\text{ R}4 \\
124\overline{)500} \\
\underline{496} \\
4
\end{array}
$$

73.
$$
\begin{array}{r}
7\text{ R}26 \\
322\overline{)2280} \\
\underline{2254} \\
26
\end{array}
$$

75.
$$
\begin{array}{r}
27 \\
129\overline{)3483} \\
\underline{258} \\
903 \\
\underline{903} \\
0
\end{array}
$$

$x = 27$

77.
$$
\begin{array}{r}
730 \\
30\overline{)21900} \\
\underline{210} \\
90 \\
\underline{90} \\
0
\end{array}
$$

730 pounds of feed per horse.

79.
$$
\begin{array}{r}
245,192 \\
15\overline{)3,677,880} \\
\underline{3\ 0} \\
67 \\
\underline{60} \\
77 \\
\underline{75} \\
28 \\
\underline{15} \\
138 \\
\underline{135} \\
30 \\
\underline{30} \\
0
\end{array}
$$

$245,192 per hour

81.
$$\begin{array}{r} 46,179 \\ 8\overline{\smash{)}369,432} \\ \underline{32} \\ 49 \\ \underline{48} \\ 1\ 4 \\ \underline{8} \\ 63 \\ \underline{56} \\ 72 \\ \underline{72} \\ 0 \end{array}$$

$46,179

83.
$$\begin{array}{r} 34 \\ 26\overline{\smash{)}884} \\ \underline{78} \\ 104 \\ \underline{104} \\ 0 \end{array}$$

34 minutes

85. If $a \div b = b \div a$
a and b must represent the same number. For example, if $a = 12$, then $b = 12$.

Cumulative Review Problems

87.
$$\begin{array}{r} 128 \\ \times\ 43 \\ \hline 384 \\ 512 \\ \hline 5504 \end{array}$$

89. $316,214 + 89,981 = 406,195$

Putting Your Skills To Work

1.
$$\begin{array}{r} 199 \\ \times\ 48 \\ \hline 9552 \end{array} \qquad \begin{array}{r} 9552 \\ +1000 \\ \hline 10,552 \end{array}$$
$10,552

3.
$$\begin{array}{r} 10,552 \\ +9,352 \\ \hline 19,904 \end{array}$$
$19,904

5. They should buy the car since $18,760 is a better deal than $19,904.

1.6 Exercises

1. 5^3 means $5 \times 5 \times 5 = 125$

3. base

5. To insure consistency we
   1. perform operations inside parentheses
   2. simplify any expressions with exponents
   3. multiply or divide from left to right
   4. add or subtract from left to right

7. $6 \times 6 \times 6 \times 6 = 6^4$

9. $5 \times 5 \times 5 = 5^3$

11. $8 \times 8 \times 8 \times 8 = 8^4$

13. $9 = 9^1$

15. $2^4 = 2 \times 2 \times 2 \times 2 = 16$

17. $4^2 = 4 \times 4 = 16$

19. $6^3 = 6 \times 6 \times 6 = 216$

21. $10^4 = 10 \times 10 \times 10 \times 10 = 10,000$

23. $1^{17} = 1$

25. $2^6 = 2 \times 2 \times 2 \times 2 \times 2 \times 2 = 64$

27. $3^4 = 3 \times 3 \times 3 \times 3 = 81$

29. $15^2 = 15 \times 15 = 225$

31. $7^3 = 7 \times 7 \times 7 = 343$

33. $4^4 = 4 \times 4 \times 4 \times 4 = 256$

35. $9^0 = 1$

37. $25^2 = 25 \times 25 = 625$

39. $10^6 = 10 \times 10 \times 10 \times 10 \times 10 \times 10$
$\quad = 1,000,000$

41. $4^5 = 4 \times 4 \times 4 \times 4 \times 4 = 1024$

43. $9^1 = 9$

45. $7^4 = 7 \times 7 \times 7 \times 7 = 2401$

47. $3^4 + 7^0 = 3 \times 3 \times 3 \times 3 + 1$
$\quad = 81 + 1$
$\quad = 82$

49. $6^3 + 3^2 = 6 \times 6 \times 6 + 3 \times 3$
$\quad = 216 + 9$
$\quad = 225$

51. $8^3 + 8 = 8 \times 8 \times 8 + 8$
$\quad = 512 + 8$
$\quad = 520$

53. $5 \times 6 - 3 + 10 = 30 - 3 + 10$
$\quad = 27 + 10$
$\quad = 37$

55. $2 + 6 \times 12 \div 2 = 2 + 72 \div 2$
$\quad = 2 + 36$
$\quad = 38$

57. $100 \div 5^2 + 3 = 100 \div 25 + 3$
$\quad = 4 + 3$
$\quad = 7$

59. $7 \times 3^2 + 4 - 8 = 7 \times 9 + 4 - 8$
$\quad = 63 + 4 - 8$
$\quad = 67 - 8$
$\quad = 59$

61. $4 \times 9^2 - 4 \times (7 - 2) = 4 \times 9^2 - 4 \times 5$
$\quad = 4 \times 81 - 4 \times 5$
$\quad = 324 - 20$
$\quad = 304$

63. $(400 \div 20) \div 20 = 20 \div 20 = 1$

65. $950 \div (25 \div 5) = 950 \div 5$
$\quad = 190$

67. $(16)(4) - (16 + 4) = 16(4) - 20$
$\quad = 64 - 20$
$\quad = 44$

69. $3^2 + 4^2 \div 2^2 = 9 + 16 \div 4$
$\quad = 9 + 4$
$\quad = 13$

71. $(6)(7) - (12 - 8) \div 4 = 6(7) - 4 \div 4$
$\quad = 42 - 1$
$\quad = 41$

73. $100 - 3^2 \times 4 = 100 - 9 \times 4$
$\quad = 100 - 36$
$\quad = 64$

75. $5^2 + 2^2 + 3^3 = 25 + 4 + 27$
$\quad = 56$

77. $100 \div 5 \times 3 \times 2 \div 2 = 20 \times 3 \times 2 \div 2$
$\quad = 60 \times 2 \div 2$
$\quad = 120 \div 2$
$\quad = 60$

79. $12^2 - 6 \times 3 \times 4 \times 0 = 144 - 6 \times 3 \times 4 \times 0$
$\quad = 144 - 72 \times 0$
$\quad = 144 - 0$
$\quad = 144$

81. $7^2 \times 5 \div 5 = 49 \times 5 \div 5$
$\quad = 245 \div 5$
$\quad = 49$

83. $5 + 6 \times 2 \div 4 - 1 = 5 + 12 \div 4 - 1$
$\quad = 5 + 3 - 1$
$\quad = 7$

85. $3 + 3^2 \times 6 + 4 = 3 + 9 \times 6 + 4$
$\quad = 3 + 54 + 4$
$\quad = 61$

87. $12 \div 2 \times 3 - 2^4 = 12 \div 2 \times 3 - 16$
$\quad = 6 \times 3 - 16$
$\quad = 18 - 16$
$\quad = 2$

89. $3^2 \times 6 \div 9 + 4 \times 3 = 9 \times 6 \div 9 + 4 \times 3$
$= 54 \div 9 + 12$
$= 6 + 12$
$= 18$

91. $4(10-6)^3 \div (2+6) = 4 \times 4^3 \div 8$
$= 4 \times 64 \div 8$
$= 256 \div 8$
$= 32$

93. $1200 - 2^3(3) \div 6 = 1200 - 8(3) \div 6$
$= 1200 - 24 \div 6$
$= 1200 - 4$
$= 1196$

95. $300 \div 25 - 10 + 2^3 = 300 \div 25 - 10 + 8$
$= 12 - 10 + 8$
$= 10$

97. $20 \div 4 \times 3 - 6 + 2 \times (1+4)$
$= 20 \div 4 \times 3 - 6 + 2 \times 5$
$= 5 \times 3 - 6 + 10$
$= 15 - 6 + 10$
$= 19$

99. $3 \times 5 + 7 \times (8-5) - 5 \times 4$
$= 3 \times 5 + 7 \times 3 - 5 \times 4$
$= 15 + 21 - 20$
$= 16$

Cumulative Review Problems

101. $156,312$
$= 100,000 + 50,000 + 6000 + 300 + 10 + 2$

103. $261,763,002$
Two hundred sixty-one million, seven hundred sixty-three thousand, two

105. $16,093$
$\underline{-14,937}$
       1156

107. $10 \times 60 + 12 = 600 + 12$
$= 612$ minutes
$612 \times 60 = 36,720$
It is approximately 36,700 seconds.

1.7 Exercises

1. Locate the rounding place. If the digit to the right of the rounding place is 5 or greater than 5, round up. If the digit to the right of the rounding place is less than 5, round down.
Examples will vary.

3. 8<u>3</u> rounds to 80 since 3 is less than 5.

5. 6<u>5</u> rounds to 70 since 5 is equal to 5.

7. 9<u>2</u> rounds to 90 since 2 is less than 5.

9. 52<u>6</u> rounds to 530 since 6 is greater than 5.

11. 423<u>5</u> rounds to 4240 since 5 is equal to 5.

13. 4<u>3</u>7 rounds to 400 since 3 is less than 5.

15. 27<u>8</u>1 rounds to 2800 since 8 is greater than 5.

17. 76<u>9</u>2 rounds to 7700 since 9 is greater than 5.

19. 7<u>6</u>21 rounds to 8000 since 6 is greater than 5.

21. <u>8</u>81 rounds to 1000 since 8 is greater than 5.

23. 27,<u>8</u>63 rounds to 28,000 since 8 is greater than 5.

25. 8<u>3</u>2,400 rounds to 800,000 since 3 is less than 5.

27. 15,<u>1</u>69,873 rounds to 15,000,000 stars since 1 is less than 5.

29. **a.**   143,<u>4</u>05 rounds to 143,000 since 4 is less than 5.

   b.   143,4<u>0</u>5 rounds to 143,400 since 0 is less than 5.

31. a. 3,7<u>0</u>5,392 rounds to 3,700,000 square
miles since 0 is less than 5.
9,5<u>9</u>6,960 rounds to 9,600,000 square
kilometers since 9 is greater than 5.

   b. 3,7<u>0</u>5,392 rounds to 3,710,000 square
miles since 5 is equal to 5.
9,5<u>9</u>6,960 rounds to 9,600,000 square
kilometers since 9 is greater than 5.

33.
$$\begin{array}{r} 500 \\ 200 \\ +\,900 \\ \hline 1600 \end{array}$$

35.
$$\begin{array}{r} 30 \\ 80 \\ 60 \\ +\,30 \\ \hline 200 \end{array}$$

37.
$$\begin{array}{r} 100,000 \\ 50,000 \\ +\,100,000 \\ \hline 250,000 \end{array}$$

39.
$$\begin{array}{r} 600,000 \\ -\,100,000 \\ \hline 500,000 \end{array}$$

41.
$$\begin{array}{r} 80,000,000 \\ -\,60,000,000 \\ \hline 20,000,000 \end{array}$$

43.
$$\begin{array}{r} 30,000,000 \\ -\,20,000,000 \\ \hline 10,000,000 \end{array}$$

45.
$$\begin{array}{r} 60 \\ \times\,50 \\ \hline 3000 \end{array}$$

47.
$$\begin{array}{r} 2000 \\ \times\quad 7 \\ \hline 14,000 \end{array}$$

49.
$$\begin{array}{r} 600,000 \\ \times\qquad 300 \\ \hline 180,000,000 \end{array}$$

51.
$$\begin{array}{r} 1,000 \\ 20\overline{)20,000} \end{array}$$

53.
$$\begin{array}{r} 5,000 \\ 40\overline{)200,000} \end{array}$$

55.
$$\begin{array}{r} 14,000 \\ 500\overline{)7,000,000} \\ \underline{5\ 00}\ \ \ \ \\ 2\ 000 \\ \underline{2\ 000} \\ 0 \end{array}$$

57.
$$\begin{array}{r} 400 \\ 500 \\ 900 \\ +\,200 \\ \hline 2000 \end{array}\ \text{Incorrect}$$

59.
$$\begin{array}{r} 100,000 \\ 50,000 \\ +\,40,000 \\ \hline 190,000 \end{array}\ \text{Incorrect}$$

61.
$$\begin{array}{r} 300,000 \\ -\,100,000 \\ \hline 200,000 \end{array}\ \text{Correct}$$

63.
$$\begin{array}{r} 80,000,000 \\ -\,50,000,000 \\ \hline 30,000,000 \end{array}\ \text{Incorrect}$$

65.
$$\begin{array}{r} 200 \\ \times\,20 \\ \hline 4000 \end{array}\ \text{Incorrect}$$

67.
$$\begin{array}{r} 6000 \\ \times\,70 \\ \hline 420,000 \end{array}\ \text{Correct}$$

69.
$$\begin{array}{r} 5000 \\ 80\overline{)400,000} \end{array}\ \text{Correct}$$

71.
$$\begin{array}{r} 500 \\ 400\overline{)200,000} \end{array}\ \text{Correct}$$

73.
$$\begin{array}{r} 100 \\ \times\,40 \\ \hline 4000 \end{array}\ \text{square yards}$$

75.

$$\begin{array}{r} 400 \\ 400 \\ 400 \\ + \; 300 \\ \hline \$1500 \end{array}$$

77.

$$\begin{array}{r} 90 \\ \times \; 60 \\ \hline 5400 \end{array} \text{ sit-ups}$$

79.

$$\begin{array}{r} 200 \\ - \; 30 \\ \hline \$170 \end{array} \text{estimate}$$

$$\begin{array}{r} 175 \\ - \; 30 \\ \hline \$145 \end{array} \text{exact}$$

81.

$$50\overline{)800} \; \begin{array}{r} 16 \\ \end{array}$$
$$\begin{array}{r} \underline{50} \\ 300 \\ \underline{300} \\ 0 \end{array}$$

$16 per week

83. a.

$$20,000\overline{)8,000,000,000} \; \begin{array}{l}400,000 \end{array} \text{ hours}$$

b.

$$20\overline{)400,000} \; \begin{array}{l}20,000 \end{array} \text{ days}$$

Cumulative Review Problems

85. $26 \times 3 + 20 \div 4 = 78 + 5$
$= 83$

87. $3 \times (16 \div 4) + 8 \times 2 = 3 \times 4 + 8 \times 2$
$= 12 + 16$
$= 28$

1.8 Exercises

1.

$$\begin{array}{r} 24,111 \\ 327 \\ + \; 793 \\ \hline 25,231 \end{array}$$

There is a total of 25,231.

3.

$$\begin{array}{r} 42,318 \\ - \; 37,650 \\ \hline 4,668 \end{array}$$

She went over budget by $4668.

5.

$$\begin{array}{r} 250 \\ \times \; 15 \\ \hline 3750 \end{array}$$

She ordered 3750 hors d'oeuvres.

7. $96 \div 16$

$$16\overline{)96} \; \begin{array}{r} 6 \\ \end{array}$$
$$\begin{array}{r} \underline{96} \\ 0 \end{array}$$

The unit cost is 6¢ per ounce.

9. $322 \div 14$

$$14\overline{)322} \; \begin{array}{r} 23 \\ \end{array}$$
$$\begin{array}{r} \underline{28} \\ 42 \\ \underline{42} \\ 0 \end{array}$$

It cost $23 each time.

11. $180 \div 20$

$$20\overline{)180} \; \begin{array}{r} 9 \\ \end{array}$$
$$\begin{array}{r} \underline{180} \\ 0 \end{array}$$

$9 \times 60 = 540$
It will take him 9 hours or 540 minutes.

13. $480 \div 60 = 8$
$100,000 \times 8 = 800,000$
800,000 people will be born.

15.

$$\begin{array}{r} 7356 \\ 3257 \\ 4777 \\ + \; 4992 \\ \hline 20,382 \end{array}$$

The gross income was $20,382.

17.

250	35	75	22
$\times 2$	$\times 2$	$\times 2$	$\times 3$
500	70	150	66

$$
\begin{array}{r}
500 \\
70 \\
150 \\
+\,66 \\
\hline
786
\end{array}
$$

The total cost was \$786.

19.

$$
\begin{array}{r}
61 \\
385 \\
945 \\
732 \\
+\,144 \\
\hline
2267
\end{array}
\qquad
\begin{array}{r}
223 \\
29 \\
98 \\
+\,435 \\
\hline
785
\end{array}
$$

$$
\begin{array}{r}
2267 \\
-\,785 \\
\hline
1482
\end{array}
$$

The balance is \$1482.

21.

$$
\begin{array}{r}
250 \\
\times\,85 \\
\hline
21,250
\end{array}
\qquad
\begin{array}{r}
85 \\
\times\,57 \\
\hline
4845
\end{array}
$$

$$
\begin{array}{r}
21,250 \\
-\,4845 \\
\hline
16,405
\end{array}
$$

Her profit is \$16,405.

23. $(15,276 - 14,926) \div 14 = 350 \div 14 = 25$
The car achieves 25 miles per gallon.

Cumulative Review Problems

25. $7^3 = 7 \times 7 \times 7 = 343$

27.

$$
\begin{array}{r}
126 \\
\times\,38 \\
\hline
1008 \\
378 \\
\hline
4788
\end{array}
$$

Chapter 1 Review Problems

1. 376 = Three hundred seventy-six

3. 109,276 = One hundred nine thousand, two hundred seventy-six

5. $4364 = 4000 + 300 + 60 + 4$

7. $1,305,128 = 1,000,000 + 300,000 + 5000 + 100 + 20 + 8$

9. Nine hundred twenty-four = 924

11. One million, three hundred twenty-eight thousand, eight hundred twenty-eight = 1,328,828

13.

$$
\begin{array}{r}
36 \\
+\,94 \\
\hline
130
\end{array}
$$

15.

$$
\begin{array}{r}
127 \\
+\,563 \\
\hline
690
\end{array}
$$

17.

$$
\begin{array}{r}
123 \\
61 \\
9 \\
84 \\
+\,123 \\
\hline
400
\end{array}
$$

19.

$$
\begin{array}{r}
937 \\
405 \\
+\,256 \\
\hline
1598
\end{array}
$$

21.

$$
\begin{array}{r}
1356 \\
2892 \\
561 \\
89 \\
+\,9805 \\
\hline
14,703
\end{array}
$$

23.

$$
\begin{array}{r}
36 \\
-\,19 \\
\hline
17
\end{array}
$$

25.

$$
\begin{array}{r}
126 \\
-\,99 \\
\hline
27
\end{array}
$$

27.

$$
\begin{array}{r}
1296 \\
-\,1137 \\
\hline
159
\end{array}
$$

29.
$$\begin{array}{r} 101,300 \\ -\ 98,274 \\ \hline 3026 \end{array}$$

31.
$$\begin{array}{r} 1,986,312 \\ -\ 1,761,555 \\ \hline 224,757 \end{array}$$

33.
$$\begin{array}{r} 12 \\ \times\ 3 \\ \hline 36 \end{array}$$

35.
$$\begin{array}{r} 36 \\ \times\ 0 \\ \hline 0 \end{array}$$

37. $1 \times 3 \times 6 = 3 \times 6 = 18$

39. $5 \times 7 \times 3 = 35 \times 3 = 105$

41. $8 \times 1 \times 9 \times 2 = 8 \times 9 \times 2 = 72 \times 2 = 144$

43. $3 \cdot 4 \cdot 2 \cdot 2 \cdot 5 = 12 \cdot 2 \cdot 2 \cdot 5 = 24 \cdot 2 \cdot 5$
$= 48 \cdot 5 = 240$

45. $26,121 \times 100 = 2,612,100$

47. $832 \times 100,000 = 83,200,000$

49.
$$\begin{array}{r} 36 \\ \times\ 24 \\ \hline 144 \\ 72\ \ \\ \hline 864 \end{array}$$

51.
$$\begin{array}{r} 150 \\ \times\ 27 \\ \hline 1050 \\ 300\ \ \\ \hline 4050 \end{array}$$

53.
$$\begin{array}{r} 709 \\ \times\ \ 36 \\ \hline 4\ 254 \\ 21\ 27\ \ \\ \hline 25,524 \end{array}$$

55.
$$\begin{array}{r} 123 \\ \times\ 714 \\ \hline 492 \\ 1\ 23\ \ \\ 86\ 1\ \ \ \\ \hline 87,822 \end{array}$$

57.
$$\begin{array}{r} 1782 \\ \times\ \ 305 \\ \hline 8\ 910 \\ 534\ 60\ \ \\ \hline 543,510 \end{array}$$

59.
$$\begin{array}{r} 300 \\ \times\ \ 500 \\ \hline 150,000 \end{array}$$

61.
$$\begin{array}{r} 1200 \\ \times\ \ \ 6000 \\ \hline 7,200,000 \end{array}$$

63.
$$\begin{array}{r} 100,000 \\ \times\ \ \ \ 20,000 \\ \hline 2,000,000,000 \end{array}$$

65. $20 \div 10 = 2$

67. $70 \div 5 = 14$

69. $0 \div 8 = 0$

71. $7 \div 1 = 7$

73. $\dfrac{49}{7} = 7$

75. $\dfrac{5}{0}$ is not possible.

77. $\dfrac{56}{8} = 7$

79. $\dfrac{72}{9} = 8$

81.
$$\begin{array}{r} 125 \\ 7\overline{)875} \\ \underline{7\ \ \ } \\ 17 \\ \underline{14} \\ 35 \\ \underline{35} \\ 0 \end{array}$$

83.
$$
\begin{array}{r}
258 \\
5\overline{)1290} \\
\underline{10} \\
29 \\
\underline{25} \\
40 \\
\underline{40} \\
0
\end{array}
$$

85.
$$
\begin{array}{r}
25,874 \\
3\overline{)77,622} \\
\underline{6} \\
17 \\
\underline{15} \\
2\,6 \\
2\,4 \\
\underline{}22 \\
21 \\
\underline{}12 \\
12 \\
\underline{}0
\end{array}
$$

87.
$$
\begin{array}{r}
36,958 \\
6\overline{)221,748} \\
18 \\
41 \\
36 \\
5\,7 \\
5\,4 \\
34 \\
30 \\
48 \\
48 \\
0
\end{array}
$$

89.
$$
\begin{array}{r}
15,986 \;\text{R2}\\
8\overline{)127,890} \\
8 \\
47 \\
40 \\
7\,8 \\
7\,2 \\
69 \\
64 \\
50 \\
48 \\
2
\end{array}
$$

91.
$$
\begin{array}{r}
7\;\text{R21}\\
67\overline{)490} \\
\underline{469} \\
21
\end{array}
$$

93.
$$
\begin{array}{r}
31\;\text{R15}\\
21\overline{)666} \\
\underline{63} \\
36 \\
\underline{21} \\
15
\end{array}
$$

95.
$$
\begin{array}{r}
38\;\text{R30}\\
68\overline{)2614} \\
\underline{204} \\
574 \\
\underline{544} \\
30
\end{array}
$$

97.
$$
\begin{array}{r}
258 \\
35\overline{)9030} \\
\underline{70} \\
203 \\
\underline{175} \\
280 \\
\underline{280} \\
0
\end{array}
$$

99.
$$
\begin{array}{r}
54 \\
132\overline{)7128} \\
\underline{660} \\
528 \\
\underline{528} \\
0
\end{array}
$$

101. $13 \times 13 = 13^2$

103. $8 \times 8 \times 8 \times 8 \times 8 = 8^5$

105. $2^6 = 2 \times 2 \times 2 \times 2 \times 2 \times 2 = 64$

107. $5^3 = 5 \times 5 \times 5 = 125$

109. $7^2 = 7 \times 7 = 49$

111. $6^3 = 6 \times 6 \times 6 = 216$

113. $6 \times 2 - 4 + 3 = 12 - 4 + 3 = 8 + 3 = 11$

115. $2^5 + 4 - \left(5 + 3^2\right) = 32 + 4 - (5 + 9)$
$= 32 + 4 - 14 = 36 - 14 = 22$

117. $3^3 \times 4 - 6 \div 6 = 27 \times 4 - 6 \div 6$
$= 108 - 1$
$= 107$

119. $2^3 \times 5 \div 8 + 3 \times 4 = 8 \times 5 \div 8 + 3 \times 4$
$= 40 \div 8 + 12$
$= 5 + 12$
$= 17$

121. $9 \times 2^2 + 3 \times 4 - 36 \div (4 + 5)$
$= 9 \times 4 + 3 \times 4 - 36 \div 9$
$= 36 + 12 - 4$
$= 44$

123. 5673 rounds to 5670.

125. 15,305 rounds to 15,310.

127. 12,350 rounds to 12,000.

129. 675,800 rounds to 676,000.

131. 5,668,243 rounds to 5,700,000.

133.
$$\begin{array}{r} 600 \\ 600 \\ 900 \\ + 900 \\ \hline 3000 \end{array}$$

135.
$$\begin{array}{r} 30,000 \\ - 20,000 \\ \hline 10,000 \end{array}$$

137.
$$\begin{array}{r} 2000 \\ \times \quad 6000 \\ \hline 12,000,000 \end{array}$$

139.
$$\begin{array}{r} 4,000 \\ 20\overline{)80,000} \\ \underline{80} \\ 0 \end{array}$$

141.
$$\begin{array}{r} 90 \\ 40 \\ 90 \\ + 60 \\ \hline 280 \end{array} \text{Correct}$$

143.
$$\begin{array}{r} 200,000 \\ \times \quad 5000 \\ \hline 1,000,000,000 \end{array} \quad \text{Incorrect}$$

145.
$$\begin{array}{r} 25 \\ \times 7 \\ \hline 175 \end{array}$$
He typed 175 words.

147.
$$\begin{array}{r} 26,300 \\ 14,520 \\ + 18,650 \\ \hline 59,470 \end{array}$$
The total price was $59,470.

149.
$$\begin{array}{r} 11,658 \\ - \quad 4630 \\ \hline 7028 \end{array}$$
She paid $7028.

151.
$$\begin{array}{r} 64 \\ 92\overline{)5888} \\ \underline{552} \\ 368 \\ \underline{368} \\ 0 \end{array}$$
The cost per share was $64.

153.

Deposits	Checks
16	29
98	128
125	100
+ 318	+ 402
557	659

$436 + 557 - 659 = 334$
Her balance will be $334.

155.
$$\begin{array}{r} 56,720 \\ - 56,320 \\ \hline 400 \text{ miles} \end{array} \qquad \begin{array}{r} 25 \\ 16\overline{)400} \\ \underline{32} \\ 80 \\ \underline{80} \\ 0 \end{array}$$
He got 25 miles per gallon.

157. $3 \times 279 + 4 \times 61 + 2 \times 1980$
$= 837 + 244 + 3960$
$= 5041$
The total price was $5041.

Chapter 1 Test

1. $44,007,635$ = Forty-four million, seven thousand, six hundred thirty-five

3. Three million, five hundred eighty-one thousand, seventy-six = $3,581,076$

5.
$$\begin{array}{r} 470 \\ 386 \\ +\ 189 \\ \hline 1045 \end{array}$$

7.
$$\begin{array}{r} 7932 \\ -\ 513 \\ \hline 7419 \end{array}$$

9.
$$\begin{array}{r} 18,400,100 \\ -\ 13,174,332 \\ \hline 5,225,768 \end{array}$$

11.
$$\begin{array}{r} 56 \\ \times\ 39 \\ \hline 504 \\ 168 \\ \hline 2184 \end{array}$$

13.
$$\begin{array}{r} 18,491 \\ \times\ \ \ \ \ 7 \\ \hline 129,437 \end{array}$$

15.
$$\begin{array}{r} 2189 \\ 7\overline{)15,323} \\ \underline{14}\ \ \ \ \ \\ 1\,3\ \ \ \ \\ \underline{7}\ \ \ \ \\ 62\ \ \\ \underline{56}\ \ \\ 63 \\ \underline{63} \\ 0 \end{array}$$

17. $11 \times 11 \times 11 = 11^3$

19. $5 + 6^2 - 2 \times (9-6)^2 = 5 + 6^2 - 2 \times 3^2$
$= 5 + 36 - 2 \times 9 = 5 + 36 - 18 = 41 - 18$
$= 23$

21. $4 \times 6 + 3^3 \times 2 + 23 \div 23$
$= 4 \times 6 + 27 \times 2 + 23 \div 23$
$= 24 + 54 + 1 = 78 + 1 = 79$

23. $6,46\underline{2},431$ rounds to $6,460,000$ since 2 is less than 5.

25. $5,000,000 \times 30,000 = 150,000,000,000$

27.
$$\begin{array}{r} 2148 \\ 15\overline{)32,220} \\ \underline{30}\ \ \ \ \ \\ 2\,2\ \ \ \ \\ \underline{1\,5}\ \ \ \ \\ 72\ \ \\ \underline{60}\ \ \\ 120 \\ \underline{120} \\ 0 \end{array}$$

Each person paid $2148.

29. $3 \times 2 + 1 \times 45 + 2 \times 21 + 2 \times 17$
$= 6 + 45 + 42 + 34 = 127$
His total bill was $127.

Chapter 2

Pretest Chapter 2

1. $\dfrac{3}{8}$

3. $\dfrac{17}{124}$

5. $\dfrac{13}{39} = \dfrac{13 \div 13}{39 \div 13} = \dfrac{1}{3}$

7. $\dfrac{35}{49} = \dfrac{35 \div 7}{49 \div 7} = \dfrac{5}{7}$

9. $1\dfrac{2}{7} = \dfrac{7 \times 1 + 2}{7} = \dfrac{9}{7}$

11. $4\overline{)97}^{24}$ $\quad \dfrac{97}{4} = 24\dfrac{1}{4}$
$\underline{8}$
17
$\underline{16}$
1

13. $17\overline{)36}^{2}$ $\quad \dfrac{36}{17} = 2\dfrac{2}{17}$
$\underline{34}$
2

15. $\dfrac{3}{7} \times \dfrac{14}{9} = \dfrac{1}{1} \times \dfrac{2}{3} = \dfrac{2}{3}$

17. $\dfrac{3}{7} \div \dfrac{3}{7} = \dfrac{3}{7} \times \dfrac{7}{3} = 1$

19. $6\dfrac{4}{7} \div 1\dfrac{5}{21} = \dfrac{46}{7} \div \dfrac{26}{21}$
$= \dfrac{46}{7} \times \dfrac{21}{26}$
$= \dfrac{23}{1} \times \dfrac{3}{13}$
$= \dfrac{69}{13}$
$= 5\dfrac{4}{13}$

21. $\dfrac{1}{8}, \dfrac{3}{4}, \dfrac{1}{2}$
$8 = 2 \times 2 \times 2$
$4 = 2 \times 2$
$2 = 2$
$\text{LCD} = 2 \times 2 \times 2 = 8$

23. $\dfrac{4}{11}, \dfrac{2}{55}$
$11 = 11$
$55 = 5 \times 11$
$\text{LCD} = 5 \times 11 = 55$

25. $\dfrac{7}{18} - \dfrac{3}{24} = \dfrac{7}{18} \times \dfrac{4}{4} - \dfrac{3}{24} \times \dfrac{3}{3}$
$= \dfrac{28}{72} - \dfrac{9}{72}$
$= \dfrac{19}{72}$

27. $8 - 3\dfrac{2}{3} = 7\dfrac{3}{3} - 3\dfrac{2}{3}$
$= 4\dfrac{1}{3} \text{ or } \dfrac{13}{3}$

29. $6\dfrac{4}{9} - 2\dfrac{3}{18} = 6\dfrac{8}{18} - 2\dfrac{3}{18}$
$= 4\dfrac{5}{18} \text{ or } \dfrac{77}{18}$

31. $4\dfrac{3}{12} + 3\dfrac{1}{18} = 4\dfrac{9}{36} + 3\dfrac{2}{36}$
$= 7\dfrac{11}{36} \text{ tons}$

2.1 Exercises

1. fraction

3. denominator

5. 3 is the numerator.
5 is the denominator.

7. 2 is the numerator.
3 is the denominator.

9. 1 is the numerator.
17 is the denominator.

11. $\dfrac{1}{2}$

13. $\dfrac{5}{6}$

15. $\dfrac{2}{3}$

17. $\frac{5}{6}$

19. $\frac{1}{4}$

21. $\frac{3}{10}$

23. $\frac{5}{8}$

25. $\frac{4}{7}$

27. $\frac{7}{8}$

29. $\frac{2}{5}$

31. $\frac{4}{5}$

33. $\frac{11}{13}$

35. $\frac{7}{10}$

37. $\frac{\text{toy makers}}{\text{exhibitors}} = \frac{29}{165}$

39. $\frac{\text{weekend earnings}}{\text{jukebox price}} = \frac{209}{750}$

41. $\frac{\text{roast beef}}{\text{total}} = \frac{89}{122+89} = \frac{89}{211}$

43. $\frac{\text{cats}}{\text{total}} = \frac{17}{17+14+4+15} = \frac{17}{50}$

45. $\frac{\text{ribs or beans}}{\text{total bowls}} = \frac{5+4}{2+3+4+5} = \frac{9}{14}$

47. a. $\frac{50+40}{94+101} = \frac{90}{195}$

b. $\frac{3+19}{94+101} = \frac{22}{195}$

49. $\frac{0}{6}$ is the amount of money each of 6 business owners get if the business has a profit of $0.

Cumulative Review Problems

51.
$$
\begin{array}{r}
18 \\
27 \\
34 \\
16 \\
125 \\
+\ 21 \\
\hline
241
\end{array}
$$

53.
$$
\begin{array}{r}
4136 \\
\times\ \ \ 29 \\
\hline
37\,224 \\
82\,72\ \ \\
\hline
119{,}944
\end{array}
$$

2.2 Exercises

1. 11, 19, 41, 5

3. composite number

5. Answers may vary. Example: $6 = 2 \times 3$

7. $15 = 3 \times 5$

9. $6 = 2 \times 3$

11. $49 = 7 \times 7 = 7^2$

13. $64 = 8 \times 8$
$= 2 \times 2 \times 2 \times 2 \times 2 \times 2$
$= 2^6$

15. $55 = 5 \times 11$

17. $35 = 5 \times 7$

19. $75 = 3 \times 25$
$= 3 \times 5 \times 5$
$= 3 \times 5^2$

21. $54 = 6 \times 9$
$ = 2 \times 3 \times 3 \times 3$
$ = 2 \times 3^3$

23. $84 = 4 \times 21$
$ = 2 \times 2 \times 3 \times 7$
$ = 2^2 \times 3 \times 7$

25. $98 = 2 \times 49$
$ = 2 \times 7 \times 7$
$ = 2 \times 7^2$

27. Prime

29. $57 = 3 \times 19$

31. Prime

33. $62 = 2 \times 31$

35. Prime

37. Prime

39. $121 = 11 \times 11 = 11^2$

41. $161 = 7 \times 23$

43. $\dfrac{18}{27} = \dfrac{18 \div 9}{27 \div 9} = \dfrac{2}{3}$

45. $\dfrac{32}{48} = \dfrac{32 \div 16}{48 \div 16} = \dfrac{2}{3}$

47. $\dfrac{30}{48} = \dfrac{30 \div 6}{48 \div 6} = \dfrac{5}{8}$

49. $\dfrac{42}{48} = \dfrac{42 \div 6}{48 \div 6} = \dfrac{7}{8}$

51. $\dfrac{3}{15} = \dfrac{3 \times 1}{3 \times 5} = \dfrac{1}{5}$

53. $\dfrac{39}{52} = \dfrac{3 \times 13}{2 \times 2 \times 13} = \dfrac{3}{4}$

55. $\dfrac{18}{24} = \dfrac{2 \times 3 \times 3}{2 \times 2 \times 2 \times 3} = \dfrac{3}{4}$

57. $\dfrac{27}{45} = \dfrac{3 \times 3 \times 3}{3 \times 3 \times 5} = \dfrac{3}{5}$

59. $\dfrac{33}{36} = \dfrac{3 \times 11}{3 \times 12} = \dfrac{11}{12}$

61. $\dfrac{65}{169} = \dfrac{5 \times 13}{13 \times 13} = \dfrac{5}{13}$

63. $\dfrac{88}{121} = \dfrac{11 \times 8}{11 \times 11} = \dfrac{8}{11}$

65. $\dfrac{150}{200} = \dfrac{3 \times 50}{4 \times 50} = \dfrac{3}{4}$

67. $\dfrac{119}{210} = \dfrac{7 \times 17}{7 \times 30} = \dfrac{17}{30}$

69. $\dfrac{3}{17} \overset{?}{=} \dfrac{15}{85}$
$3 \times 85 \overset{?}{=} 17 \times 15$
$ 255 = 255$
Yes

71. $\dfrac{12}{40} \overset{?}{=} \dfrac{9}{30}$
$12 \times 30 \overset{?}{=} 40 \times 9$
$ 360 = 360$
Yes

73. $\dfrac{23}{27} \overset{?}{=} \dfrac{92}{107}$
$23 \times 107 \overset{?}{=} 27 \times 92$
$2461 \neq 2484$
No

75. $\dfrac{35}{55} \overset{?}{=} \dfrac{69}{110}$
$55 \times 69 \overset{?}{=} 35 \times 110$
$3795 \neq 3850$
No

77. $\dfrac{65}{70} \overset{?}{=} \dfrac{13}{14}$
$64 \times 14 \overset{?}{=} 70 \times 13$
$ 910 = 910$
Yes

79. $\dfrac{4}{6} = \dfrac{2 \times 2}{2 \times 3} = \dfrac{2}{3}$

81. $\dfrac{95-65}{95} = \dfrac{30}{95} = \dfrac{5\times6}{5\times19} = \dfrac{6}{19}$

$\dfrac{6}{19}$ lasted more than one week.

83. $\dfrac{2000}{16,000+2000} = \dfrac{2000}{18,000}$

$= \dfrac{1\times2000}{9\times2000} = \dfrac{1}{9}$

Cumulative Review Problems

85.
$$
\begin{array}{r}
386 \\
\times\,425 \\
\hline
1\,930 \\
7\,72 \\
154\,4 \\
\hline
164{,}050
\end{array}
$$

87.
$$
\begin{array}{r}
200{,}000 \\
40{,}000 \\
800{,}000 \\
90{,}000 \\
500{,}000 \\
\hline
1{,}630{,}000
\end{array}
$$

2.3 Exercises

1. $3\dfrac{1}{2} = \dfrac{3\times2+1}{2} = \dfrac{7}{2}$

3. $4\dfrac{2}{3} = \dfrac{4\times3+2}{3} = \dfrac{14}{3}$

5. $2\dfrac{3}{7} = \dfrac{7\times2+3}{7} = \dfrac{17}{7}$

7. $5\dfrac{3}{10} = \dfrac{10\times5+3}{10} = \dfrac{53}{10}$

9. $4\dfrac{5}{6} = \dfrac{6\times4+5}{6} = \dfrac{29}{6}$

11. $21\dfrac{2}{3} = \dfrac{3\times21+2}{3} = \dfrac{65}{3}$

13. $9\dfrac{1}{6} = \dfrac{6\times9+1}{6} = \dfrac{55}{6}$

15. $28\dfrac{1}{6} = \dfrac{6\times28+1}{6} = \dfrac{169}{6}$

17. $10\dfrac{11}{12} = \dfrac{12\times10+11}{12} = \dfrac{131}{12}$

19. $7\dfrac{9}{10} = \dfrac{10\times7+9}{10} = \dfrac{79}{10}$

21. $8\dfrac{1}{25} = \dfrac{25\times8+1}{25} = \dfrac{201}{25}$

23. $105\dfrac{1}{2} = \dfrac{2\times105+1}{2} = \dfrac{211}{2}$

25. $164\dfrac{2}{3} = \dfrac{3\times164+2}{3} = \dfrac{494}{3}$

27. $7\dfrac{14}{15} = \dfrac{15\times7+14}{15} = \dfrac{119}{15}$

29. $5\dfrac{13}{25} = \dfrac{25\times5+13}{25} = \dfrac{138}{25}$

31. $\begin{array}{r}1\\5\overline{)7}\\5\\\hline2\end{array}$ $\dfrac{7}{5} = 1\dfrac{2}{5}$

33. $\begin{array}{r}2\\4\overline{)11}\\8\\\hline3\end{array}$ $\dfrac{11}{4} = 2\dfrac{3}{4}$

35. $\begin{array}{r}2\\6\overline{)15}\\12\\\hline3\end{array}$ $\dfrac{15}{6} = 2\dfrac{3}{6} = 2\dfrac{1}{2}$

37. $\begin{array}{r}3\\8\overline{)27}\\24\\\hline3\end{array}$ $\dfrac{27}{8} = 3\dfrac{3}{8}$

39. $\begin{array}{r}5\\13\overline{)65}\\65\\\hline0\end{array}$ $\dfrac{65}{13} = 5$

41. $\begin{array}{r}9\\9\overline{)86}\\81\\\hline5\end{array}$ $\dfrac{86}{9} = 9\dfrac{5}{9}$

43. $13\overline{)28}$ $\quad \dfrac{28}{13} = 2\dfrac{2}{13}$
$\dfrac{26}{2}$

45. $16\overline{)51}$ $\quad \dfrac{51}{16} = 3\dfrac{3}{16}$
$\dfrac{48}{3}$

47. $3\overline{)28}$ $\quad \dfrac{28}{3} = 9\dfrac{1}{3}$
$\dfrac{27}{1}$

49. $2\overline{)35}$ $\quad \dfrac{35}{2} = 17\dfrac{1}{2}$
$\dfrac{2}{15}$
$\dfrac{14}{1}$

51. $7\overline{)91}$ $\quad \dfrac{91}{7} = 13$
$\dfrac{7}{21}$
$\dfrac{21}{0}$

53. $9\overline{)200}$ $\quad \dfrac{200}{9} = 22\dfrac{2}{9}$
$\dfrac{18}{20}$
$\dfrac{18}{2}$

55. $17\overline{)102}$ $\quad \dfrac{102}{17} = 6$
$\dfrac{102}{0}$

57. $11\overline{)403}$ $\quad \dfrac{403}{11} = 36\dfrac{7}{11}$
$\dfrac{33}{73}$
$\dfrac{66}{7}$

59. $2\dfrac{9}{12} = 2\dfrac{3\times 3}{3\times 4} = 2\dfrac{3}{4}$

61. $4\dfrac{11}{66} = 4\dfrac{11\times 1}{11\times 6} = 4\dfrac{1}{6}$

63. $12\dfrac{15}{40} = 12\dfrac{5\times 3}{5\times 8} = 12\dfrac{3}{8}$

65. $\dfrac{24}{6} = \dfrac{6\times 4}{6\times 1} = 4$

67. $\dfrac{36}{15} = \dfrac{12\times 3}{5\times 3} = \dfrac{12}{5}$

69. $\dfrac{78}{9} = \dfrac{26\times 3}{3\times 3} = \dfrac{26}{3}$

71. $126\overline{)340}$
$\dfrac{252}{88}$

$\dfrac{340}{126} = 2\dfrac{88}{126} = 2\dfrac{44\times 2}{63\times 2} = 2\dfrac{44}{63}$

73. $424\overline{)986}$
$\dfrac{848}{138}$

$\dfrac{986}{424} = 2\dfrac{138}{424} = 2\dfrac{69\times 2}{212\times 2} = 2\dfrac{69}{212}$

75. $350\overline{)950}$
$\dfrac{700}{250}$

$\dfrac{950}{350} = 2\dfrac{250}{350} = 2\dfrac{50\times 5}{50\times 7} = 2\dfrac{5}{7}$

77. $360\dfrac{2}{3} = \dfrac{3\times 360 + 2}{3} = \dfrac{1082}{3}$ yards

79. $3\overline{)151}$
$\dfrac{15}{1}$
$\dfrac{0}{1}$

$\dfrac{151}{3} = 50\dfrac{1}{3}$ acres

81. No. 101 is prime and is not a factor of 5687.

Cumulative Review Problems

83.
$$16,385$$
$$4\ 126$$
$$+\ 8\ 056$$
$$\overline{28,567}$$

85.
$$200,000$$
$$\times\ \ \ \ 80,000$$
$$\overline{16,000,000,000}$$

2.4 Exercises

1. $\frac{3}{5} \times \frac{7}{11} = \frac{21}{55}$

3. $\frac{3}{4} \times \frac{5}{13} = \frac{15}{52}$

5. $\frac{6}{5} \times \frac{10}{12} = \frac{1}{1} \times \frac{2}{2} = 1$

7. $\frac{15}{7} \times \frac{8}{25} = \frac{3}{7} \times \frac{8}{5} = \frac{24}{35}$

9. $\frac{15}{28} \times \frac{7}{9} = \frac{5}{4} \times \frac{1}{3} = \frac{5}{12}$

11. $\frac{9}{10} \times \frac{35}{12} = \frac{3}{2} \times \frac{7}{4} = \frac{21}{8} = 2\frac{5}{8}$

13. $8 \times \frac{3}{7} = \frac{8}{1} \times \frac{3}{7} = \frac{24}{7} = 3\frac{3}{7}$

15. $\frac{5}{16} \times 8 = \frac{5}{16} \times \frac{8}{1} = \frac{5}{2} = 2\frac{1}{2}$

17. $\frac{3}{7} \times \frac{2}{5} \times \frac{14}{9} = \frac{1}{1} \times \frac{2}{5} \times \frac{2}{3} = \frac{4}{15}$

19. $\frac{4}{5} \times \frac{1}{8} \times \frac{35}{7} = \frac{1}{1} \times \frac{1}{2} \times \frac{1}{1} = \frac{1}{2}$

21. $3\frac{1}{5} \times \frac{7}{8} = \frac{16}{5} \times \frac{7}{8} = \frac{14}{5} = 2\frac{4}{5}$

23. $1\frac{1}{4} \times 3\frac{2}{3} = \frac{5}{4} \times \frac{11}{3} = \frac{55}{12} = 4\frac{7}{12}$

25. $2\frac{1}{2} \times 6 = \frac{5}{2} \times \frac{6}{1} = \frac{15}{1} = 15$

27. $2\frac{3}{10} \times \frac{3}{5} = \frac{23}{10} \times \frac{3}{5} = \frac{69}{50} = 1\frac{19}{50}$

29. $1\frac{3}{16} \times 0 = \frac{19}{16} \times 0 = 0$

31. $4\frac{1}{5} \times 12\frac{2}{9} = \frac{21}{5} \times \frac{110}{9} = \frac{154}{3} = 51\frac{1}{3}$

33. $8\frac{5}{6} \times \frac{2}{5} = \frac{53}{6} \times \frac{2}{5} = \frac{53}{15} = 3\frac{8}{15}$

35. $\frac{5}{5} \times 11\frac{5}{7} = 1 \times 11\frac{5}{7} = 11\frac{5}{7}$

37.
$$\frac{2}{7} \cdot x = \frac{18}{35}$$
$$\frac{2 \cdot 9}{7 \cdot 5} = \frac{18}{35}$$
$$x = \frac{9}{5}$$

39.
$$\frac{11}{12} \cdot x = \frac{121}{156}$$
$$\frac{11 \cdot 11}{12 \cdot 13} = \frac{121}{156}$$
$$x = \frac{11}{13}$$

41.
$$8\frac{3}{4} \times 4\frac{1}{3} = \frac{4 \times 8 + 3}{4} \times \frac{3 \times 4 + 1}{3}$$
$$= \frac{35}{4} \times \frac{13}{3}$$
$$= \frac{455}{12}$$
$$= 37\frac{11}{12} \text{ square miles}$$

43.
$$12 \times 11\frac{1}{6} = \frac{12}{1} \times \frac{67}{6}$$
$$= \frac{6 \times 2 \times 67}{1 \times 6}$$
$$= 134 \text{ miles}$$

45.
$$8 \times 18\frac{1}{4} = \frac{8}{1} \times \frac{73}{4}$$
$$= \frac{4 \times 2 \times 73}{1 \times 4}$$
$$= 146 \text{ yards}$$

47.
$$12\frac{1}{4} \times \frac{3}{4} = \frac{49}{4} \times \frac{3}{4}$$
$$= \frac{147}{16}$$
$$= 9\frac{3}{16} \text{ ounces}$$

49. $72\frac{1}{4} \times 85 = \frac{289}{4} \times \frac{85}{1}$

$= \frac{24,565}{4}$

$= \$6141\frac{1}{4}$

51. a. $\frac{3}{4} \times \frac{5}{6} = \frac{3 \times 5}{4 \times 3 \times 2}$

$= \frac{5}{8}$

$\frac{5}{8}$ of the students

b. $8600 \times \frac{5}{8} = \frac{8600}{1} \times \frac{5}{8}$

$= \frac{1075 \times 8 \times 5}{1 \times 8}$

$= 5375$

5375 students

Cumulative Review Problems

53.
$$\begin{array}{r} 529 \\ 31\overline{)16399} \quad \text{cars} \\ \underline{155} \\ 89 \\ \underline{62} \\ 279 \\ \underline{279} \\ 0 \end{array}$$

55.
$$\begin{array}{r} 146 \\ \times 12 \\ \hline 292 \\ 146 \\ \hline 1752 \quad \text{lines} \end{array}$$

2.5 Exercises

1. $\frac{2}{5} \div \frac{7}{2} = \frac{2}{5} \times \frac{2}{7} = \frac{4}{35}$

3. $\frac{3}{13} \div \frac{9}{26} = \frac{3}{13} \times \frac{26}{9} = \frac{3 \times 2 \times 13}{13 \times 3 \times 3} = \frac{2}{3}$

5. $\frac{5}{6} \div \frac{25}{27} = \frac{5}{6} \times \frac{27}{25} = \frac{5 \times 3 \times 9}{2 \times 3 \times 5 \times 5} = \frac{9}{10}$

7. $\frac{5}{9} \div \frac{10}{27} = \frac{5}{9} \times \frac{27}{10} = \frac{5 \times 3 \times 9}{9 \times 2 \times 5} = \frac{3}{2} = 1\frac{1}{2}$

9. $\frac{4}{5} \div 1 = \frac{4}{5} \times \frac{1}{1} = \frac{4}{5}$

11. $2 \div \frac{7}{8} = \frac{2}{1} \times \frac{8}{7} = \frac{16}{7} = 2\frac{2}{7}$

13. $\frac{2}{9} \div \frac{1}{6} = \frac{2}{9} \times \frac{6}{1} = \frac{2 \times 2 \times 3}{3 \times 3 \times 1} = \frac{4}{3} = 1\frac{1}{3}$

15. $\frac{4}{15} \div \frac{4}{15} = \frac{4}{15} \times \frac{15}{4} = 1$

17. $\frac{3}{7} \div \frac{7}{3} = \frac{3}{7} \times \frac{3}{7} = \frac{9}{49}$

19. $\frac{4}{3} \div \frac{7}{27} = \frac{4}{3} \times \frac{27}{7} = \frac{4 \times 3 \times 9}{3 \times 7} = \frac{36}{7} = 5\frac{1}{7}$

21. $0 \div \frac{3}{17} = 0 \times \frac{17}{3} = 0$

23. $\frac{18}{19} \div 0$ Cannot be done

25. $\frac{9}{16} \div \frac{3}{4} = \frac{9}{16} \times \frac{4}{3} = \frac{3}{4}$

27. $\frac{3}{7} \div \frac{15}{28} = \frac{3}{7} \times \frac{28}{15} = \frac{4}{5}$

29. $\frac{10}{25} \div \frac{20}{50} = \frac{10}{25} \times \frac{50}{20} = 1$

31. $12 \div \frac{3}{4} = \frac{12}{1} \times \frac{4}{3} = 16$

33. $\frac{7}{8} \div 4 = \frac{7}{8} \times \frac{1}{4} = \frac{7}{32}$

35. $6000 \div \frac{6}{5} = \frac{6000}{1} \times \frac{5}{6} = 5000$

37. $\frac{\frac{2}{5}}{3} = \frac{2}{5} \times \frac{1}{3} = \frac{2}{15}$

39. $\frac{\frac{5}{8}}{\frac{25}{7}} = \frac{5}{8} \times \frac{7}{25} = \frac{7}{40}$

41. $3\frac{1}{5} \div \frac{3}{10} = \frac{16}{5} \times \frac{10}{3} = \frac{32}{3} = 10\frac{2}{3}$

43. $2\dfrac{1}{3} \div 6 = \dfrac{7}{3} \times \dfrac{1}{6} = \dfrac{7}{18}$

45. $1\dfrac{7}{9} \div 2\dfrac{2}{3} = \dfrac{16}{9} \div \dfrac{8}{3} = \dfrac{16}{9} \times \dfrac{3}{8} = \dfrac{2}{3}$

47. $5 \div 1\dfrac{1}{4} = \dfrac{5}{1} \div \dfrac{5}{4} = \dfrac{5}{1} \times \dfrac{4}{5} = 4$

49. $12\dfrac{1}{2} \div 5\dfrac{5}{6} = \dfrac{25}{2} \div \dfrac{35}{6} = \dfrac{25}{2} \times \dfrac{6}{35} = \dfrac{15}{7} = 2\dfrac{1}{7}$

51. $8\dfrac{1}{4} \div 2\dfrac{3}{4} = \dfrac{33}{4} \div \dfrac{11}{4} = \dfrac{33}{4} \times \dfrac{4}{11} = 3$

53. $3\dfrac{1}{2} \div 1\dfrac{7}{9} = \dfrac{7}{2} \div \dfrac{16}{9} = \dfrac{7}{2} \times \dfrac{9}{16} = \dfrac{63}{32} = 1\dfrac{31}{32}$

55. $2\dfrac{1}{2} \div 5 = \dfrac{5}{2} \times \dfrac{1}{5} = \dfrac{1}{2}$

57. $\dfrac{4\frac{1}{2}}{\frac{3}{8}} = \dfrac{9}{2} \times \dfrac{8}{3} = 12$

59. $\dfrac{1\frac{1}{4}}{1\frac{7}{8}} = \dfrac{5}{4} \div \dfrac{15}{8} = \dfrac{5}{4} \times \dfrac{8}{15} = \dfrac{2}{3}$

61. $\dfrac{\frac{5}{9}}{2\frac{1}{3}} = \dfrac{5}{9} \div \dfrac{7}{3} = \dfrac{5}{9} \times \dfrac{3}{7} = \dfrac{5}{21}$

63. $\dfrac{5\frac{1}{3}}{2\frac{1}{2}} = \dfrac{16}{3} \div \dfrac{5}{2} = \dfrac{16}{3} \times \dfrac{2}{5} = \dfrac{32}{15} = 2\dfrac{2}{15}$

65. $x \div \dfrac{4}{3} = \dfrac{21}{20}$

$x \times \dfrac{3}{4} = \dfrac{21}{20}$

$\dfrac{7 \times 3}{5 \times 4} = \dfrac{21}{20}$

$x = \dfrac{7}{5}$

67. $x \div \dfrac{9}{5} = \dfrac{20}{63}$

$x \times \dfrac{5}{9} = \dfrac{20}{63}$

$\dfrac{4 \times 5}{7 \times 9} = \dfrac{20}{63}$

69. $20\dfrac{1}{4} \div 9 = \dfrac{81}{4} \div \dfrac{9}{1}$

$= \dfrac{81}{4} \times \dfrac{1}{9}$

$= \dfrac{9 \times 9 \times 1}{4 \times 9}$

$= \dfrac{9}{4}$

$= 2\dfrac{1}{4}$ gallons

71. $125 \div 3\dfrac{1}{3} = \dfrac{125}{1} \div \dfrac{10}{3}$

$= \dfrac{125}{1} \times \dfrac{3}{10}$

$= \dfrac{5 \times 25 \times 3}{5 \times 2}$

$= \dfrac{75}{2}$

$= 37\dfrac{1}{2}$ miles per hour

73. $87\dfrac{1}{2} \div 3\dfrac{1}{8} = \dfrac{175}{2} \div \dfrac{25}{8}$

$= \dfrac{175}{2} \times \dfrac{8}{25}$

$= \dfrac{25 \times 7 \times 2 \times 4}{2 \times 25}$

$= 28$ flags

75. If $a = 2$, $b = 3$, $c = 4$, and $d = 6$, then $\dfrac{2}{3} \div \dfrac{4}{6} = \dfrac{4}{6} \div \dfrac{2}{3}$. In general, if $\dfrac{a}{b} = \dfrac{c}{d}$ then $\dfrac{a}{b} \div \dfrac{c}{d} = \dfrac{c}{d} \div \dfrac{a}{b}$.

Cumulative Review Problems

77. 39,576,304 = Thirty-nine million, five hundred seventy-six thousand, three hundred four.

79. $126 + 34 + 9 + 891 + 12 + 27 = 1099$

2.6 Exercises

1. $5 = 5$
   $10 = 2 \times 5$
   LCD $= 2 \times 5 = 10$

3. $7 = 7$
   $4 = 2 \times 2$
   LCD $= 2 \times 2 \times 7 = 28$

5. $5 = 5$
   $7 = 7$
   LCD $= 5 \times 7 = 35$

7. $9 = 3 \times 3$
   $6 = 2 \times 3$
   LCD $= 2 \times 3 \times 3 = 18$

9. $16 = 2 \times 2 \times 2 \times 2$
   $24 = 2 \times 2 \times 2 \times 3$
   LCD $= 2 \times 2 \times 2 \times 2 \times 3 = 48$

11. $16 = 2 \times 2 \times 2 \times 2$
    $4 = 2 \times 2$
    LCD $= 2 \times 2 \times 2 \times 2 = 16$

13. $10 = 2 \times 5$
    $45 = 3 \times 3 \times 5$
    LCD $= 2 \times 3 \times 3 \times 5 = 90$

15. $12 = 2 \times 2 \times 3$
    $30 = 2 \times 3 \times 5$
    LCD $= 2 \times 2 \times 3 \times 5 = 60$

17. $21 = 3 \times 7$
    $35 = 5 \times 7$
    LCD $= 3 \times 5 \times 7 = 105$

19. $18 = 2 \times 3 \times 3$
    $12 = 2 \times 2 \times 3$
    LCD $= 2 \times 2 \times 3 \times 3 = 36$

21. $3 = 3$
    $2 = 2$
    $6 = 2 \times 3$
    LCD $= 2 \times 3 = 6$

23. $24 = 2 \times 2 \times 2 \times 3$
    $15 = 3 \times 5$
    $30 = 2 \times 3 \times 5$
    LCD $= 2 \times 2 \times 2 \times 3 \times 5 = 120$

25. $16 = 2 \times 2 \times 2 \times 2$
    $18 = 2 \times 3 \times 3$
    $24 = 2 \times 2 \times 2 \times 3$
    LCD $= 2 \times 2 \times 2 \times 2 \times 3 \times 3 = 144$

27. $12 = 2 \times 2 \times 3$
    $21 = 3 \times 7$
    $14 = 2 \times 7$
    LCD $= 2 \times 2 \times 3 \times 7 = 84$

29. $15 = 3 \times 5$
    $12 = 2 \times 2 \times 3$
    $8 = 2 \times 2 \times 2$
    LCD $= 2 \times 2 \times 2 \times 3 \times 5 = 120$

31. $\dfrac{1}{6} = \dfrac{1}{6} \times \dfrac{3}{3} = \dfrac{3}{18}$
    3

33. $\dfrac{5}{6} = \dfrac{5}{6} \times \dfrac{9}{9} = \dfrac{45}{54}$
    45

35. $\dfrac{4}{11} = \dfrac{4}{11} \times \dfrac{5}{5} = \dfrac{20}{55}$
    20

37. $\dfrac{7}{24} = \dfrac{7}{24} \times \dfrac{2}{2} = \dfrac{14}{48}$
    14

39. $\dfrac{8}{9} = \dfrac{8}{9} \times \dfrac{12}{12} = \dfrac{96}{108}$
    96

41. $\dfrac{13}{42} = \dfrac{13}{42} \times \dfrac{3}{3} = \dfrac{39}{126}$
    39

43. $\dfrac{7}{12}$ and $\dfrac{5}{9}$

    $\dfrac{7}{12} \times \dfrac{3}{3}$ and $\dfrac{5}{9} \times \dfrac{4}{4}$

    $\dfrac{21}{36}$ and $\dfrac{20}{36}$

45. $\frac{3}{25}$ and $\frac{7}{40}$

$\frac{3}{25} \times \frac{8}{8}$ and $\frac{7}{40} \times \frac{5}{5}$

$\frac{24}{200}$ and $\frac{35}{200}$

47. $\frac{19}{25}$ and $\frac{26}{75}$

$\frac{19}{25} \times \frac{6}{6}$ and $\frac{26}{75} \times \frac{2}{2}$

$\frac{114}{150}$ and $\frac{52}{150}$

49. $7 = 7$
$42 = 2 \times 3 \times 7$
$\text{LCD} = 2 \times 3 \times 7 = 42$

$\frac{5}{7}$ and $\frac{7}{42}$

$\frac{5}{7} \times \frac{6}{6}$ and $\frac{7}{42}$

$\frac{30}{42}$ and $\frac{7}{42}$

51. $12 = 2 \times 2 \times 3$
$16 = 2 \times 2 \times 2 \times 2$
$\text{LCD} = 2 \times 2 \times 2 \times 2 \times 3 = 48$

$\frac{5}{12}$ and $\frac{1}{16}$

$\frac{5}{12} \times \frac{4}{4}$ and $\frac{1}{16} \times \frac{3}{3}$

$\frac{20}{48}$ and $\frac{3}{48}$

53. $20 = 2 \times 2 \times 5$
$16 = 2 \times 2 \times 2 \times 2$
$\text{LCD} = 2 \times 2 \times 2 \times 2 \times 5 = 80$

$\frac{13}{20}$ and $\frac{11}{16}$

$\frac{13}{20} \times \frac{4}{4}$ and $\frac{11}{16} \times \frac{5}{5}$

$\frac{52}{80}$ and $\frac{55}{80}$

55. $12 = 2 \times 2 \times 3$
$30 = 2 \times 3 \times 5$
$\text{LCD} = 2 \times 2 \times 3 \times 5 = 60$

$\frac{7}{12}$ and $\frac{23}{30}$

$\frac{7}{12} \times \frac{5}{5}$ and $\frac{23}{30} \times \frac{2}{2}$

$\frac{35}{60}$ and $\frac{46}{60}$

57. $24 = 2 \times 2 \times 2 \times 3$
$36 = 2 \times 2 \times 3 \times 3$
$72 = 2 \times 2 \times 2 \times 3 \times 3$
$\text{LCD} = 2 \times 2 \times 2 \times 3 \times 3 = 72$

$\frac{5}{24} \times \frac{3}{3}, \frac{11}{36} \times \frac{2}{2}, \frac{3}{72}$

$\frac{15}{72}, \frac{22}{72}, \frac{3}{72}$

59. $56 = 2 \times 2 \times 2 \times 7$
$8 = 2 \times 2 \times 2$
$7 = 7$
$\text{LCD} = 2 \times 2 \times 2 \times 7 = 56$

$\frac{3}{56}, \frac{7}{8} \times \frac{7}{7}, \frac{5}{7} \times \frac{8}{8}$

$\frac{3}{56}, \frac{49}{56}, \frac{40}{56}$

61. $63 = 3 \times 3 \times 7$
$21 = 3 \times 7$
$9 = 3 \times 3$
$\text{LCD} = 3 \times 3 \times 7 = 63$

$\frac{5}{63}, \frac{4}{21} \times \frac{3}{3}, \frac{8}{9} \times \frac{7}{7}$

$\frac{5}{63}, \frac{12}{63}, \frac{56}{63}$

63. a. $16 = 2 \times 2 \times 2 \times 2$
$4 = 2 \times 2$
$8 = 2 \times 2 \times 2$
$\text{LCD} = 2 \times 2 \times 2 \times 2 = 16$

    b. $\frac{3}{16}, \frac{3}{4} \times \frac{4}{4}, \frac{3}{8} \times \frac{2}{2}$

$\frac{3}{16}, \frac{12}{16}, \frac{6}{16}$

Cumulative Review Problems

65. $32 \overline{)5699}$ with quotient 178

$\begin{array}{r} 178 \\ 32\overline{)5699} \\ \underline{32} \\ 249 \\ \underline{224} \\ 259 \\ \underline{256} \\ 3 \end{array}$

178 R3

67.
$$\begin{array}{r} 369 \\ \times\ 27 \\ \hline 2583 \\ 738\ \ \ \\ \hline 9963 \end{array}$$

2.7 Exercises

1. $\dfrac{5}{9} + \dfrac{2}{9} = \dfrac{5+2}{9} = \dfrac{7}{9}$

3. $\dfrac{11}{30} + \dfrac{11}{30} = \dfrac{22}{30} = \dfrac{11}{15}$

5. $\dfrac{21}{23} - \dfrac{1}{23} = \dfrac{20}{23}$

7. $\dfrac{53}{88} - \dfrac{19}{88} = \dfrac{34}{88} = \dfrac{17}{44}$

9. $\dfrac{1}{4} + \dfrac{1}{3} = \dfrac{1}{4} \times \dfrac{3}{3} + \dfrac{1}{3} \times \dfrac{4}{4}$
$= \dfrac{3}{12} + \dfrac{4}{12}$
$= \dfrac{7}{12}$

11. $\dfrac{3}{10} + \dfrac{3}{20} = \dfrac{3}{10} \times \dfrac{2}{2} + \dfrac{3}{20}$
$= \dfrac{6}{20} + \dfrac{3}{20}$
$= \dfrac{9}{20}$

13. $\dfrac{1}{8} + \dfrac{3}{4} = \dfrac{1}{8} + \dfrac{3}{4} \times \dfrac{2}{2}$
$= \dfrac{1}{8} + \dfrac{6}{8}$
$= \dfrac{7}{8}$

15. $\dfrac{4}{5} + \dfrac{7}{10} = \dfrac{4}{5} \times \dfrac{2}{2} + \dfrac{7}{10}$
$= \dfrac{8}{10} + \dfrac{7}{10} = \dfrac{15}{10} = \dfrac{3}{2}$
$= 1\dfrac{1}{2}$

17. $\dfrac{3}{10} + \dfrac{7}{100} = \dfrac{3}{10} \times \dfrac{10}{10} + \dfrac{7}{100}$
$= \dfrac{30}{100} + \dfrac{7}{100}$
$= \dfrac{37}{100}$

19. $\dfrac{3}{25} + \dfrac{1}{35} = \dfrac{3}{25} \times \dfrac{7}{7} + \dfrac{1}{35} \times \dfrac{5}{5}$
$= \dfrac{21}{175} + \dfrac{5}{175}$
$= \dfrac{26}{175}$

21. $\dfrac{7}{8} + \dfrac{5}{12} = \dfrac{7}{8} \times \dfrac{3}{3} + \dfrac{5}{12} \times \dfrac{2}{2}$
$= \dfrac{21}{24} + \dfrac{10}{24} = \dfrac{31}{24}$
$= 1\dfrac{7}{24}$

23. $\dfrac{3}{8} + \dfrac{3}{10} = \dfrac{3}{8} \times \dfrac{5}{5} + \dfrac{3}{10} \times \dfrac{4}{4}$
$= \dfrac{15}{40} + \dfrac{12}{40}$
$= \dfrac{27}{40}$

25. $\dfrac{5}{12} - \dfrac{1}{6} = \dfrac{5}{12} - \dfrac{1}{6} \times \dfrac{2}{2}$
$= \dfrac{5}{12} - \dfrac{2}{12} = \dfrac{3}{12}$
$= \dfrac{1}{4}$

27. $\dfrac{3}{7} - \dfrac{1}{5} = \dfrac{3}{7} \times \dfrac{5}{5} - \dfrac{1}{5} \times \dfrac{7}{7}$
$= \dfrac{15}{35} - \dfrac{7}{35}$
$= \dfrac{8}{35}$

29. $\dfrac{7}{8} - \dfrac{5}{16} = \dfrac{7}{8} \times \dfrac{2}{2} - \dfrac{5}{16}$
$= \dfrac{14}{16} - \dfrac{5}{16}$
$= \dfrac{9}{16}$

31. $\dfrac{5}{12} - \dfrac{7}{30} = \dfrac{5}{12} \times \dfrac{5}{5} - \dfrac{7}{30} \times \dfrac{2}{2}$
$= \dfrac{25}{60} - \dfrac{14}{60}$
$= \dfrac{11}{60}$

33. $\dfrac{11}{12} - \dfrac{2}{3} = \dfrac{11}{12} - \dfrac{2}{3} \times \dfrac{4}{4}$
$= \dfrac{11}{12} - \dfrac{8}{12}$
$= \dfrac{3}{12} = \dfrac{1}{4}$

35. $\dfrac{5}{6} - \dfrac{1}{3} = \dfrac{5}{6} - \dfrac{1}{3} \times \dfrac{2}{2}$

$\qquad\qquad = \dfrac{5}{6} - \dfrac{2}{6}$

$\qquad\qquad = \dfrac{3}{6} = \dfrac{1}{2}$

37. $\dfrac{5}{12} - \dfrac{5}{16} = \dfrac{5}{12} \times \dfrac{4}{4} - \dfrac{5}{16} \times \dfrac{3}{3}$

$\qquad\qquad = \dfrac{20}{48} - \dfrac{15}{48}$

$\qquad\qquad = \dfrac{5}{48}$

39. $\dfrac{10}{16} - \dfrac{5}{8} = \dfrac{10}{16} - \dfrac{10}{16}$

$\qquad\qquad = 0$

41. $\dfrac{20}{35} - \dfrac{4}{7} = \dfrac{20}{35} - \dfrac{4}{7} \times \dfrac{5}{5}$

$\qquad\qquad = \dfrac{20}{35} - \dfrac{20}{35}$

$\qquad\qquad = 0$

43. $\dfrac{4}{5} + \dfrac{1}{20} + \dfrac{3}{4} = \dfrac{4}{5} \times \dfrac{4}{4} + \dfrac{1}{20} + \dfrac{3}{4} \times \dfrac{5}{5}$

$\qquad\qquad = \dfrac{16}{20} + \dfrac{1}{20} + \dfrac{15}{20} = \dfrac{32}{20}$

$\qquad\qquad = \dfrac{8}{5} = 1\dfrac{3}{5}$

45. $\dfrac{5}{30} + \dfrac{3}{40} + \dfrac{1}{8} = \dfrac{5}{30} \times \dfrac{4}{4} + \dfrac{3}{40} \times \dfrac{3}{3} + \dfrac{1}{8} \times \dfrac{15}{15}$

$\qquad\qquad = \dfrac{20}{120} + \dfrac{9}{120} + \dfrac{15}{120}$

$\qquad\qquad = \dfrac{44}{120} = \dfrac{11}{30}$

47. $\dfrac{1}{5} + \dfrac{2}{3} + \dfrac{11}{15} = \dfrac{1}{5} \times \dfrac{3}{3} + \dfrac{2}{3} \times \dfrac{5}{5} + \dfrac{11}{15}$

$\qquad\qquad = \dfrac{3}{15} + \dfrac{10}{15} + \dfrac{11}{15}$

$\qquad\qquad = \dfrac{24}{15} = \dfrac{8}{5}$

$\qquad\qquad = 1\dfrac{3}{5}$

49. $x + \dfrac{1}{7} = \dfrac{5}{14}$

$x + \dfrac{1}{7} \times \dfrac{2}{2} = \dfrac{5}{14}$

$x + \dfrac{2}{14} = \dfrac{5}{14}$

$\dfrac{3}{14} + \dfrac{2}{14} = \dfrac{5}{14}$

$x = \dfrac{3}{14}$

51. $x + \dfrac{2}{3} = \dfrac{9}{11}$

$x + \dfrac{2}{3} \times \dfrac{11}{11} = \dfrac{9}{11} \times \dfrac{3}{3}$

$x + \dfrac{22}{33} = \dfrac{27}{33}$

$\dfrac{5}{33} + \dfrac{22}{33} = \dfrac{27}{33}$

$x = \dfrac{5}{33}$

53. $x - \dfrac{1}{5} = \dfrac{4}{12}$

$x - \dfrac{1}{5} \times \dfrac{12}{12} = \dfrac{4}{12} \times \dfrac{5}{5}$

$x - \dfrac{12}{60} = \dfrac{20}{60}$

$\dfrac{32}{60} - \dfrac{12}{60} = \dfrac{20}{60}$

$x = \dfrac{32}{60} = \dfrac{8}{15}$

55. $\dfrac{4}{5} + \dfrac{2}{3} = \dfrac{4}{5} \times \dfrac{3}{3} + \dfrac{2}{3} \times \dfrac{5}{5}$

$\qquad\qquad = \dfrac{12}{15} + \dfrac{10}{15}$

$\qquad\qquad = \dfrac{22}{15}$

$\qquad\qquad = 1\dfrac{7}{15}$ cups

57. $\dfrac{2}{3} + \dfrac{5}{6} = \dfrac{2}{3} \times \dfrac{2}{2} + \dfrac{5}{6}$

$\qquad\qquad = \dfrac{4}{6} + \dfrac{5}{6}$

$\qquad\qquad = \dfrac{9}{6} = \dfrac{3}{2}$

$\qquad\qquad = 1\dfrac{1}{2}$ pounds

59. $\frac{1}{3}+\frac{5}{9}+\frac{3}{4}=\frac{12}{36}+\frac{20}{36}+\frac{27}{36}$

$\qquad\qquad\quad =\frac{59}{36}$

$\qquad\qquad\quad =1\frac{23}{36}$ inches

61. $5\frac{1}{4}\div\frac{3}{4}=\frac{21}{4}\div\frac{3}{4}=\frac{21}{4}\times\frac{4}{3}=7$

$7\times\frac{1}{3}=\frac{7}{3}=2\frac{1}{3}$

$5\frac{1}{4}+2\frac{1}{3}=\frac{21}{4}+\frac{7}{3}=\frac{63}{12}+\frac{28}{12}=\frac{91}{12}$

$\qquad\quad =7\frac{7}{12}$ cups

63. $\frac{5}{6}-\frac{9}{14}=\frac{35}{42}-\frac{27}{42}$

$\qquad\qquad =\frac{8}{42}$

$\qquad\qquad =\frac{4}{21}$

$\frac{4}{21}$ of the membership

Cumulative Review Problems

65. $\frac{15}{85}=\frac{15\div 5}{85\div 5}=\frac{3}{17}$

67. $16\overline{)123}$ $\quad \frac{123}{16}=7\frac{11}{16}$
$\qquad \underline{112}$
$\qquad\;\; 11$

with quotient 7

2.8 Exercises

1. $\begin{array}{r}7\frac{1}{8}\\+2\frac{5}{8}\\\hline 9\frac{6}{8}=9\frac{3}{4}\end{array}$

3. $\begin{array}{r}15\frac{3}{14}\\-11\frac{1}{14}\\\hline 4\frac{2}{14}=4\frac{1}{7}\end{array}$

5. $\begin{array}{r}12\frac{1}{3}\\+5\frac{1}{6}\end{array}\qquad\begin{array}{r}12\frac{2}{6}\\+5\frac{1}{6}\\\hline 17\frac{3}{6}=17\frac{1}{2}\end{array}$

7. $\begin{array}{r}5\frac{4}{5}\\+10\frac{3}{10}\end{array}\qquad\begin{array}{r}5\frac{8}{10}\\+10\frac{3}{10}\\\hline 15\frac{11}{10}=16\frac{1}{10}\end{array}$

9. $\begin{array}{r}1\\-\frac{3}{7}\end{array}\qquad\begin{array}{r}\frac{7}{7}\\-\frac{3}{7}\\\hline \frac{4}{7}\end{array}$

11. $\begin{array}{r}1\frac{5}{6}\\+\frac{7}{8}\end{array}\qquad\begin{array}{r}1\frac{20}{24}\\+\frac{21}{24}\\\hline 1\frac{41}{24}=2\frac{17}{24}\end{array}$

13. $\begin{array}{r}7\frac{1}{2}\\+8\frac{3}{4}\end{array}\qquad\begin{array}{r}7\frac{2}{4}\\+8\frac{3}{4}\\\hline 15\frac{5}{4}=16\frac{1}{4}\end{array}$

15. $\begin{array}{r}8\frac{2}{3}\\-5\frac{1}{6}\end{array}\qquad\begin{array}{r}8\frac{4}{6}\\-5\frac{1}{6}\\\hline 3\frac{3}{6}=3\frac{1}{2}\end{array}$

17. $\begin{array}{r}18\frac{1}{6}\\-10\frac{3}{4}\end{array}\quad\begin{array}{r}18\frac{4}{24}\\-10\frac{18}{24}\end{array}\quad\begin{array}{r}17\frac{28}{24}\\-10\frac{18}{24}\\\hline 7\frac{10}{24}=7\frac{5}{12}\end{array}$

19. $\begin{array}{r}30\\-15\frac{3}{7}\end{array}\qquad\begin{array}{r}29\frac{7}{7}\\-15\frac{3}{7}\\\hline 14\frac{4}{7}\end{array}$

21. $\begin{array}{r}15\frac{4}{15}\\+26\frac{8}{15}\\\hline 41\frac{12}{15}=41\frac{4}{5}\end{array}$

23. $\begin{array}{r}4\frac{1}{3}\\+2\frac{1}{4}\end{array}\qquad\begin{array}{r}4\frac{4}{12}\\+2\frac{3}{12}\\\hline 6\frac{7}{12}\end{array}$

25. $\begin{array}{r}2\frac{1}{15}\\+14\frac{3}{5}\end{array}\qquad\begin{array}{r}2\frac{1}{15}\\+14\frac{9}{15}\\\hline 16\frac{10}{15}=16\frac{2}{3}\end{array}$

27. $\begin{array}{r} 47\frac{3}{10} \\ +\,26\frac{5}{8} \\ \hline \end{array}$ $\begin{array}{r} 47\frac{12}{40} \\ +\,26\frac{25}{40} \\ \hline 73\frac{37}{40} \end{array}$

29. $\begin{array}{r} 19\frac{5}{6} \\ -\,14\frac{1}{3} \\ \hline \end{array}$ $\begin{array}{r} 19\frac{5}{6} \\ -\,14\frac{2}{6} \\ \hline 5\frac{3}{6}=5\frac{1}{2} \end{array}$

31. $\begin{array}{r} 3\frac{5}{6} \\ -\,3\frac{10}{12} \\ \hline \end{array}$ $\begin{array}{r} 3\frac{10}{12} \\ -\,3\frac{10}{12} \\ \hline 0 \end{array}$

33. $\begin{array}{r} 12\frac{3}{20} \\ -\,7\frac{7}{15} \\ \hline \end{array}$ $\begin{array}{r} 12\frac{9}{60} \\ -\,7\frac{28}{60} \\ \hline \end{array}$ $\begin{array}{r} 11\frac{69}{60} \\ -\,7\frac{28}{60} \\ \hline 4\frac{41}{60} \end{array}$

35. $\begin{array}{r} 12 \\ -\,3\frac{7}{15} \\ \hline \end{array}$ $\begin{array}{r} 11\frac{15}{15} \\ -\,3\frac{7}{15} \\ \hline 8\frac{8}{15} \end{array}$

37. $\begin{array}{r} 120 \\ -\,17\frac{3}{8} \\ \hline \end{array}$ $\begin{array}{r} 119\frac{8}{8} \\ -\,17\frac{3}{8} \\ \hline 102\frac{5}{8} \end{array}$

39. $\begin{array}{r} 3\frac{1}{8} \\ 2\frac{1}{3} \\ +\,7\frac{3}{4} \\ \hline \end{array}$ $\begin{array}{r} 3\frac{3}{24} \\ 2\frac{8}{24} \\ +\,7\frac{18}{24} \\ \hline 12\frac{29}{24}=13\frac{5}{24} \end{array}$

41. $\begin{array}{r} 20\frac{3}{4} \\ +\,22\frac{3}{8} \\ \hline \end{array}$ $\begin{array}{r} 20\frac{6}{8} \\ +\,22\frac{3}{8} \\ \hline 42\frac{9}{8}=43\frac{1}{8} \end{array}$

$43\frac{1}{8}$ miles

43. $\begin{array}{r} 6\frac{3}{8} \\ -\,4\frac{1}{3} \\ \hline \end{array}$ $\begin{array}{r} 6\frac{9}{24} \\ -\,4\frac{8}{24} \\ \hline 2\frac{1}{24} \end{array}$

$2\frac{1}{24}$ pounds

45. a. $\begin{array}{r} 5\frac{1}{8} \\ +\,4\frac{2}{3} \\ \hline \end{array}$ $\begin{array}{r} 5\frac{3}{24} \\ +\,4\frac{16}{24} \\ \hline 9\frac{19}{24} \end{array}$

$9\frac{19}{24}$ pounds

b. $\begin{array}{r} 16 \\ -\,9\frac{19}{24} \\ \hline \end{array}$ $\begin{array}{r} 15\frac{24}{24} \\ -\,9\frac{19}{24} \\ \hline 6\frac{5}{24} \end{array}$

$6\frac{5}{24}$ pounds

47. $\begin{aligned} \frac{379}{8}+\frac{89}{5} &= \frac{1895}{40}+\frac{712}{40} \\ &= \frac{2607}{40} \\ &= 65\frac{7}{40} \end{aligned}$

49. $\begin{aligned} & \frac{200}{3}-\frac{153}{7} \\ &= \frac{200}{3}\times\frac{7}{7}-\frac{153}{7}\times\frac{3}{3} \\ &= \frac{1400}{21}-\frac{459}{21} \\ &= \frac{941}{21}=44\frac{17}{21} \end{aligned}$

Cumulative Review Problems

51. $\begin{array}{r} 12{,}367 \\ \times\quad 9 \\ \hline 111{,}303 \end{array}$

53. $\begin{array}{r} 6737 \\ \times\quad 76 \\ \hline 40\;422 \\ 471\;59 \\ \hline 512{,}012 \end{array}$

Putting Your Skills to Work

1. $(23\times2000)\times2\frac{1}{2}=\frac{46{,}000}{1}\times\frac{5}{2}=115{,}000$

$(23\times2000)\times1\frac{3}{4}=\frac{46{,}000}{1}\times\frac{7}{4}=80{,}500$

$115{,}000-80{,}500=34{,}500$

$34{,}500-1300=33{,}200$

$\frac{33{,}200}{2}=16{,}600$

$\$16{,}600$

3. $300(60)\left(2\frac{1}{2}\right) = 45{,}000$

$200(60) = 12{,}000$

$\frac{5}{8}(45{,}000 - 12{,}000) = \frac{5}{8}(33{,}000) = 20{,}625$

No, Loring will only earn $20,625.

$\frac{3}{4}(45{,}000 - 12{,}000) = 24{,}750$

He needs them to take $\frac{1}{4}$ of the costs and $\frac{1}{4}$ of the profits.

2.9 Exercises

1.
$$5\frac{1}{4} \qquad 5\frac{6}{24}$$
$$4\frac{7}{8} \qquad 4\frac{21}{24}$$
$$+6\frac{1}{6} \qquad +6\frac{4}{24}$$
$$\overline{\qquad\qquad 15\frac{31}{24} = 16\frac{7}{24} \text{ tons}}$$

3.
$$7\frac{5}{6} \qquad 7\frac{20}{24}$$
$$8\frac{1}{8} \qquad 8\frac{3}{24}$$
$$+9\frac{1}{2} \qquad +9\frac{12}{24}$$
$$\overline{\qquad\qquad 24\frac{35}{24}}$$

$24\frac{35}{24} = 25\frac{11}{24}$ tons

5. $\frac{1}{16} + \frac{3}{4} + \frac{1}{16} + \frac{3}{16} + \frac{1}{2}$

$= \frac{1}{16} + \frac{12}{16} + \frac{1}{16} + \frac{3}{16} + \frac{8}{16}$

$= \frac{25}{16}$

$= 1\frac{9}{16}$ inches

7. $65\frac{1}{6} \div 3\frac{5}{6}$

$= \frac{391}{6} \div \frac{23}{6}$

$= \frac{391}{6} \times \frac{6}{23}$

$= \frac{17 \times 23 \times 6}{6 \times 23}$

$= 17$

17 pieces

9. $10\frac{2}{3} \times 8\frac{3}{4} = \frac{32}{3} \times \frac{35}{4}$

$= \frac{8 \times 4 \times 35}{3 \times 4}$

$= \frac{280}{3}$

$= 93\frac{1}{3}$

$93\frac{1}{3}$

11. $36\frac{3}{4} \times 7\frac{1}{2} = \frac{147}{4} \times \frac{15}{2}$

$= \frac{2205}{8}$

$= 275\frac{5}{8}$ gallons

13. $22\frac{1}{2} \times 4\frac{3}{4}$

$= \frac{45}{2} \times \frac{19}{4}$

$= \frac{855}{8}$

$= 106\frac{7}{8}$

$106\frac{7}{8}$ nautical miles

15. $\frac{1}{5} + \frac{1}{15} + \frac{1}{20} = \frac{12}{60} + \frac{4}{60} + \frac{3}{60}$

$= \frac{12 + 4 + 3}{60}$

$= \frac{19}{60}$

$\frac{19}{60}(660) = 209$, so $209 is deducted.

$660 - 209 = 451$

She has $451 per week left.

17. a. $36\frac{3}{4} \div \frac{7}{8} = \frac{147}{4} \div \frac{7}{8}$

$= \frac{147}{4} \times \frac{8}{7}$

$= \frac{7 \times 21 \times 4 \times 2}{4 \times 7}$

$= 42$

42 bags

b. $42 \times 3\frac{1}{2} = \frac{42}{1} \times \frac{7}{2} = 147$

$147

c. $147 - 2 = 145$

$145

19. a.

$$18\frac{1}{2} - 1\frac{1}{4} - 3\frac{1}{8}$$

$$= \frac{37}{2} - \frac{5}{4} - \frac{25}{8} = \frac{148}{8} - \frac{10}{8} - \frac{25}{8}$$

$$= \frac{148 - 10 - 25}{8}$$

$$= \frac{113}{8}$$

$$= 14\frac{1}{8}$$

$14\frac{1}{8}$ ounces of bread

b.

$$
\begin{array}{cc}
14\frac{3}{4} & 14\frac{6}{8} \\
-14\frac{1}{8} & -14\frac{1}{8} \\
\hline
 & \frac{5}{8}
\end{array}
$$

$\frac{5}{8}$ of an ounce

21. a.

$$160\tfrac{1}{8} \div 5\tfrac{1}{4} = \frac{1281}{8} \div \frac{21}{4}$$

$$= \frac{1281}{8} \times \frac{4}{21}$$

$$= \frac{61}{2}$$

$$= 30\frac{1}{2} \text{ knots}$$

b.

$$213\frac{1}{2} \div \frac{61}{2} = \frac{427}{2} \div \frac{61}{2}$$

$$= \frac{427}{2} \times \frac{2}{61}$$

$$= \frac{427}{61}$$

$$= 7 \text{ hours}$$

23. a.

$$6856\frac{1}{4} \div 1\frac{1}{4} = \frac{27,425}{4} \div \frac{5}{4}$$

$$= \frac{27,425}{4} \times \frac{4}{5} = 5485 \text{ bushels}$$

b.

$$6856\frac{1}{4} \times 1\frac{3}{4} = \frac{27,425}{4} \times \frac{7}{4} = \frac{191,975}{16}$$

$$= 11,998\frac{7}{16} \text{ cubic feet}$$

c.

$$11,998\frac{7}{16} \div 1\frac{1}{4} = \frac{191,975}{16} \times \frac{4}{5}$$

$$= \frac{38,395}{4}$$

$$= 9598\frac{3}{4} \text{ bushels}$$

Cumulative Review Problems

25.
$$
\begin{array}{r}
16,846 \\
19,321 \\
+\,8,078 \\
\hline
44,245
\end{array}
$$

27.
$$
\begin{array}{r}
1683 \\
\times\ \ \ 27 \\
\hline
11\ 781 \\
33\ 66 \\
\hline
45,441
\end{array}
$$

Chapter 2 Review Problems

1. $\frac{5}{12}$

3. $\frac{4}{7}$

5. $\frac{6}{31}$

7. $42 = 6 \times 7$
$ = 2 \times 3 \times 7$

9. $168 = 8 \times 21$
$ = 2 \times 2 \times 2 \times 3 \times 7$
$ = 2^3 \times 3 \times 7$

11. $78 = 2 \times 39$
$ = 2 \times 3 \times 13$

13. $\frac{13}{52} = \frac{13}{4 \times 13} = \frac{1}{4}$

15. $\frac{21}{36} = \frac{3 \times 7}{2 \times 2 \times 3 \times 3} = \frac{7}{12}$

17. $\frac{168}{192} = \frac{2 \times 2 \times 2 \times 3 \times 7}{2 \times 2 \times 2 \times 2 \times 2 \times 3} = \frac{7}{8}$

19. $4\dfrac{3}{8} = \dfrac{4 \times 8 + 3}{8} = \dfrac{35}{8}$

21.
$$7\overline{)19} \quad \dfrac{19}{7} = 2\dfrac{5}{7}$$
$$\dfrac{2}{19}$$
$$\dfrac{14}{5}$$

23. $3\dfrac{15}{55} = 3\dfrac{5 \times 3}{5 \times 11} = 3\dfrac{3}{11}$

25.
$$240\overline{)385} \qquad \dfrac{385}{240} = 1\dfrac{145}{240}$$
$$\dfrac{1}{385}$$
$$\dfrac{240}{145} \qquad\qquad = 1\dfrac{29}{48}$$

27. $\dfrac{7}{9} \times \dfrac{21}{35} = \dfrac{1}{3} \times \dfrac{7}{5} = \dfrac{7}{15}$

29. $\dfrac{3}{5} \times \dfrac{2}{7} \times \dfrac{10}{27} = \dfrac{1}{1} \times \dfrac{2}{7} \times \dfrac{2}{9} = \dfrac{4}{63}$

31. $5\dfrac{3}{8} \times 3\dfrac{4}{5} = \dfrac{43}{8} \times \dfrac{19}{5} = \dfrac{817}{40} = 20\dfrac{17}{40}$

33. $35 \times \dfrac{7}{10} = \dfrac{35}{1} \times \dfrac{7}{10}$
$$= \dfrac{7 \times 5 \times 7}{2 \times 5} = \dfrac{49}{2} = 24\dfrac{1}{2}$$

35. $18\dfrac{1}{5} \times 26\dfrac{3}{4} = \dfrac{91}{5} \times \dfrac{107}{4} = \dfrac{9737}{20}$
$$= 486\dfrac{17}{20} \text{ square inches}$$

37. $\dfrac{9}{17} \div \dfrac{18}{5} = \dfrac{9}{17} \times \dfrac{5}{18} = \dfrac{5}{34}$

39. $\dfrac{2\frac{1}{4}}{3\frac{1}{3}} = 2\dfrac{1}{4} \div 3\dfrac{1}{3} = \dfrac{9}{4} \div \dfrac{10}{3} = \dfrac{9}{4} \times \dfrac{3}{10} = \dfrac{27}{40}$

41. $2\dfrac{1}{8} \div 20\dfrac{1}{2} = \dfrac{17}{8} \div \dfrac{41}{2} = \dfrac{17}{8} \times \dfrac{2}{41} = \dfrac{17}{164}$

43. $4\dfrac{2}{11} \div 3 = \dfrac{46}{11} \div \dfrac{3}{1} = \dfrac{46}{11} \times \dfrac{1}{3} = \dfrac{46}{33} = 1\dfrac{13}{33}$

45. $21\dfrac{7}{8} \div 3\dfrac{1}{8} = \dfrac{175}{8} \div \dfrac{25}{8} = \dfrac{175}{8} \times \dfrac{8}{25}$
$$= 7 \text{ dresses}$$

47. $40 = 2 \times 2 \times 2 \times 5$
$$30 = 2 \times 3 \times 5$$
$$\text{LCD} = 2 \times 2 \times 2 \times 3 \times 5 = 120$$

49. $\dfrac{3}{7} = \dfrac{3}{7} \times \dfrac{8}{8} = \dfrac{24}{56}$

51. $\dfrac{9}{43} = \dfrac{9}{43} \times \dfrac{4}{4} = \dfrac{36}{172}$

53. $\dfrac{3}{7} - \dfrac{5}{14} = \dfrac{3}{7} \times \dfrac{2}{2} - \dfrac{5}{14}$
$$= \dfrac{6}{14} - \dfrac{5}{14}$$
$$= \dfrac{1}{14}$$

55. $\dfrac{4}{7} + \dfrac{7}{9} = \dfrac{4}{7} \times \dfrac{9}{9} + \dfrac{7}{9} \times \dfrac{7}{7}$
$$= \dfrac{36}{63} + \dfrac{49}{63}$$
$$= \dfrac{85}{63} = 1\dfrac{22}{63}$$

57. $\dfrac{7}{30} + \dfrac{2}{21} = \dfrac{7}{30} \times \dfrac{7}{7} + \dfrac{2}{21} \times \dfrac{10}{10}$
$$= \dfrac{49}{210} + \dfrac{20}{210}$$
$$= \dfrac{69}{210} = \dfrac{23}{70}$$

59. $\dfrac{14}{15} - \dfrac{3}{25} = \dfrac{14}{15} \times \dfrac{5}{5} - \dfrac{3}{25} \times \dfrac{3}{3}$
$$= \dfrac{70}{75} - \dfrac{9}{75}$$
$$= \dfrac{61}{75}$$

61. $1 - \dfrac{17}{23} = \dfrac{23}{23} - \dfrac{17}{23}$
$$= \dfrac{6}{23}$$

63. $3 + 5\dfrac{2}{3} = 8\dfrac{2}{3}$

65. $3\dfrac{1}{4} + 1\dfrac{5}{8} = \dfrac{13}{4} + \dfrac{13}{8}$
$$= \dfrac{26}{8} + \dfrac{13}{8}$$
$$= \dfrac{39}{8} = 4\dfrac{7}{8}$$

67. $120 - 16\frac{2}{3} = \frac{360}{3} - \frac{50}{3}$
$= \frac{310}{3} = 103\frac{1}{3}$

69. $1\frac{7}{8} + 2\frac{3}{4} + 4\frac{1}{10} = \frac{15}{8} + \frac{11}{4} + \frac{41}{10}$
$= \frac{15}{8} \times \frac{5}{5} + \frac{11}{4} \times \frac{10}{10} + \frac{41}{10} \times \frac{4}{4}$
$= \frac{75}{40} + \frac{110}{40} + \frac{164}{40}$
$= \frac{349}{40} = 8\frac{29}{40}$ miles

71. $3\frac{1}{3} \times \frac{1}{2} = \frac{10}{3} \times \frac{1}{2} = \frac{5}{3} = 1\frac{2}{3}$ cups sugar
$4\frac{1}{4} \times \frac{1}{2} = \frac{17}{4} \times \frac{1}{2} = \frac{17}{8} = 2\frac{1}{8}$ cups flour

73. $48 \div 3\frac{1}{5} = \frac{48}{1} \div \frac{16}{5} = \frac{48}{1} \times \frac{5}{16} = \frac{3}{1} \times \frac{5}{1}$
$= 15$ lengths

75. $366 \div 12\frac{1}{5} = \frac{366}{1} \div \frac{61}{5} = \frac{366}{1} \times \frac{5}{61} = \frac{6}{1} \times \frac{5}{1}$
$= 30$ words per minute

77.
$\begin{array}{r} 88\frac{3}{8} \\ -79\frac{5}{8} \\ \hline \end{array}$ $\begin{array}{r} 87\frac{11}{8} \\ -79\frac{5}{8} \\ \hline 8\frac{6}{8} = 8\frac{3}{4} \end{array}$

$\$8\frac{3}{4}$

79.
$\begin{array}{l} \frac{1}{10} \times 880 \\ \frac{1}{2} \times 880 = \\ +\frac{1}{8} \times 880 \\ \hline 880 \\ -638 \\ \hline \$242 \text{ left} \end{array}$ $\begin{array}{r} 88 \\ 440 \\ +110 \\ \hline \$638 \text{ expenses} \end{array}$

Chapter 2 Test

1. $\frac{3}{5}$; 3 of the 5 parts are shaded.

3. $\frac{15}{70} = \frac{3 \times 5}{14 \times 5} = \frac{3}{14}$

5. $\frac{225}{50} = \frac{9 \times 25}{2 \times 25} = \frac{9}{2}$

7. $14\overline{)114}$ with $\frac{8}{112}$ quotient, remainder 2
$\frac{14}{114} = 8\frac{2}{14} = 8\frac{1}{7}$

9. $\frac{7}{9} \times \frac{2}{5} = \frac{7 \times 2}{9 \times 5} = \frac{14}{45}$

11. $\frac{7}{8} \div \frac{5}{11} = \frac{7}{8} \times \frac{11}{5} = \frac{7 \times 11}{8 \times 5} = \frac{77}{40} = 1\frac{37}{40}$

13. $7\frac{1}{5} \div 1\frac{1}{25} = \frac{36}{5} \div \frac{26}{25} = \frac{36}{5} \times \frac{25}{26}$
$= \frac{2 \times 18 \times 5 \times 5}{5 \times 2 \times 13} = \frac{18 \times 5}{13} = \frac{90}{13} = 6\frac{12}{13}$

15. $24 = 2 \times 2 \times 2 \times 3$
$18 = 2 \times 3 \times 3$
$\text{LCD} = 2 \times 2 \times 2 \times 3 \times 3 = 72$

17. $4 = 2 \times 2$
$8 = 2 \times 2 \times 2$
$6 = 2 \times 3$
$\text{LCD} = 2 \times 2 \times 2 \times 3 = 24$

19. $\frac{7}{9} - \frac{5}{12} = \frac{28}{36} - \frac{15}{36} = \frac{13}{36}$

21. $\frac{1}{4} + \frac{3}{7} + \frac{3}{14} = \frac{7}{28} + \frac{12}{28} + \frac{6}{28} = \frac{25}{28}$

23. $18\frac{6}{7} - 13\frac{13}{14} = 18\frac{12}{14} - 13\frac{13}{14} = 17\frac{26}{14} - 13\frac{13}{14}$
$= 4\frac{13}{14}$

25. $30 - 8\frac{3}{4} = 29\frac{4}{4} - 8\frac{3}{4} = 21\frac{1}{4}$

27. $18\frac{2}{3} \div 2\frac{1}{3} = \frac{56}{3} \div \frac{7}{3} = \frac{56}{3} \times \frac{3}{7} = \frac{8 \times 7 \times 3}{7}$
$= 8$
He can make 8 packages.

29. $4\frac{1}{8} + 3\frac{1}{6} + 6\frac{3}{4} = 4 + 3 + 6 + \frac{1}{8} + \frac{1}{6} + \frac{3}{4}$

$= 13 + \frac{3}{24} + \frac{4}{24} + \frac{18}{24} = 13 + \frac{25}{24} = 13 + 1\frac{1}{24}$

$= 14\frac{1}{24}$

She jogged $14\frac{1}{24}$ miles.

Chapters 1–2 Cumulative Test

1. $84,361,208 =$ Eighty-four million, three hundred sixty-one thousand, two hundred eight.

3.
$$\begin{array}{r} 156,200 \\ 364,700 \\ + 198,320 \\ \hline 719,220 \end{array}$$

5.
$$\begin{array}{r} 1,000,361 \\ - 983,145 \\ \hline 17,216 \end{array}$$

7.
$$\begin{array}{r} 16,908 \\ \times 12 \\ \hline 33\ 816 \\ 169\ 08 \\ \hline 202,896 \end{array}$$

9.
$$\begin{array}{r} 369 \\ 18\overline{)6642} \\ \underline{54} \\ 124 \\ \underline{108} \\ 162 \\ \underline{162} \\ 0 \end{array}$$

11. $6,037,452$ rounds to $6,037,000$.

13. $3 \times \$26 + 2 \times \$48 = \$174$

15. $\dfrac{55}{84}$

17. $18\frac{3}{4} = \dfrac{4 \times 18 + 3}{4} = \dfrac{75}{4}$

19. $3\frac{7}{8} \times 2\frac{5}{6} = \dfrac{31}{8} \times \dfrac{17}{6}$

$= \dfrac{527}{48} = 10\frac{47}{48}$

21. $13 = 13$

$39 = 3 \times 13$

$LCD = 3 \times 13 = 39$

23. $2\frac{1}{8} + 6\frac{3}{4} = 2\frac{1}{8} + 6\frac{6}{8}$

$= 8\frac{7}{8}$

25. $\dfrac{11}{14} - \dfrac{9}{28} = \dfrac{11}{14} \times \dfrac{2}{2} - \dfrac{9}{28}$

$= \dfrac{22}{28} - \dfrac{9}{28}$

$= \dfrac{13}{28}$

27. $221\frac{2}{5} \div 9 = \dfrac{1107}{5} \div \dfrac{9}{1} = \dfrac{1107}{5} \times \dfrac{1}{9} = \dfrac{123}{5}$

$= 24\frac{3}{5}$ miles per gallon

29.
$$\begin{array}{r} 30,000 \\ \times\ \ \ 2,000 \\ \hline 60,000,000 \end{array}\text{ miles}$$

Chapter 3

Pretest Chapter 3

1. 47.813 = Forty-seven and eight hundred thirteen thousandths

3. $2.11 = 2\dfrac{11}{100}$

5. 1.59, 1.6, 1.601, 1.61

7. $1.053458 \approx 1.053$

9.
```
  24.613
   0.273
+  2.305
--------
  27.191
```

11.
```
  13.000
-  4.108
--------
   8.892
```

13. $4.7805 \times 1000 = 4780.5$

15.
```
        0.354
0.09)0.03186
        27
        --
        48
        45
        --
         36
         36
         --
          0
```

17.
```
      0.4375
16)7.0000
   6 4
   ---
    60
    48
    ---
    120
    112
    ---
     80
     80
     --
      0
```

19. $(0.2)^2 + 8.7 \times 0.3 - 1.68$
$= 0.04 + 8.7 \times 0.3 - 1.68$
$= 0.04 + 2.61 - 1.68$
$= 2.65 - 1.68$
$= 0.97$

21.
```
   10.5
×   3.6
-------
   630
   315
-------
  37.80 square yards
```
```
   37.80
×  12.95
--------
  18900
  34020
   7560
   3780
--------
 489.5100
```
$489.51 cost

3.1 Exercises

1. A decimal fraction is a fraction whose denominator is a power of 10.

3. Hundred thousandths

5. 0.57 = Fifty-seven hundredths

7. 3.8 = Three and eight tenths

9. 0.124 = One hundred twenty-four thousandths

11. 28.0007 = Twenty-eight and seven ten thousandths

13. $36.18 = Thirty-six and $\dfrac{18}{100}$ dollars

15. $1236.08 = One thousand two hundred thirty-six and $\dfrac{8}{100}$ dollars

17. $10,000.76 = Ten thousand and $\dfrac{76}{100}$ dollars

19. seven tenths = 0.7

21. thirty-nine thousandths = 0.039

23. sixty-five ten thousandths = 0.0065

25. two hundred eighty-six millionths = 0.000286

41

27. $\frac{3}{10} = 0.3$

29. $\frac{76}{100} = 0.76$

31. $\frac{771}{1000} = 0.771$

33. $\frac{53}{1000} = 0.053$

35. $\frac{26}{10,000} = 0.0026$

37. $8\frac{3}{10} = 8.3$

39. $84\frac{13}{100} = 84.13$

41. $1\frac{19}{1000} = 1.019$

43. $126\frac{571}{10,000} = 126.0571$

45. $0.02 = \frac{2}{100} = \frac{1}{50}$

47. $3.6 = 3\frac{6}{10} = 3\frac{3}{5}$

49. $0.121 = \frac{121}{1000}$

51. $12.625 = 12\frac{625}{1000} = 12\frac{5}{8}$

53. $7.0015 = 7\frac{15}{10,000} = 7\frac{3}{2000}$

55. $235.1254 = 235\frac{1254}{10,000} = 235\frac{627}{5000}$

57. $0.0187 = \frac{187}{10,000}$

59. $8.0108 = 8\frac{108}{10,000} = 8\frac{27}{2500}$

61. $289.376 = 289\frac{376}{1000} = 289\frac{47}{125}$

63. $0.9889 = \frac{9889}{10,000}$

65. $\frac{2}{100,000,000} = \frac{1}{50,000,000}$

Cumulative Review Problems

67.
```
  156
   84
   39
  463
+  76
 ‾‾‾‾
  818
```

69. $56{,}758 \approx 56{,}800$

3.2 Exercises

1. $1.3 > 1.29$

3. $0.68 < 0.681$

5. $18.92 < 18.93$

7. $0.0006 > 0.0005$

9. $1.0024 < 1.003$

11. $126.34 > 125.35$

13. $16.0572 < 16.0574$

15. $\frac{8}{10} = 0.8$

   $\frac{8}{10} > 0.08$

17. $12.6, 12.65, 12.8$

19. $0.007, 0.0071, 0.05$

21. 1.1, 1.79, 1.8, 1.81

23. 26.003, 26.033, 26.034, 26.04

25. 18.006, 18.060, 18.065, 18.066, 18.606

27. 5.67 rounds to 5.7.

29. 29.49 rounds to 29.5.

31. 578.064 rounds to 578.1.

33. 2176.83 rounds to 2176.8.

35. 26.032 rounds to 26.03.

37. 5.76582 rounds to 5.77.

39. 156.1197 rounds to 156.12.

41. 2786.706 rounds to 2786.71.

43. 1.06132 rounds to 1.061.

45. 0.047357 rounds to 0.0474.

47. 5.00761238 rounds to 5.00761.

49. 0.00753682 rounds to 0.007537.

51. 129.08939 rounds to 129.

53. $2536.85 rounds to $2537.

55. $10,098.47 rounds to $10,098.

57. $56.9832 rounds to $56.98.

59. $5783.716 rounds to $5783.72.

61. 0.095 rounds to 0.10 kilogram.
0.066 rounds to 0.07 kilogram.

63. $\dfrac{6}{100} = 0.06$ and $\dfrac{6}{10} = 0.6$

0.0059, 0.006, 0.0519, $\dfrac{6}{100}$, 0.0601,

0.0612, 0.062, $\dfrac{6}{10}$, 0.61

65. You should consider only one digit to the right of the decimal place that you wish to round to. 86.23498 is closer to 86.23 than to 86.24.

Cumulative Review Problems

67.
$$
\begin{array}{ll}
3\dfrac{1}{4} & 3\dfrac{2}{8} \\[6pt]
2\dfrac{1}{2} & 2\dfrac{4}{8} \\[6pt]
+\,6\dfrac{3}{8} & +\,6\dfrac{3}{8} \\[6pt]
\hline
& 11\dfrac{9}{8} = 12\dfrac{1}{8}
\end{array}
$$

69.
$$
\begin{array}{r}
47{,}073 \\
-\ 46{,}381 \\
\hline
692 \text{ miles}
\end{array}
$$

3.3 Exercises

1.
$$
\begin{array}{r}
44.6 \\
+\ 28.2 \\
\hline
72.8
\end{array}
$$

3.
$$
\begin{array}{r}
718.98 \\
+\ 496.57 \\
\hline
1215.55
\end{array}
$$

5.
$$
\begin{array}{r}
2.107 \\
+\ 4.918 \\
\hline
7.025
\end{array}
$$

7.
$$
\begin{array}{r}
79.061 \\
+\ 57.783 \\
\hline
136.844
\end{array}
$$

9.
$$
\begin{array}{r}
6.5 \\
12.6 \\
+\ 304.8 \\
\hline
323.9
\end{array}
$$

11.
$$
\begin{array}{r}
5.60 \\
9.23 \\
+\ 8.17 \\
\hline
23.00
\end{array}
$$

13.
$$
\begin{array}{r}
4.9637 \\
28.1200 \\
+\ 3.6450 \\
\hline
36.7287
\end{array}
$$

15. $\begin{array}{r} 12.00 \\ 3.62 \\ +\ 51.80 \\ \hline 67.42 \end{array}$

17. $\begin{array}{r} 753.61 \\ 28.75 \\ 162.30 \\ 100.50 \\ +\ 67.05 \\ \hline 1112.21 \end{array}$

19. $\begin{array}{r} 6.10 \\ 5.62 \\ +\ 8.14 \\ \hline 19.86 \text{ m} \end{array}$

21. $\begin{array}{r} 7.8 \\ 12.1 \\ 9.7 \\ 10.4 \\ 8.8 \\ +\ 11.3 \\ \hline 60.1 \text{ gallons} \end{array}$

23. $\begin{array}{r} 4.99 \\ 12.50 \\ 11.85 \\ 28.50 \\ 3.29 \\ +\ 16.99 \\ \hline \$78.12 \end{array}$

25. $\begin{array}{r} 18.42 \\ 706.15 \\ 21.03 \\ 45.00 \\ +\ 621.37 \\ \hline \$1411.97 \text{ total} \end{array}$

27. $\begin{array}{r} 6.8 \\ -\ 2.9 \\ \hline 3.9 \end{array}$

29. $\begin{array}{r} 123.51 \\ -\ 96.34 \\ \hline 27.17 \end{array}$

31. $\begin{array}{r} 76.80 \\ -\ 12.62 \\ \hline 64.18 \end{array}$

33. $\begin{array}{r} 586.513 \\ -\ 78.200 \\ \hline 508.313 \end{array}$

35. $\begin{array}{r} 1.00782 \\ -\ 0.98631 \\ \hline 0.02151 \end{array}$

37. $\begin{array}{r} 24.0079 \\ -\ 19.3614 \\ \hline 4.6465 \end{array}$

39. $\begin{array}{r} 8.000 \\ -\ 1.263 \\ \hline 6.737 \end{array}$

41. $\begin{array}{r} 7362.14 \\ -\ 6173.07 \\ \hline 1189.07 \end{array}$

43. $\begin{array}{r} 1.5000 \\ -\ 0.0365 \\ \hline 1.4635 \end{array}$

45. $\begin{array}{r} 63.45 \\ -\ 29.95 \\ \hline \$33.50 \end{array}$

47. $\begin{array}{r} 7.675 \\ +\ 9.986 \\ \hline 17.661 \text{ kilograms} \end{array}$

49. $\begin{array}{r} 37{,}026.65 \\ -\ \ \ \ \ 79.49 \\ \hline \$36{,}947.16 \text{ more} \end{array}$

51. $\begin{array}{r} 47.70 \\ +\ 7.00 \\ \hline 54.70 \end{array}$

$\begin{array}{r} 100.00 \\ -\ 54.70 \\ \hline 45.30 \\ \$45.30 \text{ change} \end{array}$

53. $\begin{array}{r} 9.39 \\ -\ 7.93 \\ \hline 1.46 \text{ cm} \end{array}$

55.   12,563,784.56
    − 11,962,375.49
       $601,409.07 revenue shortage

57.   0.023
    − 0.015
     0.008 milligrams, no

59.   43.8
    − 38.1
     $5.7 billion
     5,700,000,000 dollars

61.   61.4
    − 48.1
     $13.3 billion
     13,300,000,000 dollars

63. $x + 7.1 = 15.5$
     15.5
    − 7.1
     8.4
    $x = 8.4$

65. $156.9 + x = 200.6$
     200.6
    − 156.9
      43.7
    $x = 43.7$

67. $4.162 = x + 2.053$
     4.162
    − 2.053
     2.109
    $x = 2.109$

Cumulative Review Problems

69.   2536
    ×   8
    20,288

71. $\dfrac{22}{7} \times \dfrac{49}{50} = \dfrac{77}{25}$ or $3\dfrac{2}{25}$

Putting Your Skills to Work

1. $83.24

---

3. $382.54 - 120.00 + 98.96 - 70.00 - 0.65$
         $- 0.65$
    $= \$290.20$

5.   Regina (1) hasn't included some bank charges in her account, (2) hasn't recorded a check or a deposit, or (3) has recorded a check or deposit in the wrong amount. Another possibility is that she made an arithmetic error.
She should post all charges the bank makes in her own records. Then she should compare the amount of each check and deposit on the bank's statement with the amounts listed in her records. She should also check her arithmetic.

3.4 Exercises

1.   0.6
   × 0.2
   0.12

3.   0.12
   × 0.5
   0.060 = 0.06

5.   0.0036
   ×   0.8
   0.00288

7.   0.079
   ×   0.09
   0.00711

9.   0.025
   ×   0.081
      25
     200
   0.002025

11.   10.97
   ×   0.06
   0.6582

13.   7986
   ×   0.32
   15972
   23958
   2555.52

15.
$$\begin{array}{r} 1.892 \\ \times\ 0.007 \\ \hline 0.013244 \end{array}$$

17.
$$\begin{array}{r} 0.7613 \\ \times\ 1009 \\ \hline 68517 \\ 761300 \\ \hline 768.1517 \end{array}$$

19.
$$\begin{array}{r} 9630 \\ \times\ 0.51 \\ \hline 9630 \\ 48150 \\ \hline 4911.30 \end{array} = 4911.3$$

21.
$$\begin{array}{r} 126 \\ \times\ 3.5 \\ \hline 630 \\ 378 \\ \hline 441.0 \end{array} = 441$$

23.
$$\begin{array}{r} 5030 \\ \times\ 8.62 \\ \hline 10060 \\ 30180 \\ 40240 \\ \hline 43,358.60 \end{array} = 43,358.6$$

25.
$$\begin{array}{r} 0.0034 \\ \times\ 0.07 \\ \hline 0.000238 \end{array}$$

27.
$$\begin{array}{r} 6523.7 \\ \times\ 0.001 \\ \hline 6.5237 \end{array}$$

29.
$$\begin{array}{r} 5.85 \\ \times\ 40 \\ \hline \$234.00 \end{array}$$

31.
$$\begin{array}{r} 9.55 \\ \times\ 40 \\ \hline \$382.00 \end{array}$$

33.
$$\begin{array}{r} 20.3 \\ 11.6 \\ \hline 1218 \\ 203 \\ 203 \\ \hline 235.48 \end{array}$$
235.48 square feet

35.
$$\begin{array}{r} 36.90 \\ \times\ 18 \\ \hline 29520 \\ 3690 \\ \hline \$664.20 \end{array}$$

37.
$$\begin{array}{r} 0.55 \\ \times\ 1.4 \\ \hline 220 \\ 055 \\ \hline 0.770 \end{array}$$
$0.77

39.
$$\begin{array}{r} 26.4 \\ \times\ 19.5 \\ \hline 1320 \\ 2376 \\ 264 \\ \hline 514.80 \end{array}$$ miles

41. $2.86 \times 10 = 28.6$

43. $0.701 \times 100 = 70.1$

45. $128.65 \times 1000 = 128,650$

47. $5.60982 \times 10,000 = 56,098.2$

49. $280,560.2 \times 10^2 = 28,056,020$

51. $816.32 \times 10^3 = 816,320$

53. $0.6718 \times 10^3 = 671.8$

55. $0.00081376 \times 10^5 = 81.376$

57. $5.932 \times 100 = 593.2$ cm

59. $2.98 \times 1000 = 2980$ meters

61. $3640.50 \times 10,000 = \$36,405,000.00$

63.
$$\begin{array}{r} 254.2 \\ \times\ 19.6 \\ \hline 15252 \\ 22878 \\ 2542 \\ \hline 4982.32 \end{array}\ \text{square yards}$$

$$\begin{array}{r} 4982.32 \\ \times\quad 12.50 \\ \hline 000000 \\ 2491160 \\ 996464 \\ 498232 \\ \hline \$62,279.0000 \end{array}$$

Cumulative Review Problems

65.
$$\begin{array}{r} 98 \\ 12\overline{)1176} \\ 108 \\ \hline 96 \\ 96 \\ \hline 0 \end{array}$$

67.
$$\begin{array}{r} 125\ \text{R}\ 4 \\ 37\overline{)4629} \\ 37 \\ \hline 92 \\ 74 \\ \hline 189 \\ 185 \\ \hline 4 \end{array}$$

3.5 Exercises

1.
$$\begin{array}{r} 2.1 \\ 6\overline{)12.6} \\ 12 \\ \hline 6 \\ 6 \\ \hline 0 \end{array}$$

3.
$$\begin{array}{r} 0.0369 \\ 4\overline{)0.1476} \\ 12 \\ \hline 27 \\ 24 \\ \hline 36 \\ 36 \\ \hline 0 \end{array}$$

5.
$$\begin{array}{r} 18.31 \\ 7\overline{)128.17} \\ 7 \\ \hline 58 \\ 56 \\ \hline 21 \\ 21 \\ \hline 7 \\ 7 \\ \hline 0 \end{array}$$

7.
$$\begin{array}{r} 0.0565 \\ 64\overline{)3.616} \\ 3\ 20 \\ \hline 416 \\ 384 \\ \hline 320 \\ 320 \\ \hline 0 \end{array}$$

9.
$$\begin{array}{r} 0.0029 \\ 21\overline{)0.0609} \\ 42 \\ \hline 189 \\ 189 \\ \hline 0 \end{array}$$

11.
$$\begin{array}{r} 12.2 \\ 0.8\overline{)9.76} \\ 8 \\ \hline 1\ 7 \\ 1\ 6 \\ \hline 16 \\ 16 \\ \hline 0 \end{array}$$

13.
$$\begin{array}{r} 64.3 \\ 0.5\overline{)32.15} \\ 30 \\ \hline 21 \\ 20 \\ \hline 15 \\ 15 \\ \hline 0 \end{array}$$

15.
```
         8.01
0.09)0.7209
       72
       ‾‾
       00
       00
       ‾‾
        9
        9
        ‾
        0
```

17.
```
      21
3.6)75.6
    72
    ‾‾
    36
    36
    ‾‾
     0
```

19.
```
       230
0.36)82.80
     72
     ‾‾
     10 8
     10 8
     ‾‾‾‾
       00
       00
       ‾‾
        0
```

21.
```
     5.27
7)36.92
  35
  ‾‾
  19
  14
  ‾‾
   52
   49
   ‾‾
    3
```
5.3

23.
```
      2.31
1.8)4.160
    3 6
    ‾‾‾
    56
    54
    ‾‾
    20
    18
    ‾‾
     2
```
2.3

25.
```
           33.75
0.95)32.0670
     28 5
     ‾‾‾‾
      3 56
      2 85
      ‾‾‾‾
       717
       665
       ‾‾‾
       520
       475
       ‾‾‾
        45
```
33.8

27.
```
       65.955
4)263.820
  24
  ‾‾
  23
  20
  ‾‾
   38
   36
   ‾‾
    22
    20
    ‾‾
     20
     20
     ‾‾
      0
```
65.96

29.
```
        12.235
1.7)20.8000
    17
    ‾‾
     3 8
     3 4
     ‾‾‾
      40
      34
      ‾‾
      60
      51
      ‾‾
      90
      85
      ‾‾
       5
```
12.24

31.
```
              24.922
      0.27) 6.72900
            5 4
            ‾‾‾‾
            132
            108
            ‾‾‾
            249
            243
            ‾‾‾
             60
             54
            ‾‾‾
             60
             54
            ‾‾‾
              6
```
24.92

33.
```
            31.0202
      8) 248.1620
         24
         ‾‾
          8
          8
          ‾
          16
          16
          ‾‾
           20
           16
           ‾‾
            4
```
31.020

35.
```
             12.2463
      0.69) 8.450000
            6 9
            ‾‾‾
            155
            138
            ‾‾‾
            170
            138
            ‾‾‾
            320
            276
            ‾‾‾
            440
            414
            ‾‾‾
            260
            207
            ‾‾‾
             53
```
12.246

37.
```
              49.7
      0.075) 3.7290
             3 00
             ‾‾‾‾
              729
              675
             ‾‾‾
              540
              525
             ‾‾‾
               15
```
50

39.
```
              12.7
      0.55) 7.000
            5 5
            ‾‾‾
            150
            110
            ‾‾‾
            400
            385
            ‾‾‾
             15
```
13

41.
```
            6.2
      38) 235.6
          228
          ‾‾‾
           76
           76
          ‾‾‾
            0
```
6.2 ounces in each portion

43.
```
             2 0
      15.6) 312.0
            312
```
20 miles per gallon

45.
```
           376.5
      9) 3388.5
         27
         ‾‾
         68
         63
         ‾‾
         58
         54
         ‾‾
         45
         45
         ‾‾
          0
```
$376.50 each

47.
$$125.75 \overline{)1131.75}$$
$$\underline{1131\ 75}$$
$$0$$
quotient 9

9 payments

49.
$$7.9 \overline{)300.2}$$
quotient 38
$$\underline{237}$$
$$632$$
$$\underline{632}$$
$$0$$

There are 38 blocks of chalk in the box. The error was made by placing 2 fewer blocks of chalk in the box than what was listed on the label.

51. $0.7 \times n = 0.0861$
$$0.7 \overline{)0.0861}$$
quotient 0.123
$$\underline{7}$$
$$16$$
$$\underline{14}$$
$$21$$
$$\underline{21}$$
$$0$$
$n = 0.123$

53. $1.6 \times n = 110.4$
$$1.6 \overline{)110.4}$$
quotient 6 9
$$\underline{96}$$
$$14\ 4$$
$$\underline{14\ 4}$$
$$0$$
$n = 69$

55. $n \times 0.063 = 2.835$
$$0.063 \overline{)2.835}$$
quotient 45
$$\underline{2\ 52}$$
$$315$$
$$\underline{315}$$
$$0$$
$n = 45$

57. $n \times 0.008 = 6.48$
$$0.008 \overline{)6.480}$$
quotient 810.
$$\underline{6\ 4}$$
$$8$$
$$\underline{8}$$
$$0$$
$n = 810$

59. $\dfrac{3.8702}{0.0523} \times \dfrac{10,000}{10,000} = \dfrac{38,702}{523}$
$$523 \overline{)38,702}$$
quotient 74
$$\underline{36\ 61}$$
$$2\ 092$$
$$\underline{2\ 092}$$
$$0$$
$$\dfrac{3.8702}{0.0523} = 74$$

Cumulative Review Problems

61. $\dfrac{3}{8} + 1\dfrac{2}{5} = \dfrac{15}{40} + 1\dfrac{16}{40} = 1\dfrac{31}{40}$

63. $3\dfrac{1}{2} \times 2\dfrac{1}{6} = \dfrac{7}{2} \times \dfrac{13}{6} = \dfrac{91}{12} = 7\dfrac{7}{12}$

3.6 Exercises

1. same quantity

3. The digits 8942 repeat.

5.
$$4 \overline{)1.00}$$
quotient 0.25
$$\underline{8}$$
$$20$$
$$\underline{20}$$
$$0$$
$$\dfrac{1}{4} = 0.25$$

7.
$$8\overline{)7.000} \quad 0.875$$
$$\underline{6\ 4}$$
$$60$$
$$\underline{56}$$
$$40$$
$$\underline{40}$$
$$0$$

$$\frac{7}{8} = 0.875$$

9.
$$16\overline{)7.0000} \quad 0.4375$$
$$\underline{6\ 4}$$
$$60$$
$$\underline{48}$$
$$120$$
$$\underline{112}$$
$$80$$
$$\underline{80}$$
$$0$$

$$\frac{7}{16} = 0.4375$$

11.
$$20\overline{)7.00} \quad 0.35$$
$$\underline{6\ 0}$$
$$100$$
$$\underline{100}$$
$$0$$

$$\frac{7}{20} = 0.35$$

13.
$$50\overline{)31.00} \quad 0.62$$
$$\underline{30\ 0}$$
$$100$$
$$\underline{100}$$
$$0$$

$$\frac{31}{50} = 0.62$$

15.
$$4\overline{)9.00} \quad 2.25$$
$$\underline{8}$$
$$1\ 0$$
$$\underline{8}$$
$$20$$
$$\underline{20}$$
$$0$$

$$\frac{9}{4} = 2.25$$

17.
$$8\overline{)1.000} \quad 0.125$$
$$\underline{8}$$
$$20$$
$$\underline{16}$$
$$40$$
$$\underline{40}$$
$$0$$

$$2\frac{1}{8} = 2.125$$

19.
$$16\overline{)7.0000} \quad 0.4375$$
$$\underline{6\ 4}$$
$$60$$
$$\underline{48}$$
$$120$$
$$\underline{112}$$
$$80$$
$$\underline{80}$$
$$0$$

$$1\frac{7}{16} = 1.4375$$

21.
$$3\overline{)2.000} \quad 0.666$$
$$\underline{1\ 8}$$
$$20$$
$$\underline{18}$$
$$20$$
$$\underline{18}$$
$$2$$

$$\frac{2}{3} = 0.\overline{6}$$

23.
$$\begin{array}{r} 0.555 \\ 9\overline{)5.000} \\ \underline{4\ 5} \\ 50 \\ \underline{45} \\ 50 \\ \underline{45} \\ 5 \end{array}$$

$$\frac{5}{9} = 0.\overline{5}$$

25.
$$\begin{array}{r} 0.833 \\ 6\overline{)5.000} \\ \underline{4\ 8} \\ 20 \\ \underline{18} \\ 20 \\ \underline{18} \\ 2 \end{array}$$

$$\frac{5}{6} = 0.8\overline{3}$$

27.
$$\begin{array}{r} 0.9090 \\ 11\overline{)10.0000} \\ \underline{9\ 9} \\ 100 \\ \underline{99} \\ 10 \end{array}$$

$$\frac{10}{11} = 0.\overline{90}$$

29.
$$\begin{array}{r} 0.933 \\ 15\overline{)14.000} \\ \underline{13\ 5} \\ 50 \\ \underline{45} \\ 50 \\ \underline{45} \\ 5 \end{array}$$

$$\frac{14}{15} = 0.9\overline{3}$$

31.
$$\begin{array}{r} 0.1515 \\ 33\overline{)5.0000} \\ \underline{3\ 3} \\ 1\ 70 \\ \underline{1\ 65} \\ 50 \\ \underline{33} \\ 170 \\ \underline{165} \\ 5 \end{array}$$

$$\frac{5}{33} = 0.\overline{15}$$

33.
$$\begin{array}{r} 1.037 \\ 27\overline{)28.000} \\ \underline{27} \\ 1\ 0 \\ \underline{0} \\ 1\ 00 \\ \underline{81} \\ 190 \\ \underline{189} \\ 1 \end{array}$$

$$\frac{28}{27} = 1.\overline{037}$$

35.
$$\begin{array}{r} 0.277 \\ 18\overline{)5.000} \\ \underline{3\ 6} \\ 1\ 40 \\ \underline{1\ 26} \\ 140 \\ \underline{126} \\ 14 \end{array}$$

$$2\frac{5}{18} = 2.2\overline{7}$$

37.
$$\begin{array}{r} 0.5714 \\ 7\overline{)4.0000} \\ \underline{3\ 5} \\ 50 \\ \underline{49} \\ 10 \\ \underline{7} \\ 30 \\ \underline{28} \\ 2 \end{array}$$

$$\frac{4}{7} \text{ rounds to } 0.571.$$

39.

$$
\begin{array}{r}
0.9047 \\
21\overline{)19.0000} \\
18\ 9 \\
\hline
10 \\
0 \\
\hline
100 \\
84 \\
\hline
160 \\
147 \\
\hline
13
\end{array}
$$

$\dfrac{19}{21}$ rounds to 0.905.

41.

$$
\begin{array}{r}
0.1458 \\
48\overline{)7.0000} \\
4\ 8 \\
\hline
2\ 20 \\
1\ 92 \\
\hline
280 \\
240 \\
\hline
400 \\
384 \\
\hline
16
\end{array}
$$

$\dfrac{7}{48}$ rounds to 0.146.

43.

$$
\begin{array}{r}
1.2962 \\
27\overline{)35.0000} \\
27 \\
\hline
8\ 0 \\
5\ 4 \\
\hline
2\ 60 \\
2\ 43 \\
\hline
170 \\
162 \\
\hline
80 \\
54 \\
\hline
26
\end{array}
$$

$\dfrac{35}{27}$ rounds to 1.296.

45.

$$
\begin{array}{r}
0.246 \\
81\overline{)20.0000} \\
16\ 2 \\
\hline
3\ 80 \\
3\ 24 \\
\hline
560 \\
486 \\
\hline
740 \\
729 \\
\hline
11
\end{array}
$$

$\dfrac{20}{81}$ rounds to 0.247.

47.

$$
\begin{array}{r}
0.944 \\
18\overline{)17.0} \\
16\ 2 \\
\hline
80 \\
72 \\
\hline
80 \\
72 \\
\hline
8
\end{array}
$$

$\dfrac{17}{18} = 0.9\overline{4}$

$\dfrac{17}{18}$ rounds to 0.944.

49.

$$
\begin{array}{r}
3.1428 \\
7\overline{)22.0000} \\
21 \\
\hline
1\ 0 \\
7 \\
\hline
30 \\
28 \\
\hline
20 \\
14 \\
\hline
60 \\
56 \\
\hline
4
\end{array}
$$

$\dfrac{22}{7}$ rounds to 3.143.

51.
$$
\begin{array}{r}
0.4736 \\
19\overline{)9.0000} \\
\underline{7\ 6} \\
1\ 40 \\
\underline{1\ 33} \\
70 \\
\underline{57} \\
130 \\
\underline{114} \\
16
\end{array}
$$

$\dfrac{9}{19}$ rounds to 0.474.

53.
$$
\begin{array}{r}
0.20833 \\
24\overline{)5.00000} \\
\underline{4\ 8} \\
200 \\
\underline{192} \\
80 \\
\underline{72} \\
80
\end{array}
$$

$0.208\overline{3}$ inch thick

55.
$$
\begin{array}{r}
0.375 \\
8\overline{)3.000} \\
\underline{2\ 4} \\
60 \\
\underline{56} \\
40 \\
\underline{40} \\
0
\end{array}
$$

$$
\begin{array}{r}
0.500 \\
-\ 0.375 \\
\hline
0.125
\end{array}
$$
It is too small by 0.125 inch.

57.
$$
\begin{array}{r}
0.53125 \\
32\overline{)17.00000} \\
\underline{16\ 0} \\
1\ 00 \\
\underline{96} \\
40 \\
\underline{32} \\
80 \\
\underline{64} \\
160 \\
\underline{160} \\
0
\end{array}
$$

$0.53125 > 0.53$

$$
\begin{array}{r}
0.53125 \\
-\ 0.53000 \\
\hline
0.00125
\end{array}
$$
It is too thick by 0.00125 inch.

59. $(0.2)^3 + 5.9 \times 1.3 - 2.6$
$= 0.008 + 5.9 \times 1.3 - 2.6$
$= 0.008 + 7.67 - 2.6$
$= 7.678 - 2.6$
$= 5.078$

61. $12.2 \times 9.4 - 2.68 + 1.6 \div 0.8$
$= 114.68 - 2.68 + 2$
$= 114$

63. $12 \div 0.03 - 15 \times (0.6 + 0.7)^2$
$= 12 \div 0.03 - 15 \times (1.3)^2$
$= 12 \div 0.03 - 15 \times 1.69$
$= 400 - 25.35$
$= 374.65$

65. $116.32 + (0.12)^2 + 18.06 \times 2.2$
$= 116.32 + 0.0144 + 39.732$
$= 156.0664$

67. $(1.1)^3 + 2.6 \div 0.13 + 0.083$
$= 1.331 + 20 + 0.083$
$= 21.414$

69. $(56.3 - 56.1)^2 \div 0.016 = (0.2)^2 \div 0.016$
$= 0.04 \div 0.016$
$= 2.5$

71. $(0.5)^3 + (3 - 2.6) \times 0.5$
$= (0.5)^3 + 0.4 \times 0.5$
$= 0.125 + 0.20$
$= 0.325$

73. $(0.76 + 4.24) \div 0.25 + 8.6$
$= 5.00 \div 0.25 + 8.6$
$= 20.0 + 8.6$
$= 28.6$

75. $(1.6)^3 + (2.4)^2 + 18.666 \div 3.05 + 4.86$
$= 4.096 + 5.76 + 6.12 + 4.86$
$= 20.836$

77.

```
         0.5869297
8921)5236.0000000
     4460 5
     ───────
      775 50
      713 68
      ───────
       61 820
       53 526
       ───────
        8 2940
        8 0289
        ───────
          26510
          17842
          ───────
          86680
          80289
          ───────
           63910
           62447
           ───────
            1463
```

$$\frac{5236}{8921} = 0.586930$$

79. a.

```
    0.16̄1̄6̄
  − 0.00̄1̄6̄
  ───────
    0.16
```

b.

```
    0.1616̄1̄6̄
  − 0.0166̄6̄6̄
  ─────────
    0.1449̄4̄9̄
```

c. The repeating patterns line up differently.

Cumulative Review Problems

81. $12 \times 26 = 312$ square feet

83. $56 + 81 + 42 + 198 = \$377$ was deposited

3.7 Exercises

1.

```
    167.2
    136.7
     99.3
  + 218.0
  ───────
    621.2
```
621.2 pounds

3.

```
   19,891.33
 − 11,022.45
 ───────────
    8868.88
```
$8868.88

5.

```
     103.4
  ×   76.3
  ───────
    3102
    6204
   7238
  ───────
   7889.42
```
7889.42 square meters

7.

```
          46
  0.75)34.50
       30 0
       ─────
        4 50
        4 50
        ─────
           0
```
46 packages

9.

```
    71.32
     2.16
  +  1.19
  ───────
    74.67

    75.00
  − 74.67
  ───────
     0.33
```
Yes; after she bought the eggs she had $0.33.

11.

```
    11.68
    10.42
  + 12.67
  ───────
    34.77

      11.59
  3)34.77
    3
    ─
    4
    3
    ─
    1 7
    1 5
    ───
      27
      27
      ──
       0
```
11.59 meters of rainfall per year

13.
$$3.5)\overline{42.0} \quad \frac{12}{}$$
```
         12
 3.5)42.0
      35
       7 0
       7 0
          0
```
12 days

15.
```
      43.9
      11.3
   +  63.4
     118.6

     118.6
   × 10.65
      5930
      7116
     11860
   1263.090
```
$1263.09

17. $14.30 \times 40 + 14.30 \times 1.5 \times 8$
$= 572 + 171.6$
$= 743.6$
$743.60

19.
```
    420.13
    116.32
    318.57
 +    1.86
   $856.88

     16.50
     36.89
 +  376.94
   $430.33

    856.88
 -  430.33
   $426.55  balance
```

21.
```
    288.65
 ×     60
    17,319

    17,319
 -  11,500
     5819
```
He will pay $17,319 over 5 years.
He will pay $5819 more than the loan.

23.
```
        55
 144)7920
     720
     720
     720
        0
```
$55 cost per pair to store.
```
     68
 -   55
     13
```
$13 profit on each pair
```
    144
 ×   13
    432
    144
   1872
```
$1872 profit

25.
```
      1.151
  7)8.060
    7
    1 0
    7
      36
      35
      10
       7
       3
```
```
    1.300
 -  1.151
    0.149
```
Yes, by 0.149 milligram per liter

27.
```
          137
 126.4)17316.8
       1264
       4676
       3792
        8848
        8848
```
137 minutes

29.
```
    84.1
   -66.4
    17.7
```
17.7 quadrillion Btus

31. $(33.1 + 43.8 + 66.4) \div 3 = 143.3 \div 3$
≈ 47.8
Approximately 47.8 quadrillion Btus

Cumulative Review Problems

33. $\dfrac{1}{5} + \dfrac{3}{7} + \dfrac{1}{2} = \dfrac{14}{70} + \dfrac{30}{70} + \dfrac{35}{70}$

$= \dfrac{79}{70}$ or $1\dfrac{9}{70}$

35. $\dfrac{5}{12} \times \dfrac{36}{27} = \dfrac{5}{1} \times \dfrac{3}{27}$

$= \dfrac{5}{1} \times \dfrac{1}{9} = \dfrac{5}{9}$

Chapter 3 Review Problems

1. 13.672 = thirteen and six hundred seventy-two thousandths

3. $\dfrac{7}{10} = 0.7$

5. $1\dfrac{523}{1000} = 1.523$

7. $0.17 = \dfrac{17}{100}$

9. $26.88 = 26\dfrac{88}{100} = 26\dfrac{22}{25}$

11. $\dfrac{13}{100} = 0.13$

$\dfrac{13}{100} > 0.103$

13. 0.901, 0.918, 0.98, 0.981

15. 0.613 rounds to 0.6.

17. 1.09952 rounds to 1.100.

19.
$$
\begin{array}{r}
1.800 \\
2.603 \\
0.520 \\
+ \ 1.716 \\
\hline
6.639
\end{array}
$$

21. a.
$$
\begin{array}{r}
2.9 \\
1.6 \\
+ \ 4.0 \\
\hline
8.5 \ \text{gallons}
\end{array}
$$

    b. 9 gallons

23.
$$
\begin{array}{r}
199.703 \\
- \ 108.964 \\
\hline
90.739
\end{array}
$$

25.
$$
\begin{array}{r}
0.76 \\
\times \ 0.03 \\
\hline
0.0228
\end{array}
$$

27.
$$
\begin{array}{r}
0.026 \\
\times \ 0.014 \\
\hline
104 \\
26 \ \ \ \\
\hline
0.000364
\end{array}
$$

29.
$$
\begin{array}{r}
54 \\
\times \ 1.6 \\
\hline
324 \\
54 \ \ \\
\hline
86.4
\end{array}
$$

31. $7.86 \times 10 = 78.6$

33. $0.000613 \times 10^3 = 0.613$

35.
$$
\begin{array}{r}
0.25 \\
\times \ 3.6 \\
\hline
150 \\
75 \ \ \\
\hline
\$0.900
\end{array}
$$

37.
$$
\begin{array}{r}
0.00258 \\
0.07\overline{)0.0001806} \\
\underline{14 \ \ \ \ \ \ \ } \\
40 \ \ \ \ \ \\
\underline{35 \ \ \ \ \ } \\
56 \ \ \\
\underline{56 \ \ } \\
0
\end{array}
$$

39.

$$
\begin{array}{r}
232.9 \\
8\overline{)1863.2} \\
16 \\
\hline
26 \\
24 \\
\hline
23 \\
16 \\
\hline
7\,2 \\
7\,2 \\
\hline
0
\end{array}
$$

41.

$$
\begin{array}{r}
0.0589 \\
0.06\overline{)0.03539} \\
30 \\
\hline
53 \\
48 \\
\hline
59 \\
54 \\
\hline
5
\end{array}
$$

0.059

43.

$$
\begin{array}{r}
0.277 \\
18\overline{)5.000} \\
3\,6 \\
\hline
1\,40 \\
1\,26 \\
\hline
140 \\
126 \\
\hline
14
\end{array}
$$

$\dfrac{5}{18} = 0.2\overline{7}$

45.

$$
\begin{array}{r}
0.833 \\
6\overline{)5.000} \\
4\,8 \\
\hline
20 \\
18 \\
\hline
20 \\
18 \\
\hline
2
\end{array}
$$

$1\dfrac{5}{6} = 1.8\overline{3}$

47.

$$
\begin{array}{r}
0.7857 \\
14\overline{)11.0000} \\
98 \\
\hline
120 \\
112 \\
\hline
80 \\
70 \\
\hline
100 \\
98 \\
\hline
2
\end{array}
$$

$\dfrac{11}{14}$ rounds to 0.786.

49. $1.6 \times 2.3 + 0.4 - 0.6 \times 0.8$
$= 3.68 + 0.4 - 0.48$
$= 3.6$

51. $0.03 + (1.2)^2 - 5.3 \times 0.06$
$= 0.03 + 1.44 - 0.318$
$= 1.152$

53. $6.63 + 8.24 \div (5.76 - 5.68) - 22.5$
$= 6.63 + 8.24 \div 0.08 - 22.5$
$= 6.63 + 103 - 22.5$
$= 87.13$

55.

$$
\begin{array}{r}
0.56 \\
\times\ 0.38 \\
\hline
448 \\
168 \\
\hline
0.2128
\end{array}
$$

57.

$$
\begin{array}{r}
0.6 \\
0.34\overline{)0.204} \\
204 \\
\hline
0
\end{array}
$$

59.

$$
\begin{array}{r}
2398.26 \\
-1959.07 \\
\hline
439.19
\end{array}
$$

61.

$$
\begin{array}{r}
0.0610 \\
0.0023 \\
+\ 0.7770 \\
\hline
0.8403
\end{array}
$$

63. $8 \div 0.4 + 0.1 \times (0.2)^2 = 20 + 0.1 \times 0.04$
$= 20 + 0.004 = 20.004$

65.
$$\begin{array}{r} 18.50 \\ 29.95 \\ + \ 2.42 \\ \hline \$50.87 \end{array}$$

$$\begin{array}{r} 60.00 \\ -50.87 \\ \hline \$9.13 \ \text{left} \end{array}$$

67.
$$\begin{array}{r} 49 \\ -40 \\ \hline 9 \ \text{hours} \end{array}$$

$6.88 \times 40 + 6.88 \times 1.5 \times 9$
$= 275.20 + 92.88$
$= \$368.08$

69.
$$\begin{array}{r} 189.60 \\ \times \quad 48 \\ \hline 151680 \\ 75840 \\ \hline \$9100.80 \end{array}$$

$$\begin{array}{r} 9100.80 \\ - \ 6930.50 \\ \hline \$2170.30 \ \text{extra} \end{array}$$

71.
$$12\overline{)0.0300} \quad 0.0025$$
$$\begin{array}{r} \underline{24} \\ 60 \\ \underline{60} \\ 0 \end{array}$$

$$\begin{array}{r} 0.0025 \\ - \ 0.0020 \\ \hline 0.0005 \end{array}$$
No; by 0.0005 milligram per liter

Chapter 3 Test

1. One hundred fifty-seven thousandths

3. $7.15 = 7\dfrac{15}{100} = 7\dfrac{3}{20}$

5. 2.19, 2.91, 2.9, 2.907
2.190, 2.910, 2.900, 2.907

2.190, 2.900, 2.907, 2.910
2.19, 2.9, 2.907, 2.91

7. 0.341$\underline{7}$52 rounds to 0.0342 since 7 is greater than 5.

9.
$$\begin{array}{r} \overset{1 \, 1 \ \ 1}{17.00} \\ 2.10 \\ 16.80 \\ 0.04 \\ + \ 1.59 \\ \hline 37.53 \end{array}$$

11.
$$\begin{array}{r} \overset{\quad 9}{\overset{2\,1\,0\,1\,0}{72.3\cancel{0}\cancel{0}}} \\ - \ 1.145 \\ \hline 71.155 \end{array}$$

13. $2.189 \times 100 = 218.9$

15.
$$\begin{array}{r} 47. \\ 0.69\overline{)32.43} \\ \underline{27 \ 6} \\ 4 \ 83 \\ \underline{4 \ 83} \\ 0 \end{array}$$

17.
$$\begin{array}{r} 0.5625 \\ 16\overline{)9.0000} \\ \underline{8 \ 0} \\ 1 \ 00 \\ \underline{96} \\ 40 \\ \underline{32} \\ 80 \\ \underline{80} \\ 0 \end{array}$$

$\dfrac{9}{16} = 0.5625$

19. $19.36 \div (0.24 + 0.26) \times (0.4)^2$
$= 19.36 \div 0.5 \times 0.16$
$= 38.72 \times 0.16$
$= 6.1952$

21.

$$
\begin{array}{r}
42,780.5 \\
-\ 42,620.5 \\
\hline
160.0
\end{array}
$$

$$
\begin{array}{r}
18.82 \\
8.5\overline{)160.000} \\
\underline{85} \\
75\ 0 \\
\underline{68\ 0} \\
7\ 00 \\
\underline{6\ 80} \\
200 \\
\underline{170} \\
30
\end{array}
$$

18.8 miles per gallon

Chapters 1–3 Cumulative Test

1. 38,056,954 = Thirty-eight million, fifty-six thousand, nine hundred fifty-four

3.
$$
\begin{array}{r}
1,091,000 \\
-\ 1,036,520 \\
\hline
54,480
\end{array}
$$

5.
$$
\begin{array}{r}
258 \\
17\overline{)4386} \\
\underline{34} \\
98 \\
\underline{85} \\
136 \\
\underline{136} \\
0
\end{array}
$$

7. $\dfrac{33}{88} = \dfrac{33 \div 11}{88 \div 11} = \dfrac{3}{8}$

9. $\dfrac{23}{35} - \dfrac{2}{5} = \dfrac{23}{35} - \dfrac{2}{5} \times \dfrac{7}{7}$
$= \dfrac{23}{35} - \dfrac{14}{35}$
$= \dfrac{9}{35}$

11. $52 \div 3\dfrac{1}{4} = 52 \div \dfrac{13}{4}$
$= 52 \times \dfrac{4}{13}$
$= 16$

13. $60,000 \times 400,000 = 24,000,000,000$

15. 2.01, 2.1, 2.11, 2.12, 20.1

17.
$$
\begin{array}{r}
1.90 \\
2.36 \\
15.20 \\
+\ 0.08 \\
\hline
19.54
\end{array}
$$

19.
$$
\begin{array}{r}
56.8 \\
\times\ 0.02 \\
\hline
1.136
\end{array}
$$

21.
$$
\begin{array}{r}
1.058 \\
0.06\overline{)0.06348} \\
\underline{6} \\
3 \\
0 \\
34 \\
\underline{30} \\
48 \\
\underline{48} \\
0
\end{array}
$$

23. $1.44 \div 0.12 + (0.3)^3 + 1.57$
$= 1.44 \div 0.12 + 0.027 + 1.57$
$= 12 + 0.027 + 1.57 = 12.027 + 1.57$
$= 13.597$

25.
$$
\begin{array}{r}
199.36 \\
1.03 \\
166.35 \\
+\ 93.50 \\
\hline
460.24
\end{array}
$$

$$
\begin{array}{r}
90.00 \\
37.49 \\
+\ 137.18 \\
\hline
264.67
\end{array}
$$

$$
\begin{array}{r}
460.24 \\
-\ 264.67 \\
\hline
195.57
\end{array}
$$

$195.57

Chapter 4

Pretest Chapter 4

1. $\dfrac{13}{18}$

3. $\dfrac{\$72}{\$16} = \dfrac{72 \div 8}{16 \div 8} = \dfrac{9}{2}$

5. a. $\dfrac{\$70}{\$240} = \dfrac{70 \div 10}{240 \div 10} = \dfrac{7}{24}$

   b. $\dfrac{\$22}{\$240} = \dfrac{22 \div 2}{240 \div 2} = \dfrac{11}{120}$

7. $\dfrac{620 \text{ gallons}}{840 \text{ square feet}}$

   $= \dfrac{620 \div 20}{840 \div 20} = \dfrac{31 \text{ gallons}}{42 \text{ square feet}}$

9. $\dfrac{\$592}{16 \text{ radios}} = \dfrac{592 \div 16}{16 \div 16} = \dfrac{\$37}{1 \text{ radio}}$

   or \$37/radio

11. $\dfrac{42}{78} = \dfrac{21}{39}$

13. $\dfrac{17}{33} \overset{?}{=} \dfrac{19}{45}$

    $17 \times 45 \overset{?}{=} 33 \times 19$

    $765 \neq 627$ False

15. $234 = 13 \times n$

    $\dfrac{234}{13} = \dfrac{13 \times n}{13}$

    $18 = n$

17. $\dfrac{3}{144} = \dfrac{n}{336}$

    $144 \times n = 3 \times 336$

    $\dfrac{144 \times n}{144} = \dfrac{1008}{144}$

    $n = 7$

19. $\dfrac{1.5 \text{ cups}}{6 \text{ portions}} = \dfrac{n \text{ cups}}{14 \text{ portions}}$

    $14 \times 1.5 = 6 \times n$

    $\dfrac{21}{6} = \dfrac{6 \times n}{6}$

    $n = 3.5$ cups

21. $\dfrac{5 \text{ inches}}{365 \text{ miles}} = \dfrac{2 \text{ inches}}{n \text{ miles}}$

    $5 \times n = 2 \times 365$

    $\dfrac{5 \times n}{5} = \dfrac{730}{5}$

    $n = 146$ miles

4.1 Exercises

1. ratio

3. 5 to 8

5. $18:24 = \dfrac{18}{24} = \dfrac{18 \div 6}{24 \div 6} = \dfrac{3}{4}$

7. $21:18 = \dfrac{}{} = \dfrac{21}{18} = \dfrac{21 \div 3}{18 \div 3} = \dfrac{7}{6}$

9. $55:121 = \dfrac{55}{121} = \dfrac{55 \div 11}{121 \div 11} = \dfrac{5}{11}$

11. $150:225 = \dfrac{150}{225} = \dfrac{150 \div 75}{225 \div 75} = \dfrac{2}{3}$

13. $60 \text{ to } 64 = \dfrac{60}{64} = \dfrac{60 \div 4}{64 \div 4} = \dfrac{15}{16}$

15. $28 \text{ to } 42 = \dfrac{28}{42} = \dfrac{28 \div 14}{42 \div 14} = \dfrac{2}{3}$

17. $32 \text{ to } 20 = \dfrac{32}{20} = \dfrac{32 \div 4}{20 \div 4} = \dfrac{8}{5}$

19. $8 \text{ ounces to } 12 \text{ ounces} = \dfrac{8}{12} = \dfrac{8 \div 4}{12 \div 4} = \dfrac{2}{3}$

21. $16 \text{ feet to } 24 \text{ feet} = \dfrac{16}{24} = \dfrac{16 \div 8}{24 \div 8} = \dfrac{2}{3}$

23. 50 years to 85 years $= \dfrac{50}{85} = \dfrac{50 \div 5}{85 \div 5} = \dfrac{10}{17}$

25. \$86 to \$120 $= \dfrac{86}{120} = \dfrac{86 \div 2}{120 \div 2} = \dfrac{43}{60}$

27. 153 inches to 17 inches $= \dfrac{153}{17}$

    $= \dfrac{153 \div 17}{17 \div 17} = \dfrac{9}{1}$

29. 91 tons to 133 tons $= \dfrac{91}{133} = \dfrac{91 \div 7}{133 \div 7} = \dfrac{13}{19}$

31. Ratio of take-home pay to total pay.
    $\dfrac{165}{285} = \dfrac{165 \div 15}{285 \div 15} = \dfrac{11}{19}$

33. Ratio of federal withholding to take-home pay.
    $\dfrac{35}{165} = \dfrac{35 \div 5}{165 \div 5} = \dfrac{7}{33}$

35. The ratio of sedans that lasted two years or less to the total number of sedans.
    $\dfrac{205}{1225} = \dfrac{205 \div 5}{1225 \div 5} = \dfrac{41}{245}$

37. The ratio of sedans that lasted six years or less but more than four years to the number of sedans that lasted two years or less.
    $\dfrac{450}{205} = \dfrac{450 \div 5}{205 \div 5} = \dfrac{90}{41}$

39. Ratio of labor cost to total cost.
    $\dfrac{72,000}{128,000} = \dfrac{72,000 \div 8000}{128,000 \div 8000} = \dfrac{9}{16}$

41. $\dfrac{\$60}{18 \text{ plants}} = \dfrac{\$10}{3 \text{ plants}}$

43. $\dfrac{\$170}{12 \text{ bushes}} = \dfrac{\$85}{6 \text{ bushes}}$

45. $\dfrac{310 \text{ gallons}}{625 \text{ sq ft}} = \dfrac{62 \text{ gallons}}{125 \text{ sq ft}}$

47. $\dfrac{6150 \text{ revolutions}}{15 \text{ miles}} = \dfrac{410 \text{ revolutions}}{1 \text{ mile}}$
    $= 410 \text{ rev / mile}$

49. $\dfrac{18 \text{ miles}}{8 \text{ hours}} = \dfrac{9 \text{ miles}}{4 \text{ hours}}$

51. $\dfrac{\$520}{40 \text{ hours}} = \$13 / \text{hour}$

53. $\dfrac{192 \text{ miles}}{12 \text{ gallons}} = 16 \text{ mi / gal}$

55. $\dfrac{2480 \text{ gallons}}{16 \text{ hours}} = 155 \text{ gal / hour}$

57. $\dfrac{2760 \text{ words}}{12 \text{ pages}} = 230 \text{ words / page}$

59. $\dfrac{3619 \text{ kilometers}}{7 \text{ hours}} = 517 \text{ km / hr}$

61. $\dfrac{\$3870}{129 \text{ shares}} = \$30 / \text{share}$

63. Profit $= 9800 - 6370 = \$3430$
    $\dfrac{\$3430}{245 \text{ watches}} = \$14 / \text{watch}$

65. **a.** 16-ounce box: $\dfrac{\$1.28}{16 \text{ ounces}} = \$0.08 / \text{oz}$

    24-ounce box: $\dfrac{\$1.68}{24 \text{ ounces}} = \$0.07 / \text{oz}$

    b. $\begin{array}{r} 0.08 \\ -0.07 \\ \hline \$\,0.01 / \text{ounce} \end{array}$

    c. $48(0.01) = \$0.48$

67. **a.** $\dfrac{3978 \text{ moose}}{306 \text{ acres}} = 13 \text{ moose/acre}$

    b. $\dfrac{5520 \text{ moose}}{460 \text{ acres}} = 12 \text{ moose/acre}$

    c. North Slope

69. $\dfrac{\$12,876.50}{525 \text{ shares}} = \$24.53/\text{share}$

71. Design: $\dfrac{750 \text{ meters per second}}{330 \text{ meters per second}} = $ Mach 2.3

      Modify: $\dfrac{810 \text{ meters per second}}{330 \text{ meters per second}} = $ Mach 2.5

$$\begin{array}{r} 2.5 \\ -\ 2.3 \\ \hline 0.2 \end{array}$$ Increased by Mach 0.2

Cumulative Review Problems

73. $\begin{array}{r} 2\frac{1}{4} \\ +\frac{3}{8} \\ \hline \end{array}$ $\begin{array}{r} 2\frac{2}{8} \\ +\frac{3}{8} \\ \hline 2\frac{5}{8} \end{array}$

75. $\dfrac{8}{23} \times \dfrac{5}{16} = \dfrac{5}{46}$

77. $12 \times 5.2 = 62.4$ sq yd

      $\dfrac{\$764.40}{62.4 \text{ sq yd}} = \$12.25/\text{sq yd}$

4.2 Exercises

1. equal

3. $\dfrac{48}{32} = \dfrac{3}{2}$

5. $\dfrac{8}{3} = \dfrac{32}{12}$

7. $\dfrac{20}{36} = \dfrac{5}{9}$

9. $\dfrac{27}{15} = \dfrac{9}{5}$

11. $\dfrac{22}{30} = \dfrac{11}{15}$

13. $\dfrac{45}{135} = \dfrac{9}{27}$

15. $\dfrac{5.5}{10} = \dfrac{11}{20}$

17. $\dfrac{12 \text{ pounds}}{\$4} = \dfrac{33 \text{ pounds}}{\$11}$

19. $\dfrac{10 \text{ runs}}{45 \text{ games}} = \dfrac{36 \text{ runs}}{162 \text{ games}}$

21. $\dfrac{20 \text{ pounds}}{\$75} = \dfrac{30 \text{ pounds}}{\$112.50}$

23. $\dfrac{2200 \text{ people}}{100 \text{ benches}} = \dfrac{2750 \text{ people}}{125 \text{ benches}}$

25. $\dfrac{16 \text{ pounds}}{1520 \text{ sq ft}} = \dfrac{19 \text{ pounds}}{1805 \text{ sq ft}}$

27. $\dfrac{21}{35} \overset{?}{=} \dfrac{15}{25}$

      $21 \times 25 \overset{?}{=} 35 \times 15$

      $525 = 525$ True

29. $\dfrac{18}{12} \overset{?}{=} \dfrac{42}{28}$

      $18 \times 28 \overset{?}{=} 12 \times 42$

      $504 = 504$ True

31. $\dfrac{48}{56} \overset{?}{=} \dfrac{40}{45}$

      $48 \times 45 \overset{?}{=} 40 \times 56$

      $2160 \neq 2240$ False

33. $\dfrac{9}{12} \overset{?}{=} \dfrac{15}{20}$

      $9 \times 20 \overset{?}{=} 12 \times 15$

      $180 = 180$ True

35. $\dfrac{99}{100} \overset{?}{=} \dfrac{49}{50}$

      $99 \times 50 \overset{?}{=} 100 \times 49$

      $4950 \neq 4900$ False

37. $\dfrac{315}{2100} \overset{?}{=} \dfrac{15}{100}$

      $315 \times 100 \overset{?}{=} 2100 \times 15$

      $31,500 = 31,500$ True

39. $\dfrac{6}{14} \overset{?}{=} \dfrac{4.5}{10.5}$

      $6 \times 10.5 \overset{?}{=} 14 \times 4.5$

      $63 = 63$ True

41. $\dfrac{11}{12} \overset{?}{=} \dfrac{9.5}{10}$

      $11 \times 10 \overset{?}{=} 12 \times 9.5$

      $110 \neq 114$ False

43. $\frac{2}{4\frac{1}{3}} \stackrel{?}{=} \frac{6}{13}$

$2 \times 13 \stackrel{?}{=} 6 \times 4\frac{1}{3}$

$26 \stackrel{?}{=} 6 \times \frac{13}{3}$

$26 = 26$ True

45. $\frac{8}{19} \stackrel{?}{=} \frac{2}{4\frac{3}{4}}$

$8 \times 4\frac{3}{4} \stackrel{?}{=} 19 \times 2$

$8 \times \frac{19}{4} \stackrel{?}{=} 38$

$38 = 38$ True

47. $\frac{55 \text{ feet}}{4 \text{ rolls}} \stackrel{?}{=} \frac{220 \text{ feet}}{16 \text{ rolls}}$

$55 \times 16 \stackrel{?}{=} 4 \times 220$

$880 = 880$ True

49. $\frac{286 \text{ gallons}}{12 \text{ acres}} \stackrel{?}{=} \frac{429 \text{ gallons}}{18 \text{ acres}}$

$286 \times 18 \stackrel{?}{=} 12 \times 429$

$5148 = 5148$ True

51. $\frac{48 \text{ points}}{56 \text{ games}} \stackrel{?}{=} \frac{40 \text{ points}}{45 \text{ games}}$

$48 \times 45 \stackrel{?}{=} 56 \times 40$

$2160 \neq 2240$ False

53. $\frac{9600 \text{ female}}{8200 \text{ male}} \stackrel{?}{=} \frac{12,480 \text{ female}}{10,660 \text{ male}}$

$9600 \times 10,600 \stackrel{?}{=} 8200 \times 12,480$

$102,336,000 = 102,336,000$ Yes

55. $\frac{730 \text{ boxes}}{6 \text{ hours}} \stackrel{?}{=} \frac{1090 \text{ boxes}}{9 \text{ hours}}$

$730 \times 9 \stackrel{?}{=} 6 \times 1090$

$6570 \neq 6540$

No, they did not fold boxes at the same rate.

57. a. $\frac{63}{161} \stackrel{?}{=} \frac{171}{437}$

$\frac{3 \times 3 \times 7}{23 \times 7} \stackrel{?}{=} \frac{3 \times 3 \times 19}{23 \times 19}$

$\frac{9}{23} = \frac{9}{23}$ True

b. $\frac{63}{161} \stackrel{?}{=} \frac{171}{437}$

$63 \times 437 \stackrel{?}{=} 161 \times 171$

$27,531 = 27,531$ True

c. For most students it is faster to multiply than to reduce fractions.

Cumulative Review Problems

59.   9.6000
           7.8000
           2.5600
           3.0040
        + 0.1765
          23.1405

61.   29,366.215
         − 28,963.807
             402.408

4.3 Exercises

1. $5 \times n = 40$

$\frac{5 \times n}{5} = \frac{40}{5}$

$n = 8$

3. $76 = 2 \times n$

$\frac{76}{2} = \frac{2 \times n}{2}$

$38 = n$

5. $6 \times n = 96$

$\frac{6 \times n}{6} = \frac{96}{6}$

$n = 16$

7. $117 = 9 \times n$

$\frac{117}{9} = \frac{9 \times n}{9}$

$13 = n$

9. $7 \times n = 182$

$\frac{7 \times n}{7} = \frac{182}{7}$

$n = 26$

11. $3 \times n = 16.8$

$$\frac{3 \times n}{3} = \frac{16.8}{3}$$

$$n = 5.6$$

13. $2.6 \times n = 13$

$$\frac{2.6 \times n}{2.6} = \frac{13}{2.6}$$

$$n = 5$$

15. $40.6 = 5.8 \times n$

$$\frac{40.6}{5.8} = \frac{5.8 \times n}{5.8}$$

$$7 = n$$

17. $260 \times n = 1430$

$$\frac{260 \times n}{260} = \frac{1430}{260}$$

$$n = 5.5$$

19. $\dfrac{n}{20} = \dfrac{3}{4}$

$$4 \times n = 20 \times 3$$

$$\frac{4 \times n}{4} = \frac{60}{4}$$

$$n = 15$$

Check:

$$\frac{15}{20} \stackrel{?}{=} \frac{3}{4}$$

$$4 \times 15 \stackrel{?}{=} 20 \times 3$$

$$60 = 60 \text{ True}$$

21. $\dfrac{6}{n} = \dfrac{3}{8}$

$$6 \times 8 = 3 \times n$$

$$\frac{48}{3} = \frac{3 \times n}{n}$$

$$16 = n$$

Check:

$$\frac{6}{16} \stackrel{?}{=} \frac{3}{8}$$

$$6 \times 8 \stackrel{?}{=} 3 \times 16$$

$$48 = 48$$

23. $\dfrac{12}{40} = \dfrac{n}{25}$

$$12 \times 25 = 40 \times n$$

$$\frac{300}{40} = \frac{40 \times n}{40}$$

$$7.5 = n$$

Check:

$$\frac{12}{40} \stackrel{?}{=} \frac{7.5}{25}$$

$$12 \times 25 \stackrel{?}{=} 40 \times 7.5$$

$$300 = 300$$

25. $\dfrac{25}{100} = \dfrac{8}{n}$

$$25 \times n = 100 \times 8$$

$$\frac{25 \times n}{25} = \frac{800}{25}$$

$$n = 32$$

Check:

$$\frac{25}{100} \stackrel{?}{=} \frac{8}{32}$$

$$25 \times 32 \stackrel{?}{=} 100 \times 8$$

$$800 = 800$$

27. $\dfrac{n}{32} = \dfrac{3}{4}$

$$4 \times n = 32 \times 3$$

$$\frac{4 \times n}{4} = \frac{96}{4}$$

$$n = 24$$

Check:

$$\frac{24}{32} \stackrel{?}{=} \frac{3}{4}$$

$$4 \times 24 \stackrel{?}{=} 32 \times 3$$

$$96 = 96$$

29. $\dfrac{n}{9} = \dfrac{49}{63}$

$$63 \times n = 9 \times 49$$

$$\frac{63 \times n}{63} = \frac{441}{63}$$

$$n = 7$$

Check:

$$\frac{7}{9} \stackrel{?}{=} \frac{49}{63}$$

$$63 \times 7 \stackrel{?}{=} 9 \times 49$$

$$441 = 441$$

31. $\dfrac{18}{n} = \dfrac{3}{11}$

$11 \times 18 = 3 \times n$

$\dfrac{198}{3} = \dfrac{3 \times n}{3}$

$66 = n$

Check:

$\dfrac{18}{66} \overset{?}{=} \dfrac{3}{11}$

$11 \times 18 \overset{?}{=} 3 \times 66$

$198 = 198$

33. $\dfrac{n}{5} = \dfrac{7}{4}$

$4 \times n = 5 \times 7$

$\dfrac{4 \times n}{4} = \dfrac{35}{4}$

$n = 8.8$

35. $\dfrac{12}{n} = \dfrac{3}{5}$

$12 \times 5 = 3 \times n$

$\dfrac{60}{3} = \dfrac{3 \times n}{3}$

$20 = n$

37. $\dfrac{35}{n} = \dfrac{7}{5}$

$5 \times 35 = 7 \times n$

$\dfrac{175}{7} = \dfrac{7 \times n}{7}$

$25 = n$

39. $\dfrac{9}{26} = \dfrac{n}{52}$

$9 \times 52 = 26 \times n$

$\dfrac{468}{26} = \dfrac{26 \times n}{26}$

$18 = n$

41. $\dfrac{12}{8} = \dfrac{21}{n}$

$12 \times n = 8 \times 21$

$\dfrac{12 \times n}{12} = \dfrac{168}{12}$

$n = 14$

43. $\dfrac{n}{18} = \dfrac{3.5}{1}$

$1 \times n = 18 \times 3.5$

$\dfrac{1 \times n}{1} = \dfrac{63}{1}$

$n = 63$

45. $\dfrac{2.5}{n} = \dfrac{0.5}{10}$

$2.5 \times 10 = 0.5 \times n$

$\dfrac{25}{0.5} = \dfrac{0.5 \times n}{0.5}$

$50 = n$

47. $\dfrac{3}{4} = \dfrac{n}{3.8}$

$3 \times 3.8 = 4 \times n$

$\dfrac{11.4}{4} = \dfrac{4 \times n}{4}$

$2.9 = n$

49. $\dfrac{12.5}{16} = \dfrac{n}{12}$

$12 \times 12.5 = 16 \times n$

$\dfrac{150}{16} = \dfrac{16 \times n}{16}$

$9.4 = n$

51. $\dfrac{16}{100} = \dfrac{5}{n}$

$16 \times n = 5 \times 100$

$\dfrac{16 \times n}{16} = \dfrac{500}{16}$

$n \approx 31.3$

53. $\dfrac{n \text{ grams}}{10 \text{ liters}} = \dfrac{7 \text{ grams}}{25 \text{ liters}}$

$25 \times n = 10 \times 7$

$\dfrac{25 \times n}{25} = \dfrac{70}{25}$

$n = 2.8$

55. $\dfrac{76 \text{ dollars}}{5 \text{ tons}} = \dfrac{n \text{ dollars}}{8 \text{ tons}}$

$76 \times 8 = 5 \times n$

$\dfrac{608}{5} = \dfrac{5 \times n}{5}$

$n = 121.60$

57. $\dfrac{50 \text{ gallons}}{12 \text{ acres}} = \dfrac{36 \text{ gallons}}{n \text{ acres}}$

$50 \times n = 12 \times 36$

$\dfrac{50 \times n}{50} = \dfrac{432}{50}$

$n = 8.64$

59. $\dfrac{10 \text{ miles}}{16.1 \text{ kilometers}} = \dfrac{n \text{ miles}}{7 \text{ kilometers}}$

$10 \times 7 = 16.1 \times n$

$\dfrac{10 \times 7}{16.1} = \dfrac{16.1 \times n}{16.1}$

$n = 4.35$

61. $\dfrac{5 \text{ pounds}}{2.27 \text{ kilograms}} = \dfrac{3 \text{ pounds}}{n \text{ kilograms}}$

$5 \times n = 2.27 \times 3$

$\dfrac{5 \times n}{5} = \dfrac{6.81}{5}$

$n = 1.36$

63. $\dfrac{6.3 \text{ acres}}{2 \text{ people}} = \dfrac{n \text{ acres}}{5 \text{ people}}$

$6.3 \times n = 2 \times n$

$\dfrac{31.5}{2} = \dfrac{2 \times n}{2}$

$n = 15.75$

65. $\dfrac{n}{2\frac{1}{3}} = \dfrac{4\frac{5}{6}}{3\frac{1}{9}}$

$\dfrac{28}{9} \times n = \dfrac{7}{3} \times \dfrac{29}{6}$

$\dfrac{\frac{28}{9} \times n}{\frac{28}{9}} = \dfrac{\frac{203}{18}}{\frac{28}{9}}$

$n = \dfrac{203}{18} \times \dfrac{9}{28}$

$n = \dfrac{28}{8} \text{ or } 3\dfrac{5}{8}$

67. $\dfrac{8\frac{1}{6}}{n} = \dfrac{5\frac{1}{2}}{7\frac{1}{3}}$

$\dfrac{22}{3} \times \dfrac{49}{6} = \dfrac{11}{2} \times n$

$\dfrac{\frac{539}{9}}{\frac{11}{2}} = \dfrac{\frac{11}{2} \times n}{\frac{11}{2}}$

$\dfrac{539}{9} \times \dfrac{2}{11} = n$

$\dfrac{98}{9} \text{ or } 10\dfrac{8}{9} = n$

Cumulative Review Problems

69. $4^3 + 20 \div 5 + 6 \times 3 - 5 \times 2$

$= 64 + 20 \div 5 + 6 \times 3 - 5 \times 2$

$= 64 + 4 + 18 - 10$

$= 76$

71. $0.563 =$ five hundred sixty-three thousandths

4.4 Exercises

1. $\dfrac{19 \text{ desserts}}{16 \text{ people}} = \dfrac{n \text{ desserts}}{320 \text{ people}}$

$16 \times n = 19 \times 320$

$\dfrac{16 \times n}{16} = \dfrac{6080}{16}$

$n = 380$

380 desserts

3. $\dfrac{90 \text{ shots}}{5 \text{ thrown}} = \dfrac{162 \text{ shots}}{n \text{ thrown}}$

$90 \times n = 5 \times 162$

$\dfrac{90 \times n}{90} = \dfrac{810}{90}$

$n = 9$

9 shots thrown

5. $\dfrac{35 \text{ clear}}{4 \text{ pigment}} = \dfrac{8015 \text{ clear}}{n \text{ pigment}}$

$35 \times n = 4 \times 8015$

$\dfrac{35 \times n}{35} = \dfrac{32,060}{35}$

$n = 916$

916 drops of pigment

7. $\dfrac{\$7.5\text{ U.S.}}{\$10.5\text{ Canadian}} = \dfrac{\$240\text{ U.S.}}{\$n\text{ Canadian}}$

$7.5 \times n = 10.5 \times 240$

$\dfrac{7.5 \times n}{7.5} = \dfrac{2520}{7.5}$

$n = 336$

$\$336$ Canada

9. $\dfrac{80\text{ rpm}}{18\text{ miles per hour}} = \dfrac{75\text{ rpm}}{n\text{ miles per hour}}$

$80 \times n = 18 \times 75$

$\dfrac{80 \times n}{80} = \dfrac{1350}{80}$

$n = 16.875$

16.9 miles per hour

11. $\dfrac{6.5\text{ ft}}{5\text{ ft}} = \dfrac{n\text{ ft}}{152\text{ ft}}$

$152 \times 6.5 = 5 \times n$

$\dfrac{988}{5} = \dfrac{5 \times n}{5}$

$197.6 = n$

197.6 feet

13. $\dfrac{4\text{ pages}}{12\text{ minutes}} = \dfrac{11\text{ pages}}{n\text{ minutes}}$

$4 \times n = 12 \times 11$

$\dfrac{4 \times n}{4} = \dfrac{132}{4}$

$n = 33$

33 minutes

15. $\dfrac{4\text{ inches}}{250\text{ miles}} = \dfrac{5.7\text{ inches}}{n\text{ miles}}$

$4 \times n = 250 \times 5.7$

$\dfrac{4 \times n}{4} = \dfrac{1425}{4}$

$n = 356.25$

356 miles

17. $\dfrac{100\text{ watts}}{30\text{ mm}} = \dfrac{140\text{ watts}}{n\text{ mm}}$

$100 \times n = 30 \times 140$

$\dfrac{100 \times n}{100} = \dfrac{4200}{100}$

$n = 42$

42 millimeters

19. $\dfrac{5\text{ cups}}{12\text{ people}} = \dfrac{n\text{ cups}}{28\text{ people}}$

$5 \times 28 = 12 \times n$

$\dfrac{140}{12} = \dfrac{12 \times n}{12}$

$11.\overline{6} = n$

$11\dfrac{2}{3}$ cups

21. $\dfrac{7\text{ cars}}{24\text{ customers}} = \dfrac{n\text{ cars}}{50\text{ customers}}$

$7 \times 50 = 24 \times n$

$\dfrac{350}{24} = \dfrac{24 \times n}{24}$

$14.58 = n$

15 cars

23. $\dfrac{14\text{ errors}}{110\text{ points}} = \dfrac{n\text{ errors}}{275\text{ points}}$

$14 \times 275 = 110 \times n$

$\dfrac{3850}{110} = \dfrac{110 \times n}{110}$

$35 = n$

35 errors

25. $\dfrac{7\text{ flights}}{79\text{ people}} = \dfrac{434\text{ flights}}{n\text{ people}}$

$7 \times n = 79 \times 434$

$\dfrac{7 \times n}{7} = \dfrac{34,286}{7}$

$n = 4898$

4898 people

27. $\dfrac{26\text{ tagged}}{n\text{ total}} = \dfrac{6\text{ tagged}}{18\text{ total}}$

$26 \times 18 = 6 \times n$

$\dfrac{468}{6} = \dfrac{6 \times n}{6}$

$78 = n$

78 giraffes

29. $\dfrac{425 \text{ pounds}}{3 \text{ acres}} = \dfrac{n \text{ pounds}}{14 \text{ acres}}$

$14 \times 425 = 3 \times n$

$\dfrac{5950}{3} = \dfrac{3 \times n}{3}$

$1983.\overline{3} = n$

$1983\dfrac{1}{3}$ pounds

$1983\dfrac{1}{3} \times 1.8 = 3570$

$\$3570$

31. $\dfrac{8 \text{ ft}}{86 \text{ lb}} = \dfrac{12 \text{ ft}}{n \text{ lb}}$

$8 \times n = 86 \times 12$

$\dfrac{8 \times n}{8} = \dfrac{1032}{8}$

$n = 129$

129 pounds

$129 \times 7 = 903$

903 pounds

33. $\dfrac{22 \text{ respond}}{100 \text{ people}} = \dfrac{n \text{ respond}}{15,500 \text{ people}}$

$22 \times 15,500 = 100 \times n$

$\dfrac{341,000}{100} = \dfrac{100 \times n}{100}$

$3410 = n$

3410 people will respond.

35. Yes; the units show that the parts of the proportion correspond correctly.

$\dfrac{88 \text{ feet per second}}{n \text{ feet per second}} = \dfrac{60 \text{ miles per hour}}{49 \text{ miles per hour}}$

37. No; look at the denominators: 49 miles per hour does not correspond to 88 feet per second; 60 miles per hour does. This should be $\dfrac{n \text{ feet per second}}{88 \text{ feet per second}} = \dfrac{49 \text{ miles per hour}}{60 \text{ miles per hour}}$.

Cumulative Review Problems

39. 56,179 rounds to 56,200.

41. 56.148 rounds to 56.1.

43. 0.07615382 rounds to 0.0762.

Putting Your Skills to Work

1. $\dfrac{364,114}{78} \approx 4668$

$\dfrac{465,648}{116} \approx 4014$

There are 4668 people per square mile in Cincinnati and 4014 people per square mile in Austin. Cincinnati is more densely populated.

3. Anaheim:

$\dfrac{219,494 \text{ in } 1980}{266,406 \text{ in } 1990} = \dfrac{266,406 \text{ in } 1990}{n \text{ in } 2000}$

$219,494 \times n = 266,406 \times 266,406$

$\dfrac{219,494 \times n}{219,494} = \dfrac{266,406 \times 266,406}{219,494}$

$n \approx 323,344$

$\dfrac{323,344 \text{ in } 2000}{41 \text{ mi}^2} \approx 7886$

Detroit:

$\dfrac{1,203,368 \text{ in } 1980}{1,027,974 \text{ in } 1990} = \dfrac{1,027,974 \text{ in } 1990}{n \text{ in } 2000}$

$\dfrac{1,203,368 \times n}{1,203,368} = \dfrac{1,027,974 \times 1,027,974}{1,203,368}$

$n \approx 878,144$

$\dfrac{878,144 \text{ in } 2000}{136 \text{ mi}^2} \approx 6457$

In the year 2000, there will be approximately 7886 people per square mile in Anaheim and 6457 people per square mile in Detroit.

Chapter 4 Review Problems

1. $88:40 = \dfrac{88}{40} = \dfrac{11}{5}$

3. $28:35 = \dfrac{28}{35} = \dfrac{4}{5}$

5. $50 \text{ to } 124 = \dfrac{50}{124} = \dfrac{25}{62}$

7. $156 \text{ to } 441 = \dfrac{156}{441} = \dfrac{52}{147}$

9. 26 tons to 65 tons $= \dfrac{26}{65} = \dfrac{2}{5}$

11. 150 kg to 200 kg $= \dfrac{150}{200} = \dfrac{3}{4}$

13. $\dfrac{35}{215} = \dfrac{7}{43}$

15. $\dfrac{10 \text{ gallons}}{18 \text{ people}} = \dfrac{5 \text{ gallons}}{9 \text{ people}}$

17. $\dfrac{188 \text{ vibrations}}{16 \text{ seconds}} = \dfrac{47 \text{ vibrations}}{4 \text{ seconds}}$

19. $\dfrac{\$2125}{125 \text{ shares}} = \$17.00 / \text{share}$

21. $\dfrac{\$742.50}{55 \text{ square yards}} = \$13.50 / \text{square yard}$

23. a. $\dfrac{\$2.96}{4} = \$0.74$

 b. $\dfrac{\$5.22}{9} = \$0.58$

 c. $0.74 - 0.58 = \$0.16$

25. $\dfrac{12}{48} = \dfrac{7}{28}$

27. $\dfrac{7.5}{45} = \dfrac{22.5}{135}$

29. $\dfrac{136}{17} = \dfrac{408}{51}$

31. $\dfrac{4.50 \text{ dollars}}{15 \text{ pounds}} = \dfrac{8.10 \text{ dollars}}{27 \text{ pounds}}$

33. $\dfrac{16}{48} \overset{?}{=} \dfrac{2}{12}$
$16 \times 12 \overset{?}{=} 48 \times 2$
$192 \neq 96$
False

35. $\dfrac{24}{20} \overset{?}{=} \dfrac{18}{15}$
$24 \times 15 \overset{?}{=} 20 \times 18$
$360 = 360$
True

37. $\dfrac{37}{33} \overset{?}{=} \dfrac{22}{19}$
$37 \times 19 \overset{?}{=} 33 \times 22$
$703 \neq 726$
False

39. $\dfrac{84 \text{ miles}}{7 \text{ gallons}} \overset{?}{=} \dfrac{108 \text{ miles}}{9 \text{ gallons}}$
$84 \times 9 \overset{?}{=} 7 \times 108$
$756 = 756$
True

41. $\dfrac{1.6 \text{ pounds}}{32 \text{ feet}} \overset{?}{=} \dfrac{4.8 \text{ pounds}}{96 \text{ feet}}$
$1.6 \times 96 \overset{?}{=} 32 \times 4.8$
$153.6 = 153.6$
True

43. $7 \times n = 161$
$\dfrac{7 \times n}{7} = \dfrac{161}{7}$
$n = 23$

45. $558 = 18 \times n$
$\dfrac{558}{18} = \dfrac{18 \times n}{18}$
$31 = n$

47. $\dfrac{3}{11} = \dfrac{9}{n}$
$3 \times n = 11 \times 9$
$\dfrac{3 \times n}{3} = \dfrac{99}{3}$
$n = 33$

49. $\dfrac{n}{28} = \dfrac{6}{24}$
$24 \times n = 28 \times 6$
$\dfrac{24 \times n}{24} = \dfrac{168}{24}$
$n = 7$

51. $\dfrac{3}{7} = \dfrac{n}{9}$

$3 \times 9 = 7 \times n$

$\dfrac{27}{7} = \dfrac{7 \times n}{7}$

$3.9 = n$

53. $\dfrac{54}{72} = \dfrac{n}{4}$

$54 \times 4 = 72 \times n$

$\dfrac{216}{72} = \dfrac{72 \times n}{72}$

$3 = n$

55. $\dfrac{6}{n} = \dfrac{2}{29}$

$6 \times 29 = 2 \times n$

$\dfrac{174}{2} = \dfrac{2 \times n}{2}$

$87 = n$

57. $\dfrac{25}{7} = \dfrac{60}{n}$

$25 \times n = 7 \times 60$

$\dfrac{25 \times n}{25} = \dfrac{420}{25}$

$n = 16.8$

59. $\dfrac{35 \text{ miles}}{28 \text{ gallons}} = \dfrac{15 \text{ miles}}{n \text{ gallons}}$

$35 \times n = 28 \times 15$

$\dfrac{35 \times n}{35} = \dfrac{420}{35}$

$n = 12$

61. $\dfrac{7 \text{ tons}}{5.5 \text{ horsepower}} = \dfrac{16 \text{ tons}}{n \text{ horsepower}}$

$7 \times n = 5.5 \times 16$

$\dfrac{7 \times n}{7} = \dfrac{88}{7}$

$n = 12.6$

63. $\dfrac{3 \text{ gallons}}{2 \text{ rooms}} = \dfrac{n \text{ gallons}}{10 \text{ rooms}}$

$3 \times 10 = 2 \times n$

$\dfrac{30}{2} = \dfrac{2 \times n}{2}$

$15 = n$

15 gallons

65. $\dfrac{84 \text{ patients}}{7 \text{ nurses}} = \dfrac{108 \text{ patients}}{n \text{ nurses}}$

$84 \times n = 7 \times 108$

$\dfrac{8 \times n}{84} = \dfrac{756}{84}$

$n = 9$

9 nurses

67. $\dfrac{24 \text{ francs}}{5 \text{ dollars}} = \dfrac{n \text{ francs}}{420 \text{ dollars}}$

$24 \times 420 = 5 \times n$

$\dfrac{10,080}{5} = \dfrac{5 \times n}{5}$

$2016 = n$

2016 francs

69. $\dfrac{225 \text{ miles}}{3 \text{ inches}} = \dfrac{n \text{ miles}}{8 \text{ inches}}$

$8 \times 225 = 3 \times n$

$\dfrac{1800}{3} = \dfrac{3 \times n}{3}$

$600 = n$

600 miles

71. $\dfrac{34,720 \text{ feet}}{31 \text{ seconds}} = \dfrac{n \text{ feet}}{60 \text{ seconds}}$

$34,720 \times 60 = 31 \times n$

$\dfrac{2,083,200}{31} = \dfrac{31 \times n}{31}$

$67,200 = n$

67,200 feet

73. $\dfrac{6 \text{ feet}}{16 \text{ feet}} = \dfrac{n \text{ feet}}{320 \text{ feet}}$

$6 \times 320 = 16 \times n$

$\dfrac{1920}{16} = \dfrac{16 \times n}{16}$

$120 = n$

Putting Your Skills to Work

1. First year: $\dfrac{\text{Tuition costs}}{\text{Total expenses}} = \dfrac{12,350}{20,000} = \dfrac{247}{400}$

    Second year:

    $\dfrac{\text{Tuition costs}}{\text{Total expenses}} = \dfrac{13,500}{22,000} = \dfrac{27}{44}$

    $\dfrac{27}{44} = 0.614, \dfrac{247}{400} = 0.618$

    No, the ratio is slightly less.

3. $\dfrac{13,500}{12,350} = \dfrac{n}{20,000}$

    $20,000 \times 13,500 = 12,350 \times n$

    $270,000,000 = 12,350 \times n$

    $\dfrac{270,000,000}{12,350} = \dfrac{12,350 \times n}{12,350}$

    $21,862 = n$

5. Tuition: $\dfrac{13,500}{12,350} = 1.093$

    Room: $\dfrac{2700}{2400} = 1.125$

    Board: $\dfrac{3000}{2700} = 1.111$

    Churches & Charities: $\dfrac{380}{350} = 1.086$

    Greatest ratio: Room

    Least ratio: Churches & Charities

Chapter 4 Test

1. $\dfrac{18}{52} = \dfrac{18 \div 2}{52 \div 2} = \dfrac{9}{26}$

3. $\dfrac{784 \text{ miles}}{24 \text{ gal}} = \dfrac{784 \text{ miles} \div 8}{24 \text{ gal} \div 8}$

    $= \dfrac{98 \text{ miles}}{3 \text{ gal}}$

5. $\dfrac{19 \text{ tons}}{5 \text{ days}} = \dfrac{19 \text{ tons} \div 5}{5 \text{ days} \div 5} = 3.8 \text{ tons/day}$

7. $\dfrac{5400 \text{ ft}}{22 \text{ poles}} = \dfrac{5400 \text{ ft} \div 22}{22 \text{ poles} \div 22} = 245.45 \text{ ft/pole}$

9. $\dfrac{17}{29} = \dfrac{51}{87}$

11. $\dfrac{490 \text{ miles}}{21 \text{ gallons}} = \dfrac{280 \text{ miles}}{12 \text{ gallons}}$

13. $\dfrac{50}{24} \overset{?}{=} \dfrac{34}{16}$

    $50 \times 16 \overset{?}{=} 24 \times 34$

    $800 \neq 816$

    False

15. $\dfrac{32 \text{ smokers}}{46 \text{ nonsmokers}} \overset{?}{=} \dfrac{160 \text{ smokers}}{230 \text{ nonsmokers}}$

    $32 \times 230 \overset{?}{=} 46 \times 160$

    $7360 = 7360$

    True

17. $\dfrac{n}{20} = \dfrac{4}{5}$

    $n \times 5 = 20 \times 4$

    $n \times 5 = 80$

    $\dfrac{n \times 5}{5} = \dfrac{80}{5}$

    $n = 16$

19. $\dfrac{33}{n} = \dfrac{11}{4}$

    $33 \times 4 = n \times 11$

    $132 = n \times 11$

    $\dfrac{132}{11} = \dfrac{n \times 11}{11}$

    $12 = n$

21. $\dfrac{45 \text{ women}}{15 \text{ men}} = \dfrac{n \text{ women}}{40 \text{ men}}$

    $45 \times 40 = 15 \times n$

    $1800 = 15 \times n$

    $\dfrac{1800}{15} = \dfrac{15 \times n}{15}$

    $120 = n$

    120 women

23. $\dfrac{n \text{ inches of snow}}{14 \text{ inches of rain}} = \dfrac{12 \text{ inches of snow}}{1.4 \text{ inches of rain}}$

$n \times 1.4 = 14 \times 12$

$n \times 1.4 = 168$

$\dfrac{n \times 1.4}{1.4} = \dfrac{168}{1.4}$

$n = 120$

120 inches of snow

25. $\dfrac{3 \text{ eggs}}{11 \text{ people}} = \dfrac{n \text{ eggs}}{22 \text{ people}}$

$3 \times 22 = 11 \times n$

$66 = 11 \times n$

$\dfrac{66}{11} = \dfrac{11 \times n}{11}$

$6 = n$

6 eggs

27. $\dfrac{9 \text{ inches}}{57 \text{ miles}} = \dfrac{3 \text{ inches}}{n \text{ miles}}$

$9 \times n = 57 \times 3$

$9 \times n = 171$

$\dfrac{9 \times n}{9} = \dfrac{171}{9}$

$n = 19$

19 miles

29. $\dfrac{1.5 \text{ quarts}}{3000 \text{ miles}} = \dfrac{n \text{ quarts}}{8000 \text{ miles}}$

$1.5 \times 8000 = 3000 \times n$

$12{,}000 = 3000 \times n$

$\dfrac{12{,}000}{3000} = \dfrac{3000 \times n}{3000}$

$4 = n$

4 quarts

Chapters 1–4 Cumulative Test

1. 26,597,089 = Twenty-six million, five hundred ninety-seven thousand, eighty-nine

3.
$$
\begin{array}{r}
208 \\
\times\ \ 67 \\
\hline
1456 \\
1248\ \ \\
\hline
13{,}936
\end{array}
$$

5. $\dfrac{1}{5} + \dfrac{1}{8} + \dfrac{3}{4} = \dfrac{1}{5} \times \dfrac{8}{8} + \dfrac{1}{8} \times \dfrac{5}{5} + \dfrac{3}{4} \times \dfrac{10}{10}$

$= \dfrac{8}{40} + \dfrac{5}{40} + \dfrac{30}{40}$

$= \dfrac{43}{40} \text{ or } 1\dfrac{3}{40}$

7. $4\dfrac{1}{2} \times 3\dfrac{1}{4} = \dfrac{9}{2} \times \dfrac{13}{4} = \dfrac{117}{8} \text{ or } 14\dfrac{5}{8}$

9. 163.578314 rounds to 163.58.

11.
$$
\begin{array}{r}
0.8163 \\
\times\ \ 0.22 \\
\hline
16326 \\
16326\ \ \\
\hline
0.179586
\end{array}
$$

13. $\dfrac{81 \text{ miles}}{27 \text{ miles}} = \dfrac{81 \div 27}{27 \div 27} = \dfrac{3}{1}$

15. $\dfrac{12 \text{ yen}}{3 \text{ pesos}} = \dfrac{4 \text{ yen}}{1 \text{ peso}}$

17. $\dfrac{5}{7} \overset{?}{=} \dfrac{15}{21}$

$5 \times 21 \overset{?}{=} 7 \times 15$

$105 = 105$

True

19. $\dfrac{50}{20} = \dfrac{5}{n}$

$50 \times n = 20 \times 5$

$\dfrac{50 \times n}{50} = \dfrac{100}{50}$

$n = 2$

21. $\dfrac{7}{n} = \dfrac{28}{36}$

$7 \times 36 = n \times 28$

$\dfrac{252}{28} = \dfrac{n \times 28}{28}$

$n = 9$

23. $\dfrac{3\frac{1}{3}}{7} = \dfrac{10}{n}$

$3\dfrac{1}{3} \times n = 7 \times 10$

$\dfrac{\frac{10}{3} \times n}{\frac{10}{3}} = \dfrac{70}{\frac{10}{3}}$

$n = 70 \times \dfrac{3}{10}$

$n = 21$

25. $\dfrac{\$7}{\$84} = \dfrac{n}{\$9000}$

$7 \times 9000 = 84 \times n$

$\dfrac{63,000}{84} = \dfrac{84 \times n}{84}$

$n = \$750$

Chapter 5

Pretest Chapter 5

1. $0.13 = \dfrac{13}{100} = 13\%$

3. $0.185 = \dfrac{18.5}{100} = 18.5\%$

5. $1.34 = \dfrac{134}{100} = 134\%$

7. $0.002 = \dfrac{0.2}{100} = 0.2\%$

9. $\dfrac{17}{100} = 17\%$

11. $\dfrac{13.4}{100} = 13.4\%$

13. $\dfrac{6\frac{1}{2}}{100} = 6\frac{1}{2}\%$

15.
$$\begin{array}{r} 0.60 \\ 10\overline{)6.00} \\ \underline{6\ 0} \\ 0 \end{array}$$
$\dfrac{6}{10} = 60\%$

17.
$$\begin{array}{r} 1.15 \\ 20\overline{)23.00} \\ \underline{20} \\ 3\ 0 \\ \underline{2\ 0} \\ 1\ 00 \\ \underline{1\ 00} \\ 0 \end{array}$$
$\dfrac{23}{20} = 115\%$

19.
$$\begin{array}{r} 0.71428 \\ 7\overline{)5.00000} \\ \underline{4\ 9} \\ 10 \\ \underline{7} \\ 30 \\ \underline{28} \\ 20 \\ \underline{14} \\ 60 \\ \underline{56} \\ 4 \end{array}$$
$\dfrac{5}{7} = 71.43\%$

21.
$$\begin{array}{r} 0.95652 \\ 23\overline{)22.00000} \\ \underline{20\ 7} \\ 1\ 30 \\ \underline{1\ 15} \\ 150 \\ \underline{138} \\ 120 \\ \underline{115} \\ 50 \\ \underline{46} \\ 4 \end{array}$$
$\dfrac{22}{23} = 95.65\%$

23.
$$\begin{array}{r} 4.40 \\ 5\overline{)22.00} \\ \underline{20} \\ 2\ 0 \\ \underline{2\ 0} \\ 0 \end{array}$$
$4\dfrac{2}{5} = 440\%$

25.
$$\begin{array}{r} 0.00333 \\ 300\overline{)1.00000} \\ \underline{900} \\ 1000 \\ \underline{900} \\ 1000 \\ \underline{900} \\ 100 \end{array}$$
$\dfrac{1}{300} = 0.33\%$

27. $22\% = \dfrac{22}{100} = \dfrac{11}{50}$

29. $53\% = \dfrac{53}{100}$

31. $150\% = \dfrac{150}{100} = \dfrac{3}{2}$ or $1\dfrac{1}{2}$

33. $6\dfrac{1}{3}\% = \dfrac{6\frac{1}{3}}{100} = \dfrac{19}{300}$

35. $51\dfrac{1}{4}\% = \dfrac{205/4}{100} = \dfrac{205}{400} = \dfrac{41}{80}$

37. Find 24% of 230 = 0.24(230) = 55.2

75

39. 68 is what percent of 72?
$68 = n \times 72$
$n = \frac{68}{72} = 0.9\overline{4} = 94.44\%$

41. 8% of what number is 240?
$8\% \times n = 240$
$n = \frac{240}{0.08} = 3000$

43. $\frac{24}{38} = 0.6316$
They won 63.16% of the games.

45. $5\% \times n = 0.72$
$n = \frac{0.72}{0.05} = 14.4$
The dinner was $14.40 without tax.

5.1 Exercises

1. hundred

3. move the decimal point *two* places to the *left. Drop* the % symbol.

5. $\frac{45}{100} = 45\%$

7. $\frac{7}{100} = 7\%$

9. $\frac{80}{100} = 80\%$

11. $\frac{245}{100} = 245\%$

13. $\frac{5.3}{100} = 5.3\%$

15. $\frac{0.6}{100} = 0.6\%$

17. $\frac{29}{100} = 29\%$

19. $\frac{78}{100} = 78\%$

21. $\frac{32}{100} = 32\%$

23. $51\% = 0.51$

25. $7\% = 0.07$

27. $20\% = 0.2$

29. $43.6\% = 0.436$

31. $0.3\% = 0.003$

33. $0.72\% = 0.0072$

35. $126\% = 1.26$

37. $366\% = 3.66$

39. $0.74 = 74\%$

41. $0.50 = 50\%$

43. $0.08 = 8\%$

45. $0.563 = 56.3\%$

47. $0.002 = 0.2\%$

49. $0.0057 = 0.57\%$

51. $1.35 = 135\%$

53. $2.72 = 272\%$

55. $0.27 = 27\%$

57. $\frac{36}{100} = 36\%$

59. $\frac{143}{100} = 143\%$

61. $0.3 = 30\%$

63. $\frac{0.5}{100} = 0.5\%$

65. $62\% = \frac{62}{100} = 0.62$

67. $128\% = \frac{128}{100} = 1.28$

69. $0.5\% = \frac{0.5}{100} = 0.005$

71. $\frac{80}{100} = 0.8$

73. $\frac{49}{100} = 49\%$

75. $0.03413 = 3.413\%$

77. $36\% = 36$ percent $= 36$ "per one hundred"

$= 36 \times \frac{1}{100} = \frac{36}{100} = 0.36$

The rule is using the fact that 36% means 36 per one hundred.

79. a. $55,562\% = 555.62$

b. $55,562\% = \frac{55,562}{10^2} = \frac{55,562}{100}$

c. $55,562\% = \frac{55,562}{100} = \frac{27,781}{50}$

Cumulative Review Problems

81. $0.56 = \frac{56}{100} = \frac{14}{25}$

83.
$$\begin{array}{r} 0.6875 \\ 16\overline{)11.0000} \\ \underline{9\ 6} \\ 1\ 40 \\ \underline{1\ 28} \\ 120 \\ \underline{112} \\ 80 \end{array}$$
$\qquad \frac{11}{16} = 0.6875$

5.2 Exercises

1. $88\% = \frac{88}{100} = \frac{22}{25}$

3. $7\% = \frac{7}{100}$

5. $33\% = \frac{33}{100}$

7. $55\% = \frac{55}{100} = \frac{11}{20}$

9. $75\% = \frac{75}{100} = \frac{3}{4}$

11. $20\% = \frac{20}{100} = \frac{1}{5}$

13. $14.5\% = 0.145 = \frac{145}{1000} = \frac{29}{200}$

15. $17.6\% = 0.176 = \frac{176}{1000} = \frac{22}{125}$

17. $64.8\% = 0.648 = \frac{648}{1000} = \frac{81}{125}$

19. $71.25\% = 0.7125 = \frac{7125}{10,000} = \frac{57}{80}$

21. $176\% = \frac{176}{100} = \frac{44}{25} = 1\frac{19}{25}$

23. $340\% = \frac{340}{100} = \frac{17}{5} = 3\frac{2}{5}$

25. $1200\% = \frac{1200}{100} = 12$

27. $2\frac{1}{6}\% = \frac{\frac{13}{6}}{100} = \frac{13}{600}$

29. $12\frac{3}{8}\% = \frac{\frac{99}{8}}{100} = \frac{99}{800}$

31. $8\frac{4}{5}\% = \frac{\frac{44}{5}}{100} = \frac{44}{500} = \frac{11}{125}$

33. $2\frac{2}{13}\% = \frac{28}{13}\% = \frac{\frac{28}{13}}{100} = \frac{7}{325}$

35. $4\frac{1}{11}\% = \frac{\frac{45}{11}}{100} = \frac{45}{1100} = \frac{9}{220}$

37. $\frac{3}{4} = 0.75 = 75\%$

39. $\frac{1}{3} = 0.3333 = 33.33\%$

41. $\frac{5}{16} = 0.3125 = 31.25\%$

43. $\frac{7}{25} = 0.28 = 28\%$

45. $\frac{11}{40} = 0.275 = 27.5\%$

47. $\frac{5}{12} = 0.4167 = 41.67\%$

49. $\frac{18}{5} = 3.6 = 360\%$

51. $2\frac{5}{6} = \frac{17}{6} = 2.8333 = 283.33\%$

53. $4\frac{1}{8} = \frac{33}{8} = 4.125 = 412.5\%$

55. $\frac{3}{7} = 0.4286 = 42.86\%$

57. $\frac{15}{16} = 0.9375 = 93.75\%$

59. $\frac{26}{50} = 0.52 = 52\%$

61. $\frac{47}{137} = 0.3431 = 34.31\%$

63. $\frac{316}{907} = 0.3484 = 34.84\%$

65.
$$
\begin{array}{r}
0.025 \\
40\overline{)1.000} \\
\underline{80} \\
200 \\
\underline{200} \\
0
\end{array}
\qquad \frac{1}{40} = 2.5\%
$$

67.
$$
\begin{array}{r}
0.01233 \\
3000\overline{)37.00000} \\
\underline{30\ 00} \\
7\ 000 \\
\underline{6\ 000} \\
1\ 0000 \\
\underline{9000} \\
10000 \\
\underline{9000} \\
1000
\end{array}
$$
$$
\frac{37}{3000} = 1.23\%
$$

69.
$$
\begin{array}{r}
0.83 \\
6\overline{)5.00} \\
\underline{4\ 8} \\
20 \\
\underline{18} \\
2
\end{array}
\qquad \frac{5}{6} = 0.83\frac{2}{6} = 0.83\frac{1}{3} = 83\frac{1}{3}\%
$$

71.
$$
\begin{array}{r}
.68 \\
16\overline{)11.00} \\
\underline{9\ 6} \\
1\ 40 \\
\underline{1\ 28} \\
12
\end{array}
$$
$$
\frac{11}{16} = 0.68\frac{12}{16}
$$
$$
= 0.68\frac{3}{4}
$$
$$
= 68\frac{3}{4}\%
$$

73.
$$
\begin{array}{r}
0.37 \\
8\overline{)3.00} \\
\underline{2\ 4} \\
60 \\
\underline{56} \\
4
\end{array}
\qquad \frac{3}{8} = 0.37\frac{4}{8} = 0.37\frac{1}{2} = 37\frac{1}{2}\%
$$

75.
$$
\begin{array}{r}
0.07 \\
40\overline{)3.00} \\
\underline{2\ 80} \\
20
\end{array}
\qquad \frac{3}{40} = 0.07\frac{20}{40} = 0.07\frac{1}{2} = 7\frac{1}{2}\%
$$

77.
$$
\begin{array}{r}
0.41666 \\
12\overline{)5.00000} \\
\underline{4\ 8} \\
20 \\
\underline{12} \\
80 \\
\underline{72} \\
80 \\
\underline{72} \\
80 \\
\underline{72} \\
8
\end{array}
$$
$$
\frac{5}{12}; \ 0.4167; \ 41.67\%
$$

79. $0.06 = \dfrac{6}{100} = \dfrac{3}{50}$

$\dfrac{3}{50}$; 0.06; 6%

81. $40\% = 0.4 = \dfrac{4}{10} = \dfrac{2}{5}$

$\dfrac{2}{5}$; 0.4; 40%

83. $0.345 = \dfrac{345}{1000} = \dfrac{69}{200}$

$\dfrac{69}{200}$; 0.345; 34.5%

85.
$$
\begin{array}{r}
0.015 \\
200\overline{)3.000} \\
2\ 00 \\
\overline{1\ 000} \\
1\ 000 \\
\overline{0}
\end{array}
$$

$\dfrac{3}{200}$; 0.015; 1.5%

87.
$$
\begin{array}{r}
0.555 \\
9\overline{)5.0} \\
4\ 5 \\
\overline{50} \\
45 \\
\overline{50} \\
45 \\
\overline{5}
\end{array}
$$

$\dfrac{5}{9} = 0.\overline{5}$

$\dfrac{5}{9}$; 0.5556; 55.56%

89. $\dfrac{1}{8} = 0.125$

$3\dfrac{1}{8}\% = 0.03125 = 0.0313$

$0.03125 = \dfrac{3125}{100,000} = \dfrac{1}{32}$

$\dfrac{1}{32}$; 0.0313; $3\dfrac{1}{8}\%$

91. $28\dfrac{15}{16}\% = \dfrac{463}{16} \times \dfrac{1}{100} = \dfrac{463}{1600}$

93. $\dfrac{123}{800} = \dfrac{n}{100}$
$800 \times n = 123 \times 100$
$800 \times n = 12{,}300$
$\dfrac{800 \times n}{800} = \dfrac{12{,}300}{800}$
$n = 15.375$
$\dfrac{123}{800} = 15.375\%$

Cumulative Review Problems

95. $\dfrac{15}{n} = \dfrac{8}{3}$
$8 \times n = 15 \times 3$
$\dfrac{8 \times n}{8} = \dfrac{45}{8}$
$n = 5.625$

97. $\dfrac{n}{11} = \dfrac{32}{4}$
$4 \times n = 11 \times 32$
$\dfrac{4 \times n}{4} = \dfrac{352}{4}$
$n = 88$

5.3A Exercises

1. What is 38% of 500?
$n = 38\% \times 500$

3. 50% of what is 7?
$50\% \times n = 7$

5. 17 is what percent of 85?
$17 = n \times 85$

7. Find 128% of 4000.
$n = 128\% \times 4000$

9. What percent of 400 is 15?
$n \times 400 = 15$

11. 136 is 145% of what?
$136 = 145\% \times n$

13. What is 60% of 250?
$n = 60\% \times 250$
$n = 0.6 \times 250$
$n = 150$

15. Find 152% of 600
$n = 152\% \times 600$
$n = 1.52 \times 600$
$n = 912$

17. 6% of $106.50 is what?
$6\% \times 106.50 = n$
$0.06 \times 106.50 = \$6.39$

19. 26% of what is 312?
$26\% \times n = 312$
$0.26 \times n = 312$
$\dfrac{0.26n}{0.26} = \dfrac{312}{0.26}$
$n = 1200$

21. 52 is 4% of what?
$52 = 4\% \times n$
$52 = 0.04n$
$\dfrac{52}{0.04} = \dfrac{0.04n}{0.04}$
$1300 = n$

23. 22% of what is $33?
$22\% \times n = 33$
$0.22n = 33$
$\dfrac{0.22n}{0.22} = \dfrac{33}{0.22}$
$n = 150$
$150

25. What percent of 30 is 18?
$n \times 30 = 18$
$\dfrac{n \times 30}{30} = \dfrac{18}{30}$
$n = 0.6$
$n = 60\%$

27. 56 is what percent of 200?
$56 = n \times 200$
$\dfrac{56}{200} = \dfrac{n \times 200}{200}$
$0.28 = n$
$28\% = n$

29. 14 is what percent of 280?
$14 = n \times 280$
$\dfrac{14}{280} = \dfrac{n \times 280}{280}$
$0.05 = n$
5% defective

31. 18% of 280 is what?
$18\% \times 280 = n$
$0.18 \times 2800 = n$
$50.4 = n$

33. 150% of what is 102?
$150\% \times n = 102$
$1.5n = 102$
$\dfrac{1.5n}{1.5} = \dfrac{102}{1.5}$
$n = 68$

35. 84 is what percent of 700?
$84 = n \times 700$
$\dfrac{84}{700} = \dfrac{n \times 700}{700}$
$0.12 = n$
$12\% = n$

37. Find 0.4% of 820.
$n = 0.4\% \times 820$
$n = 0.004 \times 820$
$n = 3.28$

39. What percent of 35 is 22.4?
$n \times 35 = 22.4$
$\dfrac{n \times 35}{35} = \dfrac{22.4}{35}$
$n = 0.64$
$n = 64\%$

41. 89 is 20% of what?
$89 = 20\% \times n$
$89 = 0.2n$
$\dfrac{89}{0.2} = \dfrac{0.2n}{0.2}$
$445 = n$

43. 42 is what percent of 120?
$42 = n \times 120$
$\dfrac{42}{120} = \dfrac{n \times 120}{120}$
$0.35 = n$
$35\% = n$

45. What is 16.5% of 240?
$n = 16.5\% \times 240$
$n = 0.165 \times 240$
$n = 39.6$

47. Find 0.06% of 2400.
$n = 0.06\% \times 2400$
$n = 0.0006 \times 2400$
$n = 1.44$

49. What is 38.5% of 2345?
$n = 38.5\% \times 2345$
$n = 0.385 \times 2345$
$n = 902.825$

51. 3458 is what percent of 5832?
$3458 = n \times 5832$
$\dfrac{3458}{5832} = \dfrac{n \times 5832}{5832}$
$0.5929 \approx n$
$n = 59.29\%$ (rounded)

53. 68 is what percent of 80?
$68 = n \times 80$
$\dfrac{68}{80} = \dfrac{n \times 80}{80}$
$0.85 = n$
$85\% = n$
85% were acceptable

55. 44% of 1260 is what?
$44\% \times 1260 = n$
$0.44 \times 1260 = n$
$554.4 = n$
554 students

57. 60% of what is 24
$60\% \times n = 24$
$0.60 \times n = 34$
$\dfrac{0.60 \times n}{0.60} = \dfrac{24}{0.60}$
$n = 40$
40 years

59. Find 12% of 30% of $1600.
$n = 12\% \times 30\% \times 1600$
$n = 0.12 \times 0.30 \times 1600$
$n = 57.60$

Cumulative Review Problems

61.
$$\begin{array}{r} 1.36 \\ \times\ 1.8 \\ \hline 1088 \\ 136\ \ \\ \hline 2.448 \end{array}$$

63.
$$\begin{array}{r} 2834. \\ 0.06\overline{)170.04} \\ \underline{12}\ \ \ \ \ \\ 50\ \ \ \ \\ \underline{48}\ \ \ \ \\ 2\ 0\ \ \\ \underline{1\ 8}\ \ \\ 24 \\ \underline{24} \\ 0 \end{array}$$

5.3B Exercises

		p	b	a
1.	75% of 660 is 495	75	660	495
3.	What is 42% of 400	42	400	a
5.	49% of what is 2450?	49	b	2450
7.	30 is what percent of 50?	p	50	30
9.	What percent of 25 is 10?	p	25	10
11.	400 is 160% of what?	160	b	400

13. 24% of 300 is what?
$\dfrac{a}{300} = \dfrac{24}{100}$
$100a = 300 \times 24$
$\dfrac{100a}{100} = \dfrac{24,7200}{100}$
$a = 72$

15. Find 250% of 30.
$\dfrac{a}{30} = \dfrac{250}{100}$
$100a = 30 \times 250$
$\dfrac{100a}{100} = \dfrac{7500}{100}$
$a = 75$

17. 0.7% of 8000 is what?

$$\frac{a}{8000} = \frac{0.7}{100}$$
$$100a = 8000 \times 0.7$$
$$\frac{100a}{100} = \frac{5600}{100}$$
$$a = 56$$

19. 45 is 60% of what?

$$\frac{45}{b} = \frac{60}{100}$$
$$45 \times 100 = 60b$$
$$\frac{4500}{60} = \frac{60b}{60}$$
$$75 = b$$

21. 150% of what is 90?

$$\frac{90}{b} = \frac{150}{100}$$
$$90 \times 100 = 150b$$
$$\frac{9000}{150} = \frac{150b}{150}$$
$$60 = b$$

23. 3000 is 0.5% of what?

$$\frac{3000}{b} = \frac{0.5}{100}$$
$$3000 \times 100 = 0.5b$$
$$\frac{300,000}{0.5} = \frac{0.5b}{0.5}$$
$$600,000 = b$$

25. 70 is what percent of 280?

$$\frac{p}{100} = \frac{70}{280}$$
$$280p = 70 \times 100$$
$$\frac{280p}{280} = \frac{7000}{280}$$
$$p = 25$$

27. What percent of 140 is 3.5?

$$\frac{p}{100} = \frac{3.5}{140}$$
$$140p = 3.5 \times 100$$
$$\frac{140p}{140} = \frac{350}{140}$$
$$p = 2.5$$

29. What percent of $5000 is $90?

$$\frac{p}{100} = \frac{90}{5000}$$
$$5000p = 90 \times 100$$
$$\frac{5000p}{5000} = \frac{9000}{5000}$$
$$p = 1.8$$

31. 26% of 350 is what?

$$\frac{a}{350} = \frac{26}{100}$$
$$100a = 350 \times 26$$
$$\frac{100a}{100} = \frac{9100}{100}$$
$$a = 91$$

33. 180% of what is 540?

$$\frac{180}{100} = \frac{540}{b}$$
$$180b = 100 \times 540$$
$$\frac{180b}{180} = \frac{54,000}{180}$$
$$b = 300$$

35. 82 is what percent of 500?

$$\frac{p}{100} = \frac{82}{500}$$
$$500p = 100 \times 82$$
$$\frac{500p}{500} = \frac{8200}{500}$$
$$p = 16.4$$
$$16.4\%$$

37. Find 0.7% of 520.

$$\frac{a}{520} = \frac{0.7}{100}$$
$$100a = 520 \times 0.7$$
$$\frac{100a}{100} = \frac{364}{100}$$
$$a = 3.64$$

39. What percent of 66 is 16.5?

$$\frac{p}{100} = \frac{16.5}{66}$$
$$66p = 100 \times 16.5$$
$$\frac{66p}{66} = \frac{1650}{66}$$
$$p = 25$$
$$25\%$$

41. 68 is 40% of what?

$$\frac{40}{100} = \frac{68}{b}$$
$$40b = 100 \times 68$$
$$\frac{40b}{40} = \frac{6800}{40}$$
$$b = 170$$

43. 94.6 is what percent of 220?

$$\frac{p}{100} = \frac{94.6}{220}$$
$$220p = 100 \times 94.6$$
$$\frac{220p}{220} = \frac{9460}{220}$$
$$p = 43$$
43%

45. What is 12.5% of 380?

$$\frac{a}{380} = \frac{12.5}{100}$$
$$100a = 380 \times 12.5$$
$$\frac{100a}{100} = \frac{4750}{100}$$
$$a = 47.5$$

47. Find 0.05% of 5600.

$$\frac{a}{5600} = \frac{0.05}{100}$$
$$100a = 5600 \times 0.05$$
$$\frac{100a}{100} = \frac{280}{100}$$
$$a = 2.8$$

49. What percent of 4550 is 720?

$$\frac{p}{100} = \frac{720}{4550}$$
$$4550p = 720 \times 100$$
$$p = \frac{72,000}{4550}$$
$$p = 15.82$$
15.82%

51. 4.25% of 256.75 is what number?

$$\frac{4.25}{100} = \frac{a}{256.75}$$
$$4.25 \times 256.75 = 100a$$
$$\frac{1091}{100} = a$$
$$10.91 = a$$

53. What is $19\frac{1}{4}\%$ of 798?

$$\frac{a}{798} = \frac{19\frac{1}{4}}{100}$$
$$\frac{a}{798} = \frac{19.25}{1000}$$
$$100a = 798 \times 19.25$$
$$\frac{100a}{100} = \frac{15,361.5}{100}$$
$$a = 153.62$$

55. First find 20% of $3300.

$$\frac{a}{3300} = \frac{20}{100}$$
$$100 \times a = 3300 \times 20$$
$$\frac{100a}{100} = \frac{66,000}{100}$$
$$a = 660$$
Next find 18% of $660.
$$\frac{a}{660} = \frac{18}{100}$$
$$100 \times a = 660 \times 18$$
$$\frac{100a}{100} = \frac{11,880}{100}$$
$$a = 118.8$$
$118.80

Cumulative Review Problems

57. $\frac{4}{5} + \frac{8}{9} = \frac{4}{5} \times \frac{9}{9} + \frac{8}{9} \times \frac{5}{5}$

$$= \frac{36}{45} + \frac{40}{45}$$
$$= \frac{76}{45} = 1\frac{31}{45}$$

59. $\left(2\frac{4}{5}\right)\left(1\frac{1}{2}\right) = \frac{14}{5} \times \frac{3}{2}$

$= \frac{42}{10} = \frac{21}{5} = 4\frac{1}{5}$

5.4 Exercises

1. $n \times 2.5\% = 4500$

$\dfrac{n \times 0.025}{0.025} = \dfrac{4500}{0.025}$

$n = 180,000$

180,000 pencils

3. $n = 1885 \times 5\%$

$n = 1885 \times 0.05$

$n = 94.25$

$94.25

5. $n \times 95 = 76$

$\dfrac{n \times 95}{95} = \dfrac{76}{95}$

$n = 0.8$

80% do not need adjustment.

20% need adjustment.

7. $48.60 = 115\% \times n$

$48.6 = 1.15n$

$\dfrac{48.6}{1.15} = \dfrac{1.15n}{1.15}$

$42.26 = n$

Approximately $42.26

9. $n = 7\% \times 92$

$n = 0.07 \times 92$

$n = 6.44$

$6.44

11. $400 \times n = 36$

$\dfrac{400 \times n}{400} = \dfrac{36}{400}$

$n = 0.09$

9%

13. $n = 450 \times 74\%$

$n = 450 \times 0.74$

$n = 333$

333 people

15. $n \times 4\% = 9.60$

$0.04n = 9.6$

$\dfrac{0.04n}{0.04} = \dfrac{9.6}{0.04}$

$n = 240$

$240

17. $n \times 5060 = 1265$

$\dfrac{n \times 5060}{5060} = \dfrac{1265}{5060}$

$n = 0.25$

25%

19. $n \times 75\% = 7,200,000$

$\dfrac{0.75n}{0.75} = \dfrac{7,200,000}{0.75}$

$n = 9,600,000$

$9,600,000

21. $n = 6.5\% \times 21,000$

$n = 0.065 \times 21,000$

$n = 1365$

1365 blue M&M's

23. $n = 3\% \times 2,500,000$

$n = 0.03 \times 2,500,000$

$n = 75,000$

$75,000

25. $n = 0.9\% \times 24,000$

$n = 0.009 \times 24,000$

$n = 216$

216 babies

27. $650,000 \times n = 26,000$

$\dfrac{650,000n}{650,000} = \dfrac{26,000}{650,000}$

$n = 0.04$

4%

29. $100\% \times n + 20\% \times n = 66$

$120\% \times n = 66$

$1.2n = 66$

$\dfrac{1.2n}{1.2} = \dfrac{66}{1.2}$

$n = 55$

$55

31. $(15\% + 12\% + 10\%) \times 33{,}000{,}000 = n$
$(37\%) \times 33{,}000{,}000 = n$
$0.37 \times 33{,}000{,}000 = n$
$12{,}210{,}000 = n$
$33{,}000{,}000 - 12{,}210{,}000 = 20{,}790{,}000$
$12{,}210{,}000 for personnel, food, and decorations.
$20{,}790{,}000 for security, facility rental and all other expenses

33. a. $6\% \times 236.00 = n$
$0.06 \times 236 = n$
$14.16 = n$
$14.16

b. $236.00 + 14.16 = 250.16$
$250.16

35. $7600 - 5550 = 2050$
$2050 = n \times 5550$
$$\frac{2050}{5550} = \frac{n \times 5550}{5550}$$
$0.3694 \approx n$
36.94%

37. $985 - 394 = 591$
Percent of decrease $= \dfrac{591}{985} = 0.6$
60%

39. a. $n = 8\% \times 15{,}990$
$n = 0.08 \times 15{,}990$
$n = 1279.2$
$1279.20

b. $15{,}990 - 1279.20 = 14{,}710.80$
$14{,}710.80

41. a. $n = 12\% \times 2125$
$n = 0.12 \times 2125$
$n = 255$
$255

b. $2125 - 255 = 1870$
$1870

43. a. $n = 8\% \times 2500$
$n = 0.08 \times 2500$
$n = 200$
$200

b. $2500 + 200 = 2700$
$2700

45. a. $n = 3.2\% \times 3700$
$n = 0.032 \times 3700$
$n = 118.4$
$118.40

b. $3700 + 118.4 = 3818.4$
$3818.40

47. $n = 4.6\% \times 18{,}456.82$
$n = 0.046 \times 18{,}456.82$
$n = 849.01$
$849.01

49. $n = 1.4575\% \times 698.44$
$n = 0.014575 \times 698.44$
$n = 10.18$
$698.44 + 10.18 = 708.62$
$10.18
$708.62

51. discount $= 0.12 \times 9346.8 = 1121.62$
price $= 9346.8 - 1121.62 = 8225.18$
tax $= 0.04 \times 8225.18 \approx 329.01$
total price for two $= 2(8225.18 + 329.01)$
$= 2(8554.19) = 17{,}108.38$
$17{,}108.38

Cumulative Review Problems

53. 1,698,481 rounds to 1,698,000.

55. 1.63474 rounds to 1.63.

57. 0.055613 rounds to 0.0556.

Putting Your Skills to Work

1. $3.3 - 1.3 = 2$
$1.3 \times n = 2$
$$\frac{1.3n}{1.3} = \frac{2}{1.3}$$
$n \approx 1.538$
153.8% increase health benefits of reducing the amount of fat consumed in milk

3. 1970 total = 25.5 + 4.4 + 1.3 = 31.2
1995 total = 9.2 + 12.7 + 3.3 = 25.2
31.2 − 25.2 = 6
31.2 × n = 6
$$\frac{31.2n}{31.2} = \frac{6}{31.2}$$
n ≈ 0.192
Overall use of milk decreased by 19.2%

Chapter 5 Review Problems

1. 0.87 = 87%

3. 0.276 = 27.6%

5. 0.0713 = 7.13%

7. 2.52 = 252%

9. 1.036 = 103.6%

11. 0.006 = 0.6%

13. 0.0029 = 0.29%

15. $\frac{72}{100} = 72\%$

17. $\frac{19.5}{100} = 19.5\%$

19. $\frac{0.24}{100} = 0.24\%$

21. $\frac{4\frac{1}{12}}{100} = 4\frac{1}{12}\%$

23. $\frac{317}{100} = 317\%$

25. $\frac{16}{25} = 0.64 = 64\%$

27. $\frac{18}{20} = 0.9 = 90\%$

29. $\frac{5}{11} = 0.4545 = 45.45\%$

31. $2\frac{1}{4} = \frac{9}{4} = 2.25 = 225\%$

33. $4\frac{3}{7} = 4.4286 = 442.86\%$

35. $\frac{152}{80} = 1.9 = 190\%$

37. $\frac{3}{800} = 0.00375 = 0.38\%$

39. 0.2% = 0.002

41. 21.9% = 0.219

43. 166% = 1.66

45. $32\frac{1}{8}\% = 32.125\% = 0.32125$

47. $82\% = \frac{82}{100} = \frac{41}{50}$

49. $185\% = \frac{185}{100} = \frac{37}{20}$

51. $16.4\% = \frac{16.4}{100} = \frac{164}{1000} = \frac{41}{250}$

53. $31\frac{1}{4}\% = \frac{\frac{125}{4}}{100} = \frac{125}{400} = \frac{5}{16}$

55. $0.05\% = \frac{0.05}{100} = \frac{5}{10,000} = \frac{1}{2000}$

57. $5\overline{)3.0}$
$\underline{3\,0}$
0

$\frac{3}{5}$; 0.6; 60%

59. $37.5\% = 0.375 = \frac{375}{1000} = \frac{3}{8}$

$\frac{3}{8}$; 0.375; 37.5%

61. $0.008 = \dfrac{8}{1000} = \dfrac{1}{125}$

$\dfrac{1}{125}; \ 0.008; \ 0.8\%$

63. What is 96% of 300?
$n = 96\% \times 300$
$= 0.96 \times 300$
$= 288$

65. 3 is 20% of what number?
$3 = 20\% \times n$
$\dfrac{3}{0.2} = \dfrac{0.2n}{0.2}$
$15 = n$

67. 50 is what percent of 125?
$50 = n \times 125$
$\dfrac{50}{125} = \dfrac{n \times 125}{125}$
$0.4 = n$
40%

69. Find 125% of 46.
$125\% \times 46 = n$
$1.25 \times 46 = n$
$57.5 = n$

71. 92% of what number is 147.2?
$92\% \times n = 147.2$
$\dfrac{0.92b}{0.92} = \dfrac{147.2}{0.92}$
$n = 160$

73. What percent of 70 is 14?
$n \times 70 = 14$
$\dfrac{n \times 70}{70} = \dfrac{14}{70}$
$n = 0.2 = 20\%$

75. 0.5% of 2600 is what number?
$0.5\% \times 2600 = n$
$0.005 \times 2600 = n$
$13 = n$

77. What percent of 28 is 130?
$n \times 28 = 130$
$\dfrac{n \times 28}{28} = \dfrac{130}{28}$
$n = 4.6429 = 464.29\%$

79. Left handed = 34% × # students
$= 0.34 \times 150$
$= 51$

81. Percent defective = $\dfrac{\text{Number defective}}{\text{Computers}}$

$= \dfrac{6}{144}$
$= 0.041\overline{6}$
$= 4.17\%$

83. Today's value = 61% × previous value
$6832 = 61\% \times n$
$\dfrac{6832}{0.61} = \dfrac{0.61n}{0.61}$
$\$11,200 = n$

85. Percent failed = $\dfrac{\text{Number failed}}{\text{tires}}$

$= \dfrac{3}{20}$
$= 0.15$
$= 15\%$

87. Commission = 7.5% × sales
$= 7.5\% \times 16,000$
$= 0.075 \times 16,000$
$= \$1200$

89. Increase = 45.8 − 44 = 1.8
Percent increase = $\dfrac{\text{Increase}}{\text{Average temperature}}$

$= \dfrac{1.8}{44}$
$= 0.04\overline{09}$
$= 4.09\%$

91. a. Discount = 20% × list price
$= 0.2 \times 1595$
$= \$319$

b. Sale price = list price – discount
= 1595 – 319
= $1276

Chapter 5 Test

1. $0.42 = 42\%$

3. $0.006 = 0.6\%$

5. $2.18 = 218\%$

7. $\dfrac{2.7}{100} = 2.7\%$

9.

$$\begin{array}{r} 0.475 \\ 40\overline{)19.000} \\ 16\ 0 \\ \hline 3\ 00 \\ 2\ 80 \\ \hline 200 \\ 200 \\ \hline 0 \end{array}$$

$\dfrac{19}{40} = 0.475 = 47.5\%$

11.

$$\begin{array}{r} 1.4 \\ 75\overline{)105.0} \\ 75 \\ \hline 30\ 0 \\ 30\ 0 \\ \hline 0 \end{array}$$

$\dfrac{105}{75} = 1.4 = 140\%$

13. $0.1713 = 17.13\%$

15. $152\% = \dfrac{152}{100} = \dfrac{38}{25}$ or $1\dfrac{13}{25}$

17. $n = 17\% \times 157$
$n = (0.17)(157)$
$n = 26.69$

19. $n \times 72 = 40$
$\dfrac{n \times 72}{72} = \dfrac{40}{72}$
$n = 0.5556 = 55.56\%$

21. $16\% \times n = 800$
$0.16n = 800$
$\dfrac{0.16n}{0.16} = \dfrac{800}{0.16}$
$n = 5000$

23. $132\% \times 530 = n$
$(1.32)(530) = n$
$699.6 = n$

25. $n = 4\% \times 152{,}300$
$n = (0.04)(152{,}300)$
$n = 6092$
$\$6092$

27. $75 = n \times 84$
$\dfrac{75}{84} = \dfrac{n \times 84}{84}$
$n = 0.8929 = 89.29\%$

29. $5160 = 43\% \times n$
$5160 = 0.43n$
$\dfrac{5160}{0.43} = \dfrac{0.43n}{0.43}$
$12{,}000 = n$
12,000 registered voters

Chapters 1–5 Cumulative Test

1.
$$\begin{array}{r} 38 \\ 196 \\ +\ 2007 \\ \hline 2241 \end{array}$$

3.
$$\begin{array}{r} 126 \\ \times\ 42 \\ \hline 252 \\ 504 \\ \hline 5292 \end{array}$$

5. $2\dfrac{1}{4} + 3\dfrac{1}{3} = \dfrac{9}{4} + \dfrac{10}{3}$

$= \dfrac{9}{4} \times \dfrac{3}{3} + \dfrac{10}{3} \times \dfrac{4}{4}$

$= \dfrac{27}{12} + \dfrac{40}{12}$

$= \dfrac{67}{12}$ or $5\dfrac{7}{12}$

7. $3\dfrac{17}{36} \times \dfrac{21}{25} = \dfrac{125}{36} \times \dfrac{21}{25}$

$= \dfrac{2625}{900}$

$= \dfrac{35}{12}$ or $2\dfrac{11}{12}$

9. 5731.652 rounds to 5731.7.

11.
$$\begin{array}{r} 5.62 \\ \times\ 0.3 \\ \hline 1.686 \end{array}$$

13. $\dfrac{78 \div 26}{130 \div 26} = \dfrac{3 \text{ pounds}}{5 \text{ square feet}}$

15. $\dfrac{8}{2.5} = \dfrac{n}{7.5}$

$8 \times 7.5 = 2.5 \times n$

$\dfrac{60}{2.5} = \dfrac{2.5 \times n}{2.5}$

$n = 24$

17. $0.023 = 2.3\%$

19. $1.98 = 198\%$

21. $243\% = 2.43$

23. What percent of 214 is 38?

$n \times 214 = 38$

$\dfrac{n \times 214}{214} = \dfrac{38}{214}$

$n = 0.1776$

$n = 17.76\%$

25. 219 is 73% of what number?

$219 = 73\% \times n$

$\dfrac{219}{0.73} = \dfrac{0.73 \times n}{0.73}$

$n = 300$

27. $9000 \times 0.07 = 630$

$9000 - 630 = \$8370$

29. $8.86 - 7.96 = 0.9$

$\dfrac{7.96 \times n}{7.96} = \dfrac{0.9}{7.96}$

$n = 0.1131$

$= 11.31\%$ increase

Chapter 6

Pretest Chapter 6

1. $17 \text{ ft} \times \dfrac{12 \text{ in.}}{1 \text{ ft}} = 204 \text{ in.}$

3. $2 \text{ mi} \times \dfrac{1760 \text{ yd}}{1 \text{ mi}} = 3520 \text{ yd}$

5. $22 \text{ min} \times \dfrac{60 \text{ sec}}{1 \text{ min}} = 1320 \text{ sec}$

7. $5.32 \text{ km} = 5320 \text{ m}$ (move 3 places right)

9. $986 \text{ mm} = 98.6 \text{ cm}$ (move 1 place left)

11. $5296 \text{ mm} = 529.6 \text{ cm}$ (move 1 place left)

13. $12 \text{ km} + 192 \text{ m} + 984 \text{ m}$
    $= 1200 \text{ m} + 192 \text{ m} + 984 \text{ m}$
    $= 2376 \text{ m}$

15. $3.82 \text{ L} = 3820 \text{ mL}$ (move 3 places right)

17. $56.3 \text{ kg} = 0.0563 \text{ t}$ (move 3 places left)

19. $568 \text{ mg} = 0.568 \text{ g}$ (move 3 places left)

21. $12 \text{ cm} \times \dfrac{0.394 \text{ in.}}{1 \text{ cm}} = 4.73 \text{ in.}$

23. $96 \text{ km} \times \dfrac{0.62 \text{ mi}}{1 \text{ km}} = 59.52 \text{ mi}$

25. $1.4 \text{ oz} \times \dfrac{28.35 \text{ g}}{1 \text{ oz}} = 39.69 \text{ g}$

27. $7\dfrac{4}{5} \text{ yd} + 4\dfrac{1}{5} \text{ yd} + 6\dfrac{3}{5} \text{ yd} = 18\dfrac{3}{5} \text{ yd}$
    $= \dfrac{93}{5} \text{ yd} \times \dfrac{3 \text{ feet}}{1 \text{ yd}} = \dfrac{279}{5} \text{ feet}$
    $= 55.8 \text{ feet}$

29. $2 \times 95 \text{ km} = 190 \text{ km}$
    $190 \text{ km} \times \dfrac{0.62 \text{ mi}}{1 \text{ km}} = 117.8$
    $130 - 117.8 = 12.2 \text{ miles farther}$

6.1 Exercises

1. 1 foot = 12 inches

3. 1760 yards = 1 mile

5. 1 ton = 2000 pounds

7. 4 quarts = 1 gallon

9. 1 quart = 2 pints

11. 60 seconds = 1 minute

13. $15 \text{ feet} = 15 \text{ feet} \times \dfrac{1 \text{ yard}}{3 \text{ feet}} = 5 \text{ yards}$

15. $84 \text{ inches} = 84 \text{ inches} \times \dfrac{1 \text{ foot}}{12 \text{ inches}} = 7 \text{ feet}$

17. $10,560 \text{ feet}$
    $= 10,560 \text{ feet} \times \dfrac{1 \text{ mile}}{5280 \text{ feet}} = 2 \text{ miles}$

19. $7 \text{ miles} = 7 \text{ miles} \times \dfrac{1760 \text{ yards}}{1 \text{ mile}}$
    $= 12,320 \text{ yards}$

21. $12 \text{ feet} = 12 \text{ feet} \times \dfrac{12 \text{ inches}}{1 \text{ foot}} = 144 \text{ inches}$

23. $41 \text{ yards} = 41 \text{ yards} \times \dfrac{3 \text{ feet}}{1 \text{ yard}} = 123 \text{ feet}$

25. $75 \text{ inches} = 75 \text{ inches} \times \dfrac{1 \text{ foot}}{12 \text{ inches}}$
    $= 6.25 \text{ feet}$

27. 192 ounces
    $= 192 \text{ ounces} \times \dfrac{1 \text{ pound}}{16 \text{ ounces}}$
    $= 12 \text{ pounds}$

29. $13 \text{ tons} = 13 \text{ tons} \times \dfrac{2000 \text{ pounds}}{1 \text{ ton}}$
    $= 26,000 \text{ pounds}$

31. 2.25 pounds

$$= 2.25 \text{ pounds} \times \frac{16 \text{ ounces}}{1 \text{ pound}}$$

$$= 36 \text{ ounces}$$

33. 7 gallons $= 7 \text{ gallons} \times \frac{4 \text{ quarts}}{1 \text{ gallon}}$

$$= 28 \text{ quarts}$$

35. 18 pints $= 18 \text{ pints} \times \frac{1 \text{ quart}}{2 \text{ pints}}$

$$= 9 \text{ quarts}$$

37. 31 pints $= 31 \text{ pints} \times \frac{2 \text{ cups}}{1 \text{ pint}}$

$$= 62 \text{ cups}$$

39. 8 gallons $= 8 \text{ gallons} \times \frac{4 \text{ quarts}}{1 \text{ gallon}} \times \frac{2 \text{ pints}}{1 \text{ quart}}$

$$= 64 \text{ pints}$$

41. 12 weeks $= 12 \text{ weeks} \times \frac{7 \text{ days}}{1 \text{ week}}$

$$= 84 \text{ days}$$

43. 660 minutes

$$= 660 \text{ minutes} \times \frac{1 \text{ hour}}{60 \text{ minutes}}$$

$$= 11 \text{ hours}$$

45. 11 days $= 11 \text{ days} \times \frac{24 \text{ hours}}{1 \text{ day}}$

$$= 264 \text{ hours}$$

47. 70 minutes

$$= 70 \text{ minutes} \times \frac{60 \text{ seconds}}{1 \text{ minute}}$$

$$= 4200 \text{ seconds}$$

49. 18 hours

$$= 18 \text{ hours} \times \frac{60 \text{ minutes}}{1 \text{ hour}} \times \frac{60 \text{ seconds}}{1 \text{ minute}}$$

$$= 64,800 \text{ seconds}$$

51. 180 seconds $= 180 \text{ seconds} \times \frac{1 \text{ minute}}{60 \text{ seconds}}$

$$= 3 \text{ minutes}$$

53. 6755 yards $= 6755 \text{ yards} \times \frac{3 \text{ feet}}{1 \text{ yard}}$

$$= 20,265 \text{ feet}$$

55. $2\frac{1}{2} = \frac{5}{2}$

$$\frac{5}{2} \text{ days} \times \frac{24 \text{ hours}}{1 \text{ day}} \times \frac{\$2.25}{1 \text{ hour}} = \$135$$

57. 26 ounces $\times \frac{1 \text{ pound}}{16 \text{ ounces}} \times \frac{\$6.00}{1 \text{ pound}} = \$9.75$

59. 37.7 miles $\times \frac{5280 \text{ feet}}{1 \text{ mile}} = 199,056 \text{ feet}$

61. 13 feet $\times \frac{12 \text{ inches}}{1 \text{ foot}} = 156 \text{ inches}$

$$156 + 5\frac{3}{4} = 161\frac{3}{4} \text{ inches}$$

63. 267,905,993 pounds $\times \frac{1 \text{ ton}}{2000 \text{ pounds}}$

$$= 133,953 \text{ tons}$$

65. 3 years $\times \frac{365 \text{ days}}{1 \text{ years}} \times \frac{24 \text{ hours}}{1 \text{ day}}$

$$= 26,280 \text{ hours}$$

67. 12,800 nautical miles $\times \frac{38 \text{ land miles}}{33 \text{ nautical miles}}$

$$= 14,739 \text{ land miles}$$

6.2 Exercises

  1. hecto-

  3. deci-

  5. kilo-

  7. 37 centimeters $= 370$ millimeters

  9. 3.6 kilometers $= 3600$ meters

11. 328 millimeters $= 0.328$ meter

13. 56.3 centimeters $= 0.563$ meter

15. 2 kilometers = 200,000 centimeters

17. 78,000 millimeters = 0.078 kilometer

19. 0.5386 kilometer = 538,600 millimeters

21. 35 mm = 3.5 cm = 0.035 m

23. 3582 mm = 3.582 m = 0.003582 km

25. 0.32 cm = 0.0032 m = 0.0000032 km

27. (a)

29. (c)

31. 3 kilometers = 30 hectometers

33. 27 meters = 270 decimeters

35. 198 millimeters = 1.98 decimeters

37. 48.2 meters = 0.482 hectometers

39. 0.5236 hectometers = 5236 centimeters

41. 243 m + 2.7 km + 312 m
= 243 m + 2700 m + 312 m
= 3255 m

43. 5.2 cm + 361 cm + 968 mm
= 5.2 cm + 361 cm + 96.8 cm = 463 cm

45. 82 m + 471 cm + 0.32 km
= 82 m + 4.71 m + 320 m = 406.71 m

47. 0.95 cm + 1.35 cm + 2.464 mm
= 0.95 cm + 1.35 cm + 0.2464 cm
= 2.5464 cm

49. False; 1 m = 100 cm

51. True

53. True

55. False

57. True

59. a. 1,192,000 cm = 11.92 km
(move 5 places left)

b. 1,192,000 cm = 11,920 m
(move 2 places left)

61. a. 4818 m = 481,800 cm
(move 2 places right)

b. 4818 m = 4.818 km
(move 3 places left)

63. 0.004 mm = 0.000000004 km
(move 6 places left)

6.3 Exercises

1. 1 kL

3. 1 mg

5. 1 t

7. 64 kL = 64,000 L

9. 4.7 L = 4700 mL

11. 18.9 mL = 0.0189 L

13. 752 L = 0.752 kL

15. 2.43 kL = 2,430,000 mL

17. 82 mL = 82 cm^3

19. 5261 mL = 0.005261 kL

21. 74 L = 74,000 cm^3

23. 162 g = 0.162 kg

25. 35 mg = 0.035 g

27. 6328 mg = 6.328 g

29. 2.92 kg = 2920 g

31. 17 t = 17,000 kg

33. 0.32 g = 0.00032 kg

35. 7896 g = 0.007896 t

37. 5.9 kg = 5,900,000 mg

39. $7 \text{ mL} = 0.007 \text{ L} = 0.000007 \text{ kL}$

41. $128 \text{ cm}^3 = 0.128 \text{ L} = 0.000128 \text{ kL}$

43. $522 \text{ mg} = 0.522 \text{ g} = 0.000522 \text{ kg}$

45. $3607 \text{ g} = 3.607 \text{ kg} = 0.003607 \text{ t}$

47. (b)

49. (a)

51. $83 \text{ L} + 822 \text{ mL} + 30.1 \text{ L}$
$= 83 \text{ L} + 0.822 \text{ L} + 30.1 \text{ L} = 113.922 \text{ L}$

53. $5 \text{ t} + 3.82 \text{ t} + 983 \text{ kg}$
$= 5 \text{ t} + 3.82 \text{ t} + 0.983 \text{ t}$
$= 9.803 \text{ t}$

55. $24 \text{ mg} + 136 \text{ mg} + 0.26 \text{ kg}$
$= 24 \text{ mg} + 136 \text{ mg} + 260,000 \text{ mg}$
$= 260,160 \text{ mg}$

57. True

59. False; deciliter jugs are possible.

61. True

63. False; 1 metric ton = 1,000,000 grams

65. True

67. $\dfrac{\$358,000}{1 \text{ liter}} = \dfrac{\$358,000}{1 \text{ liter}} \times \dfrac{1 \text{ liter}}{1000 \text{ mL}} = \$358$

69. $\dfrac{\$95.50}{1 \text{ g}} \times \dfrac{1000 \text{ g}}{1 \text{ kg}} \times 6 \text{ kg} = \$573,000$

71. $0.4 \text{ L} = 400 \text{ mL}$
$850 \times 400 = 340,000$
$\$340,000$

73. $0.45 \text{ t} = 450 \text{ kg}$
$450 \text{ kg} \times \dfrac{\$22,450}{1 \text{ kg}} = \$10,102,500$

75. $5632 \text{ picograms} = 0.005632 \text{ micrograms}$

Cumulative Review Problems

77. $14 \text{ out of } 70 = \dfrac{14}{70} = 0.20 = 20\%$

79. What is 1.7% of $18,900?
$1.7\% \times 18,900 = 0.017 \times 18,900$
$= 321.30$
$\$321.30$

6.4 Exercises

1. $7 \text{ ft} = 7 \text{ ft} \times \dfrac{0.305 \text{ m}}{1 \text{ ft}} = 2.14 \text{ m}$

3. $9 \text{ in.} = 9 \text{ in.} \times \dfrac{2.54 \text{ cm}}{1 \text{ in.}} = 22.86 \text{ cm}$

5. $14 \text{ m} = 14 \text{ m} \times \dfrac{1.09 \text{ yards}}{1 \text{ m}} = 15.26 \text{ yd}$

7. $26.5 \text{ m} = 26.5 \text{ m} \times \dfrac{1.09 \text{ yd}}{1 \text{ m}} = 28.89 \text{ yd}$

9. $15 \text{ km} = 15 \text{ km} \times \dfrac{0.62 \text{ mi}}{1 \text{ km}} = 9.3 \text{ mi}$

11. $24 \text{ yd} = 24 \text{ yd} \times \dfrac{0.914 \text{ m}}{1 \text{ yd}} = 21.94 \text{ m}$

13. $82 \text{ mi} = 82 \text{ mi} \times \dfrac{1.61 \text{ km}}{1 \text{ mi}} = 132.02 \text{ km}$

15. $25 \text{ m} = 25 \text{ m} \times \dfrac{3.28 \text{ ft}}{1 \text{ m}} = 82 \text{ ft}$

17. $17.5 \text{ cm} = 17.5 \text{ cm} \times \dfrac{0.394 \text{ in.}}{1 \text{ cm}} = 6.90 \text{ in.}$

19. $200 \text{ m} = 200 \text{ m} \times \dfrac{1.09 \text{ yd}}{1 \text{ m}} = 218 \text{ yd}$

21. $5 \text{ gal} = 5 \text{ gal} \times \dfrac{3.79 \text{ L}}{1 \text{ gal}} = 18.95 \text{ L}$

23. $280 \text{ gal} = 280 \text{ gal} \times \dfrac{3.79 \text{ L}}{1 \text{ gal}} = 1061.2 \text{ L}$

25. $23 \text{ qt} = 23 \text{ qt} \times \dfrac{0.946 \text{ L}}{1 \text{ qt}} = 21.76 \text{ L}$

27. $19 \text{ L} = 19 \text{ L} \times \dfrac{0.264 \text{ gal}}{1 \text{ L}} = 5.02 \text{ gal}$

29. $4.5 \text{ L} = 4.5 \text{ L} \times \dfrac{1.06 \text{ qt}}{1 \text{ L}} = 4.77 \text{ qt}$

31. $32 \text{ lb} = 32 \text{ lb} \times \dfrac{0.454 \text{ kg}}{1 \text{ lb}} = 14.53 \text{ kg}$

33. $7 \text{ oz} = 7 \text{ oz} \times \dfrac{28.35 \text{ g}}{1 \text{ oz}} = 198.45 \text{ g}$

35. $16 \text{ kg} = 16 \text{ kg} \times \dfrac{2.2 \text{ lb}}{1 \text{ kg}} = 35.2 \text{ lb}$

37. $126 \text{ g} = 126 \text{ g} \times \dfrac{0.0353 \text{ oz}}{1 \text{ g}} = 4.45 \text{ oz}$

39. $166 \text{ cm} = 166 \text{ cm} \times \dfrac{0.394 \text{ in.}}{1 \text{ cm}} \times \dfrac{1 \text{ ft}}{12 \text{ in.}}$
$= 5.45 \text{ ft}$

41. $16.5 \text{ ft} = 16.5 \text{ ft} \times \dfrac{12 \text{ in.}}{1 \text{ ft}} \times \dfrac{2.54 \text{ cm}}{1 \text{ in.}}$
$= 502.92 \text{ cm}$

43. $50 \text{ km/hr} = \dfrac{50 \text{ km}}{1 \text{ hr}} \times \dfrac{0.62 \text{ mi}}{1 \text{ km}} = \dfrac{31 \text{ mi}}{1 \text{ hr}}$
$= 31 \text{ mi/hr}$

45. $60 \text{ mi/hr} = \dfrac{60 \text{ mi}}{1 \text{ hr}} \times \dfrac{1.61 \text{ km}}{1 \text{ mi}} = \dfrac{96.6 \text{ km}}{1 \text{ hr}}$
$= 96.6 \text{ km/hr}$

47. $13 \text{ mm} = 1.3 \text{ cm} \times \dfrac{0.394 \text{ in.}}{1 \text{ cm}} = 0.51 \text{ in.}$

49. $F = 1.8 \times C + 32$
$= 1.8 \times 40 + 32$
$= 104$
$104°F$

51. $F = 1.8 \times C + 32$
$= 1.8 \times 85 + 32$
$= 185$
$185°F$

53. $F = 1.8 \times C + 32$
$= 1.8 \times 12 + 32$
$= 53.6$
$53.6°F$

55. $C = \dfrac{5 \times F - 160}{9}$
$= \dfrac{5 \times 68 - 160}{9}$
$= \dfrac{180}{9}$
$= 20$
$20°C$

57. $C = \dfrac{5 \times F - 160}{9}$
$= \dfrac{5 \times 168 - 160}{9}$
$= \dfrac{680}{9} = 75.56$
$75.56°C$

59. $C = \dfrac{5 \times F - 160}{9}$
$= \dfrac{5 \times 86 - 160}{9}$
$= \dfrac{270}{9} = 30$
$30°C$

61. $67 \text{ mi} \times \dfrac{1.61 \text{ km}}{1 \text{ mi}} = 107.87 \text{ km}$
$107.87 + 36 = 143.87$
143.87 km

63. $15 \text{ gal} = 15 \text{ gal} \times \dfrac{3.79 \text{ L}}{1 \text{ gal}} = 56.85 \text{ L}$
$56.85 \text{ L} - 38 \text{ L} = 18.85 \text{ liters}$

65. $635 \text{ kg} \times \dfrac{2.2 \text{ pounds}}{1 \text{ kg}} = 1397 \text{ pounds}$

67. $F = 1.8 \times C + 32$
4 A.M.: $F = 1.8 \times 19 + 32 = 66.2$
7 A.M.: $F = 1.8 \times 45 + 32 = 113$
It is 66.2°F at 4 A.M.
The temperature may reach 113°F after
7 A.M.

69. $C = \dfrac{5 \times F - 160}{9} = \dfrac{5 \times 6188 - 160}{9}$
$= \dfrac{30,780}{9} = 3420$
3420°C

71. $0.768 \text{ oz} \times \dfrac{28.35 \text{ g}}{1 \text{ oz}} = 21.773$
21.773 g

73. 28 square inches
$= 28 \text{ sq in.} \times \dfrac{2.54 \text{ cm}}{1 \text{ in.}} \times \dfrac{2.54 \text{ cm}}{1 \text{ in.}}$
$= 180.6448 \text{ sq cm}$

75. 48 ft/sec
$= \dfrac{48 \text{ ft}}{1 \text{ sec}} \times \dfrac{1 \text{ mi}}{5280 \text{ ft}} \times \dfrac{60 \text{ sec}}{1 \text{ min}} \times \dfrac{60 \text{ min}}{1 \text{ hr}}$
$= 32.7273 \text{ mi/hr}$

Cumulative Review Problems

77. $2^3 \times 6 - 4 + 3 = 8 \times 6 - 4 + 3$
$= 48 - 4 + 3$
$= 44 + 3$
$= 47$

79. $2^2 + 3^2 + 4^3 + 2 \times 7 = 4 + 9 + 64 + 14$
$= 13 + 64 + 14 = 77 + 14 = 91$

Putting Your Skills to Work

1. 1.2 GB − 16.5 MB − 867 K
$= 1,200,000,000 - 16,500,000 - 867,000$
$= 1,182,633,000$ bytes

3. 1 GHz = 1000 MHz
$\dfrac{1000}{40} = 25$
The new computer would be 25 times faster
than Mary's.
$\dfrac{3.2}{25} = 0.128$
0.128 second

6.5 Exercises

1. $7\dfrac{2}{3} \text{ ft} + 10\dfrac{1}{3} \text{ ft} + 6 \text{ ft} = 24 \text{ feet}$
$24 \text{ ft} \times \dfrac{1 \text{ yd}}{3 \text{ ft}} = 8 \text{ yd}$

3. 86 yd + 77 yd = 163 yd
$522 \text{ ft} \times \dfrac{1 \text{ yd}}{3 \text{ ft}} = 174 \text{ yd}$
174 yd − 163 yd = 11 yd
11 yards left over

5. Perimeter = $2 \times 87 + 2 \times 152$
$= 174 \times 304$
$= 478 \text{ cm} = 4.78 \text{ m}$
Cost $= 4.78 \text{ m} \times \dfrac{\$7.00}{1 \text{ m}}$
$= \$33.46$

7. 62 L = 62,000 mL
$\dfrac{62,000}{80} = 775$
775 mL/bottle

9. 12.4 m = 1240 cm
$\dfrac{1240}{4} = 310$
310 cm/piece

11. 67 m = 6700 cm
$\dfrac{6700}{5} = 1340$
1340 cm

13. 3 L = 3000 mL
$\dfrac{3000}{24} = 125$
125 samples

15. $F = 1.8 \times 27 + 32 = 80.6°F$
$85 - 80.6 = 4.4$
The discrepancy is 4.4°F. The sign in the store is 4.4°F less than it should be.

17. $F = 1.8 \times 180 + 32 = 356°F$
$356 - 350 = 6$
The difference is 6°F. The temperature reading of 180°C is hotter.

19. $95 \text{ km/hr} \times 6.2 \text{ hr} = 589 \text{ km}$
$589 \text{ km} \times \dfrac{0.62 \text{ mi}}{1 \text{ km}} = 365 \text{ mi}$
$560 - 365 = 195$
195 miles farther

21. a. $\dfrac{520 \text{ mi}}{8 \text{ hr}} = 65 \text{ mi/hr}$
$\dfrac{65 \text{ mi}}{1 \text{ hr}} \times \dfrac{1.61 \text{ km}}{1 \text{ mi}} = 105 \text{ km/hr}$

    b. Probably not, but we cannot be sure. They may have gone faster or slower than their average speed.

23. $\dfrac{8 \text{ pt}}{1 \text{ min}} \times \dfrac{1 \text{ qt}}{2 \text{ pt}} \times \dfrac{1 \text{ gal}}{4 \text{ qt}} \times \dfrac{60 \text{ min}}{1 \text{ hr}} = 60 \text{ gal/hr}$

25. $3.4 \text{ tons} \times \dfrac{2000 \text{ lb}}{1 \text{ ton}} \times \dfrac{\$0.015}{1 \text{ lb}} = \$102$

27. $14 \text{ oz} - 11 \text{ oz} = 3 \text{ oz of raisins}$
$3 \text{ oz} \times \dfrac{28.35 \text{ g}}{1 \text{ oz}} = 85.05 \text{ grams of raisins}$

29. a. $12 \text{ L} \times \dfrac{1.06 \text{ qt}}{1 \text{ L}} = 12.72 \text{ qt}$
$18 - 12.72 = 5.28$
She bought 5 qt extra.

    b. $5 \text{ qt} \times \dfrac{\$1.39}{1 \text{ qt}} = \$6.95$

31. a. $392 \text{ km} \times \dfrac{1 \text{ L}}{6 \text{ km}} \times \dfrac{\$0.78}{1 \text{ L}} = \$5.46$

    b. 56 km/L
$= \dfrac{56 \text{ km}}{1 \text{ L}} \times \dfrac{0.62 \text{ m}}{1 \text{ km}} \times \dfrac{1 \text{ L}}{0.264 \text{ gal}}$
$= \dfrac{132 \text{ mi}}{1 \text{ gal}}$
132 mi/gal

Cumulative Review Problems

33. $\dfrac{n}{16} = \dfrac{2}{50}$
$50n = 16 \times 2$
$\dfrac{50n}{50} = \dfrac{32}{50}$
$n = 0.64$

35. $6 \text{ in.} \times \dfrac{7.75 \text{ mi}}{3 \text{ in.}} = 15.5 \text{ mi}$

Chapter 6 Review Problems

1. $27 \text{ ft} = 27 \text{ ft} \times \dfrac{1 \text{ yd}}{3 \text{ ft}} = 9 \text{ yd}$

3. $3 \text{ mi} = 3 \text{ mi} \times \dfrac{1760 \text{ yd}}{1 \text{ mi}} = 5280 \text{ yd}$

5. $90 \text{ in.} = 90 \text{ in.} \times \dfrac{1 \text{ ft}}{12 \text{ in.}} = 7.5 \text{ ft}$

7. $15,840 \text{ ft} = 15,840 \text{ ft} \times \dfrac{1 \text{ mi}}{5280 \text{ ft}}$
$= 3 \text{ mi}$

9. $4 \text{ tons} = 4 \text{ tons} \times \dfrac{2000 \text{ lb}}{1 \text{ ton}} = 8000 \text{ lb}$

11. $92 \text{ oz} = 92 \text{ oz} \times \dfrac{1 \text{ lb}}{16 \text{ oz}} = 5.75 \text{ lb}$

13. $15 \text{ gal} = 15 \text{ gal} \times \dfrac{4 \text{ qt}}{1 \text{ gal}} = 60 \text{ qt}$

15. $31 \text{ pt} = 31 \text{ pt} \times \dfrac{1 \text{ qt}}{2 \text{ pt}} = 15.5 \text{ qt}$

17. $2160 \text{ sec} = 2160 \text{ sec} \times \dfrac{1 \text{ min}}{60 \text{ sec}} = 36 \text{ min}$

19. $14 \text{ hr} = 14 \text{ hr} \times \dfrac{60 \text{ min}}{1 \text{ hr}} = 840 \text{ min}$

21. $56 \text{ cm} = 560 \text{ mm}$

23. $1763 \text{ mm} = 176.3 \text{ mm}$

25. $9.2 \text{ m} = 920 \text{ cm}$

27. $5 \text{ km} = 5000 \text{ m}$

29. $285 \text{ m} = 0.285 \text{ km}$

31. $6.2 \text{ m} + 121 \text{ cm} + 0.52 \text{ m}$
$= 6.2 \text{ m} + 1.21 \text{ m} + 0.52 \text{ m}$
$= 7.93 \text{ m}$

33. $0.024 \text{ km} + 1.8 \text{ m} + 983 \text{ cm}$
$= 24 \text{ m} + 1.8 \text{ m} + 9.83 \text{ m}$
$= 35.63 \text{ m}$

35. $17 \text{ kL} = 17{,}000 \text{L}$

37. $59 \text{ mL} = 0.059 \text{ L}$

39. $196 \text{ kg} = 196{,}000 \text{ g}$

41. $778 \text{ mg} = 0.778 \text{ g}$

43. $125 \text{ kg} = 0.125 \text{ t}$

45. $76 \text{ kg} = 76{,}000 \text{ g}$

47. $765 \text{ cm}^3 = 765 \text{ mL}$

49. $2.43 \text{ L} = 2430 \text{ mL} = 2430 \text{ cm}^3$

51. $42 \text{ kg} = 42 \text{ kg} \times \dfrac{2.2 \text{ lb}}{1 \text{ kg}} = 92.4 \text{ lb}$

53. $15 \text{ ft} = 15 \text{ ft} \times \dfrac{0.305 \text{ m}}{1 \text{ ft}} = 4.58 \text{ m}$

55. $13 \text{ oz} = 13 \text{ oz} \times \dfrac{28.35 \text{ g}}{1 \text{ oz}} = 368.55 \text{ g}$

57. $1.8 \text{ ft} = 1.8 \text{ ft} \times \dfrac{12 \text{ in.}}{1 \text{ ft}} \times \dfrac{2.54 \text{ cm}}{1 \text{ in.}}$
$= 54.86 \text{ cm}$

59. $14 \text{ cm} = 14 \text{ cm} \times \dfrac{0.394 \text{ in.}}{1 \text{ cm}} = 5.52 \text{ in.}$

61. $20 \text{ lb} = 20 \text{ lb} \times \dfrac{0.454 \text{ kg}}{1 \text{ lb}} = 9.08 \text{ kg}$

63. $12 \text{ yd} = 12 \text{ yd} \times \dfrac{0.914 \text{ m}}{1 \text{ yd}} = 10.97 \text{ m}$

65. $80 \text{ km/hr} = \dfrac{80 \text{ km}}{1 \text{ hr}} \times \dfrac{0.62 \text{ mi}}{1 \text{ km}} = 49.6 \dfrac{\text{mi}}{\text{hr}}$

67. $F = 1.8 \times C + 32 = 1.8 \times 15 + 32 = 59°\text{F}$

69. $C = \dfrac{5 \times F - 160}{9} = \dfrac{5 \times 221 - 160}{9} = 105°\text{C}$

71. $C = \dfrac{5 \times F - 160}{9}$
$= \dfrac{5 \times 32 - 160}{9}$
$= 0°\text{C}$

73. a. $7\dfrac{2}{3} \text{ ft} + 4\dfrac{1}{3} \text{ ft} + 5 \text{ ft} = 16\dfrac{3}{3} \text{ feet}$
$= 17 \text{ feet}$

    b. $17 \text{ feet} \times \dfrac{12 \text{ in.}}{1 \text{ foot}} = 204 \text{ inches}$

75. $450 \text{ g} \times \dfrac{0.0353 \text{ oz}}{1 \text{ g}} = 15.89 \text{ oz}$
$\dfrac{\$0.14}{1 \text{ oz}} \times 15.89 \text{ oz} = \$2.22$

77. $12.6 \text{ m} \times \dfrac{3.28 \text{ feet}}{1 \text{ m}} = 41.33 \text{ feet}$
Yes, she had enough.
$43 - 41.33 = 1.67 \text{ feet extra}$

79. 2 tons = 4000 pounds

$$4000 \text{ pounds} \times \frac{0.454 \text{ kg}}{1 \text{ pound}} = 1816 \text{ kg}$$

$$\frac{\$0.32}{1 \text{ kg}} \times 1816 \text{ kg} = \$581.12$$

81. $F = 1.8 \times C + 32$
$= 1.8 \times 185 + 32 = 365°F$
$390 - 365 = 25°F$ too hot

Chapter 6 Test

1. $1.6 \text{ tons} \times \dfrac{2000 \text{ lb}}{1 \text{ ton}} = 3200 \text{ lb}$

3. $21 \text{ gal} \times \dfrac{4 \text{ qt}}{1 \text{ gal}} = 84 \text{ qt}$

5. $3 \text{ cups} \times \dfrac{1 \text{ pt}}{2 \text{ cups}} \times \dfrac{1 \text{ qt}}{2 \text{ pt}} = 0.75 \text{ qt}$

7. 27.3 cm = 0.273 m (move 2 places left)

9. 46 mm = 4.6 cm (move 1 place left)

11. 12.7 m = 1270 cm (move 2 places right)

13. 46 L = 0.046 kL (move 3 places left)

15. 28.9 mg = 0.0289 g (move 3 places left)

17. 0.92 L = 920 mL (move 3 places right)

19. $42 \text{ mi} \times \dfrac{1.61 \text{ km}}{1 \text{ mi}} = 67.62 \text{ km}$

21. $9 \text{ cm} \times \dfrac{0.394 \text{ in.}}{1 \text{ cm}} = 3.55 \text{ in.}$

23. $7.3 \text{ kg} \times \dfrac{2.2 \text{ lb}}{1 \text{ kg}} = 16.06 \text{ lb}$

25. a. $3 \text{ m} + 7 \text{ m} + 3 \text{ m} + 7 \text{ m} = 20 \text{ m}$

 b. $20 \text{ m} \times \dfrac{1.09 \text{ yd}}{1 \text{ m}} = 21.8 \text{ yd}$

27. $\dfrac{5.5 \text{ qt}}{1 \text{ min}} \times \dfrac{1 \text{ gal}}{4 \text{ qt}} \times \dfrac{60 \text{ min}}{1 \text{ hr}} = 82.5 \text{ gal/hr}$

Chapters 1–6 Cumulative Test

1. $\begin{array}{r} 9824 \\ -\ 3796 \\ \hline 6028 \end{array}$

3. $28\overline{)1932}$, 69
$\begin{array}{r} 168 \\ \hline 252 \\ 252 \\ \hline 0 \end{array}$

5. $3\frac{1}{8} \quad 2\frac{9}{8}$
$-1\frac{3}{4} = -1\frac{6}{8}$
$\rule{1cm}{0.4pt}$
$1\frac{3}{8}$

7. $\dfrac{0.4}{n} = \dfrac{2}{30}$
$0.4 \times 30 = n \times 2$
$\dfrac{12}{2} = \dfrac{n \times 2}{2}$
$n = 6$

9. What percent of 66 is 165?
$n \times 66 = 165$
$\dfrac{n \times 66}{66} = \dfrac{165}{66}$
$n = 2.5 = 250\%$

11. 0.5% of what number is 100?
$0.5\% \times n = 100$
$\dfrac{0.005 \times n}{0.005} = \dfrac{100}{0.005}$
$n = 20,000$

13. $2.5 \text{ tons} \times \dfrac{2000 \text{ lb}}{1 \text{ ton}} = 5000 \text{ lb}$

15. $25 \text{ feet} \times \dfrac{12 \text{ in.}}{1 \text{ ft}} = 300 \text{ in.}$

17. $62.8 \text{ g} = 0.0628 \text{ kg}$
(move left 3 places)

19. $5 \text{ cm} = 0.05 \text{ m}$
(move left 2 places)

21. $28 \text{ gal} \times \dfrac{3.79 \text{ L}}{1 \text{ gal}} = 106.12 \text{ L}$

23. $7.87 \text{ m} \times \dfrac{3.28 \text{ ft}}{1 \text{ m}} = 25.81 \text{ feet}$

25. $6 \text{ yd} + 4 \text{ yd} + 3 \text{ yd} = 13 \text{ yd}$
$13 \text{ yd} \times \dfrac{0.914 \text{ m}}{1 \text{ yd}} = 11.88 \text{ m}$

27. $\dfrac{100 \text{ km}}{1 \text{ hr}} \times 1\dfrac{1}{2} \text{ hr} = 150 \text{ km}$
$150 \text{ km} \times \dfrac{0.62 \text{ mi}}{1 \text{ km}} = 93 \text{ mi}$
$100 - 93 = 7$
He needs to travel 7 miles farther.

Chapter 7

1. $P = 2l + 2w = 2(6.5) + 2(2.5) = 13 + 5$
   $= 18$ m

3. $A = s^2 = (4.8)^2 = 23$ sq cm

5. $P = 2 \times 9.2 + 2 \times 3.6 = 18.4 + 7.2$
   $= 25.6$ yd

7. $A = bh = 27 \times 5 = 135$ in.^{2}

9. Total Area $=$ Area$_1$ + Area$_2$
   $= lw + \dfrac{h(B+b)}{2}$
   $= 9 \times 7 + \dfrac{4(10+7)}{2}$
   $= 63 + 34 = 97$ m^2

11. $P = 7.2 + 4.3 + 3.8 = 15.3$ m

13. $\sqrt{64} = 8$

15. $\sqrt{46} \approx 6.782$

17. Leg $= \sqrt{(\text{hypotenuse})^2 - (\text{leg})^2}$
    $= \sqrt{(13)^2 - (5)^2}$
    $= \sqrt{169 - 25}$
    $= \sqrt{144} = 12$ ft

19. $C = \pi d = 3.14 \times 30 \approx 94.2$ cm

21. Shaded area
    $=$ area of rectangle $-$ area of circle
    $= l \times w - \pi r^2$
    $= 8 \times 5 - 3.14(2)^2$
    $\approx 40 - 12.56 \approx 27.4$ sq m

23. $V = \dfrac{4\pi r^3}{3} = \dfrac{4 \times 3.14 \times (3)^3}{3}$
    ≈ 113 cu ft

25. $V = \dfrac{Bh}{3} = \dfrac{(25)^2 \times 21}{3} = 4375$ cu m

27. $\dfrac{4}{30} = \dfrac{16}{n}$
    $4 \times n = 16 \times 30$
    $\dfrac{4 \times n}{4} = \dfrac{480}{4}$
    $n = 120$ cm

29. **a.** Total area
    $=$ area of rectangle $+$ area of semicircles
    $= l \times w + 2\left(\dfrac{\pi r^2}{2}\right)$
    $= 100 \times 30 + \dfrac{2 \times 3.14 \times (15)^2}{2}$
    ≈ 3706.5 yd^2

    b. $\dfrac{\$0.15}{1 \text{ yd}^2} \times 3706.5 \text{ yd}^2 = \$555.98$

7.1 Exercises

1. **a.** perpendicular

   b. equal

3. multiply

5. $P = 2l + 2w = 2(5.5) + 2(2) = 11 + 4$
   $P = 15$ mi

7. $2.5 + 9.3 + 2.5 + 9.3 = 23.6$ ft

9. $P = 4s = 4(12.3)$
   $P = 49.2$ ft

11. $P = 2l + 2w = 2(0.84) + 2(0.12)$
    $= 1.68 + 0.24$
    $P = 1.92$ mm

13. $P = 2l + 2w = 2(7) + 2(5.73) = 14 + 11.46$
    $P = 25.46$ in.

15. $P = 4s = 4(4.28)$
    $P = 17.12$ km

17. $2(0.0089) + 2(0.0034) = 0.0178 + 0.0068$
$= 0.0246$ cm

19. $2(15.2) + 2(6.65) = 30.4 + 13.3 = 43.7$ m

21. $s = 13$ m
$P = 4s = 4(13)$
$P = 52$ m

23. $s = 1.2$ mi
$P = 4s = 4(1.2)$
$P = 4.8$ mi

25. $4(0.0052) = 0.0208$ mm

27. $4(7.96) = 31.84$ cm

29. $P = 11 + 16 + 7 + 20 + 4 + 36$
$P = 94$ m

31. $P = 41 + 36 + 41 + 9 + 13 + 11 + 13 + 16$
$P = 180$ cm

33. $(18)(4) = 72$ in^2

35. $(9.8)(9.8) = 96.04$ ft^2

37. Area $= lw = 0.96 \times 0.3 = 0.288$ m^2

39. Area $= lw = 156 \times 96 = 14{,}976$ yd^2

41. Shaded area $=$ area$_1 +$ area$_2$
$= l_1 w_1 + l_2 w_2$
$= 21 \times 12 + 7 \times 6$
$= 252 + 42 = 294$ m^2

43. $A = 220 \times 50 = 11{,}000$ ft^2
Cost $= 11{,}000 \times 12 = 132{,}000$
\$132,000

45. $P = 2(8.25) + 2(5) = 16.5 + 10 = 26.5$ feet
Cost $= 26.5 \times 3.8 = 100.7$
\$100.07

47. $A = 20.24 \times 16.82 = 340.4368$ m^2
Cost $= 340.4368 \times 2.8 \approx 953.22$
\$953.22

49. Total area $=$ area$_1 +$ area$_2$
$= l_1 w_1 + l_2 w_2$
$= 24 \times 12 + 8 \times 7$
$= 288 + 56$
$= 344 \text{ ft}^2 \times \dfrac{1 \text{ yd}}{9 \text{ ft}^2}$
$= 38.\overline{2} \text{ yd}^2$
Perimeter $= 24 + 12 + 17 + 8 + 7 + 20$
$= 88 \text{ ft} \times \dfrac{1 \text{ yd}}{3 \text{ ft}}$
$= 29.\overline{3}$ yd
Total cost
$=$ cost per yd$^2 \times$ area $+$ cost per yard
$\times$ perimeter
$= \dfrac{\$14.50}{1 \text{ yd}^2} \times 38.\overline{2} \text{ yd}^2 + \dfrac{\$1.50}{1 \text{ yd}} \times 29.\overline{3} \text{ yd}$
$= \$554.22 + \$44.090 = \$598.22$

Cumulative Review Problems

51. $156.8 + 27.2 + 39.3 = 223.3$

53.
$$
\begin{array}{r}
1076 \\
\times\ \ 20.3 \\
\hline
322\ 8 \\
21520\ \ \ \\
\hline
21842.8
\end{array}
$$

7.2 Exercises

1. adding

3. perpendicular

5. $2(2.8) + 2(17.3) = 5.6 + 34.6 = 40.2$ m

7. $2(2.6) + 2(12.3) = 5.2 + 24.6 = 29.8$ in.

9. $A = bh = 25 \times 42.3$
Area $= 1057.5$ m^2

11. $(20.5)(21.5) = 440.75$ m^2

13. $A = bh = 126 \times 28$
Area $= 3528$ yd^2

15. $P = 13 + 20 + 15 + 34$
$P = 82$ m

17. $130 + 100 + 70 + 80 = 380$ cm

19. $A = \dfrac{h(b + B)}{2} = \dfrac{7(3 + 9)}{2}$

    Area $= 42$ m^2

21. $A = \dfrac{1}{2}(4)(14 + 29) = 2(43) = 86$ cm^2

23. $h = 16$ yd, $b = 15$ yd, $B = 28$ yd

    $A = \dfrac{h(b + B)}{2} = \dfrac{16(15 + 28)}{2} = 344$ yd^2

25. $h = 20$ km, $b = 24$ km, $B = 31$ km

    $A = \dfrac{h(b + B)}{2} = \dfrac{20(24 + 31)}{2} = 550$ km^2

27. $A = lw + \dfrac{h(b + B)}{2} = 28 \times 16 + \dfrac{9(28 + 32)}{2}$

    $= 448 + 270$

    Area $= 718$ m^2

29. $A = \dfrac{h_1(b_1 + B_1)}{2} + \dfrac{h_2(b_2 + B_2)}{2}$

    $= \dfrac{5(12 + 18)}{2} + \dfrac{7(7 + 18)}{2}$

    $= 75 + 87.5 = 162.5$ cm^2

31. $A = lw + bh = 15 \times 11 + 15 \times 12$

    $= 165 + 180$

    Area $= 345$ ft^2

33. $A = b_1 h_1 + b_2 h_2 = 46 \times 31 + 46 \times 49$

    $= 1426 + 2254 = 3680$ yd^2

    Cost $= 3680$ yd$^2 \times \dfrac{\$22,00}{\text{yd}^2} = \$80,960.00$

35. $A = \dfrac{h(b + B)}{2} = \dfrac{34.569(17.398 + 22.782)}{2}$

    Area ≈ 694.49 in.^{2}

$2 \times \left[\dfrac{1}{2} \times .71 \times b \times \left(b + 2.6 \times b \right) \right] + 2.65 \times b \times b$

37. $A = \dfrac{h(b + B)}{2} + \dfrac{h(b + B)}{2} + lw$

    $= 2\left[\dfrac{0.71b(b + 2.65b)}{2} \right] + b \times 2.65b$

    $= (0.71b)(3.65b) + 2.65b^2$

    $= 2.5915b^2 + 2.65b^2$

    Area $= 5.2415b^2$ sq units

Cumulative Review Problems

39. 10 yd $= 10$ yd $\times \dfrac{3 \text{ ft}}{1 \text{ yd}} = 30$ ft

41. 18 m $= 1800$ cm

7.3 Exercises

1. right

3. Take $180°$ and subtract the sum of the degrees of the other two angles.

5. You could conclude that all three sides of the triangle are equal.

7. Two lines that meet at a $90°$ angle are perpendicular. True

9. The sum of the angles of a triangle is $180°$. True

11. An equilateral triangle has one angle greater than $90°$. False

13. Known angles: $30°$ and $90°$
    Missing angle $= 180° - 30° - 90° = 60°$

15. Known angles: $130°$ and $20°$
    Missing angle $= 180° - 130° - 20° = 30°$

17. Known angles: $45°$ and $45°$
    Missing angle $= 180° - 45° - 45° = 90°$

19. Known angles: $44°$ and $8°$
    Missing angle $= 180° - 44° - 8° = 128°$

21. Sides: 36 m, 27 m, 41 m
    $P = 36 + 27 + 41 = 104$ m

23. Sides: 50 in., 40 in., 40 in.
$P = 50 + 40 + 40 = 130$ in.

25. Sides: 3.5 mi each
$P = 3(3.5 \text{ mi}) = 10.5$ mi

27. Sides: 8.5 in., 7.5 in., 9.5 in.
$P = 8.5 + 7.5 + 9.5 = 25.5$ in.

29. $\text{Area} = \dfrac{bh}{2} = \dfrac{9 \times 5}{2} = 22.5 \text{ ft}^2$

31. $\text{Area} = \dfrac{bh}{2} = \dfrac{4.5 \times 7}{2} = 15.75 \text{ in.}^2$

33. $b = 17.5$ cm, $h = 9.5$ cm
$\text{Area} = \dfrac{bh}{2} = \dfrac{17.5 \times 9.5}{2} = 83.125 \text{ cm}^2$

35. $b = 67$ m, $h = 42$ m
$\text{Area} = \dfrac{bh}{2} = \dfrac{67 \times 42}{2} = 14.07 \text{ m}^2$

37. $b = 3.5$ yd, $h = 7$ yd
$\text{Area} = \dfrac{bh}{2} = \dfrac{3.5 \times 7}{2} = 12.25 \text{ yd}^2$

39. Perimeter $= 3.6 + 4.5 + 3.6 + 2.8 + 1.9$
$= 16.4$ cm

41. $\text{Area} = lw + \dfrac{bh}{2} = 16 \times 9.5 + \dfrac{16 \times 4.5}{2}$
$= 152 + 36 = 188 \text{ yd}^2$

43. Total area
$= \text{area of front} + \text{area of back}$
$\qquad\qquad + \text{area of 2 sides}$
$= \left(\dfrac{bh}{2} + lw\right) + \left(\dfrac{bh}{2} + lw\right) + 2(lw)$
$= \left(\dfrac{20 \times 12}{2} + 15 \times 20\right) + \left(\dfrac{20 \times 12}{2} + 15 \times 20\right)$
$\qquad\qquad + 2(30 \times 15)$
$= 420 + 420 + 900 = 1740 \text{ ft}^2$

45. Painted area = area of complete triangle
$\qquad\quad$ – area of unshaded triangle
$= \dfrac{26 \times 25}{2} - \dfrac{26 \times 7}{2}$
$= 325 - 91$
$= 234 \text{ yd}^2$
$\text{Cost} = 234 \text{ yd}^2 \times \dfrac{\$90.00}{\text{yd}^2}$
$= \$21,060.00$

Cumulative Review Problems

47. $\dfrac{5}{n} = \dfrac{7.5}{18}$
$5 \times 18 = 7.5n$
$\dfrac{90}{7.5} = \dfrac{7.5n}{7.5}$
$n = 12$

49. $\dfrac{4}{15} = \dfrac{n}{2685}$
$4 \times 2685 = 15n$
$\dfrac{10,740}{15} = \dfrac{15n}{15}$
$n = 716$
716 waitstaff

7.4 Exercises

1. $\sqrt{25} = 5$

3. 32 is not a perfect square because no whole number multiplied by itself equals 32.

5. $\sqrt{1} = 1$

7. $\sqrt{16} = 4$

9. $\sqrt{25} = 5$

11. $\sqrt{49} = 7$

13. $\sqrt{100} = 10$

15. $\sqrt{121} = 11$

17. $\sqrt{169} = 13$

19. $\sqrt{0} = 0$

21. $\sqrt{49} + \sqrt{9} = 7 + 3 = 10$

23. $\sqrt{100} + \sqrt{1} = 10 + 1 = 11$

25. $\sqrt{36} + \sqrt{64} = 6 + 8 = 14$

27. $\sqrt{0} + \sqrt{16} = 0 + 4 = 4$

29. $\sqrt{144} - \sqrt{4} = 12 - 2 = 10$

31. $\sqrt{121} - \sqrt{36} = 11 - 6 = 5$

33. $\sqrt{1} + \sqrt{9} + \sqrt{25} + \sqrt{36} + \sqrt{49}$
$= 1 + 3 + 5 + 6 + 7 = 22$

35. a. Yes, $7 \times 7 = 49$

    b. $\sqrt{49} = 7$

37. a. Yes, $16 \times 16 = 256$

    b. $\sqrt{256} = 16$

39. $\sqrt{18} \approx 4.243$

41. $\sqrt{31} \approx 5.568$

43. $\sqrt{83} \approx 9.110$

45. $\sqrt{120} \approx 10.954$

47. $\sqrt{125} \approx 11.180$

49. $\sqrt{121 \ m^2} = 11 \ m$

51. $\sqrt{26 \ m^2} \approx 5.099 \ m$

53. $\sqrt{75 \ m^2} \approx 8.660 \ m$

55. a. $\sqrt{4} = 2$

    b. $\sqrt{0.04} = 0.02$

    c. $\sqrt{0.0004} = 0.02$

    d. Each answer is obtained from the previous answer by dividing by 10.

    e. No, because 0.004 isn't a perfect square.

57. $\sqrt{42,036} \approx 205.027$

59. $\sqrt{456} + \sqrt{322} \approx 39.299$

Cumulative Review Problems

61. Area $= 60 \times 80 = 4800$
4800 in.^{2}

63. $92 \ cm = 92 \ cm \times \dfrac{1 \ m}{100 \ cm} = 0.92$ meters

7.5 Exercises

1. Hypotenuse $= \sqrt{(\text{leg})^2 + (\text{leg})^2}$
$= \sqrt{(3)^2 + (4)^2} = \sqrt{9 + 16} = \sqrt{25} = 5$ in.

3. Hypotenuse $= \sqrt{(\text{leg})^2 + (\text{leg})^2}$
$= \sqrt{(8)^2 + (3)^2} = \sqrt{64 + 9} = \sqrt{73}$
≈ 8.544 yd

5. Leg $= \sqrt{(\text{Hypotenuse})^2 - (\text{leg})^2}$
$= \sqrt{256 - 25} = \sqrt{231} \approx 15.199$ ft

7. Leg $= \sqrt{(\text{Hypotenuse})^2 - (\text{leg})^2}$
$= \sqrt{(7)^2 - (6)^2} = \sqrt{49 - 36} = \sqrt{13}$
≈ 3.606 ft

9. Leg $= \sqrt{(\text{Hypotenuse})^2 - (\text{leg})^2}$
$= \sqrt{(13)^2 - (8)^2} = \sqrt{169 - 64} = \sqrt{105}$
≈ 10.247 km

11. $\text{Hypotenuse} = \sqrt{(\text{leg})^2 + (\text{leg})^2}$
$= \sqrt{(11)^2 + (3)^2} = \sqrt{121 + 9} = \sqrt{130}$
$\approx 11.402 \text{ m}$

13. $\text{Hypotenuse} = \sqrt{(\text{leg})^2 + (\text{leg})^2}$
$= \sqrt{(5)^2 + (5)^2} = \sqrt{25 + 25} = \sqrt{50}$
≈ 7.071

15. $\text{Leg} = \sqrt{(\text{Hypotenuse})^2 - (\text{leg})^2}$
$= \sqrt{(5)^2 - (4)^2} = \sqrt{25 - 16} = \sqrt{9}$
$= 3 \text{ ft}$

17. $\text{Hypotenuse} = \sqrt{(\text{leg})^2 + (\text{leg})^2}$
$= \sqrt{(12)^2 + (9)^2} = \sqrt{144 + 81} = \sqrt{225}$
$= 15 \text{ in.}$

19. $\text{Leg} = \sqrt{(\text{Hypotenuse})^2 - (\text{leg})^2}$
$= \sqrt{(13)^2 - (11)^2} = \sqrt{169 - 121} = \sqrt{48}$
$\approx 6.928 \text{ yd}$

21. $\text{Hypotenuse} = \sqrt{(\text{leg})^2 + (\text{leg})^2}$
$= \sqrt{(15)^2 + (8)^2} = \sqrt{225 + 64} = \sqrt{289}$
$= 17 \text{ ft}$

23. $\text{Hypotenuse} = \sqrt{(\text{leg})^2 + (\text{leg})^2}$
$= \sqrt{(3)^2 + (4)^2} = \sqrt{9 + 16} = \sqrt{25} \approx 5 \text{ mi}$

25. $\text{Leg} = \sqrt{(\text{Hypotenuse})^2 - (\text{leg})^2}$
$= \sqrt{(20)^2 - (18)^2} = \sqrt{400 - 324} = \sqrt{76}$
$\approx 8.7 \text{ ft}$

27. $\text{Leg opposite } 30° = \frac{1}{2} \times \text{hypotenuse}$
$= \frac{1}{2} \times 8 = 4 \text{ in.}$
$\text{Other leg} = \sqrt{(\text{Hypotenuse})^2 - (\text{leg})^2}$
$= \sqrt{(8)^2 - (4)^2} = \sqrt{64 - 16} = \sqrt{48}$
$\approx 6.9 \text{ in.}$

29. $\text{Leg opposite } 30° = \frac{1}{2} \times \text{hypotenuse}$
$= \frac{1}{2} \times 14 = 7 \text{ m}$
$\text{Other leg} = \sqrt{(\text{Hypotenuse})^2 - (\text{leg})^2}$
$= \sqrt{(14)^2 - (7)^2} = \sqrt{196 - 49} = \sqrt{147}$
$\approx 12.1 \text{ m}$

31. $\text{Hypotenuse} = \sqrt{2} \times \text{leg}$
$= \sqrt{2} \times 6 \approx 8.5 \text{ m}$

33. $\text{Hypotenuse} = \sqrt{2} \times \text{leg}$
$= \sqrt{2} \times 11 \approx 15.6 \text{ cm}$

35. $\text{Leg} = \sqrt{(\text{Hypotenuse})^2 - (\text{leg})^2}$
$= \sqrt{(10)^2 - (7)^2} = \sqrt{100 - 49} = \sqrt{51}$
$\approx 7.1 \text{ in.}$

37. $\text{Hypotenuse} = \sqrt{(\text{leg})^2 + (\text{leg})^2}$
$= \sqrt{(48)^2 + (20)^2} = \sqrt{2304 + 400} = \sqrt{2704}$
$= 52 \text{ yd}$

Cumulative Review Problems

39. $h = 22 \text{ m}, b = 31 \text{ m}$
$A = \frac{bh}{2} = \frac{31 \times 22}{2} = 341 \text{ m}^2$

41. $s = 21 \text{ in.}$
$A = s^2 = (21)^2 = 441 \text{ in.}^2$

7.6 Exercises

1. circumference

3. radius

5. $r = 29$ in.
   Diameter $= 2r = 2 \times 29 = 58$ in.

7. $r = 7.5$ mm
   Diameter $= 2r = 2 \times 7.5 = 15$ mm

9. $d = 45$ yd
   Radius $= \dfrac{d}{2} = \dfrac{45 \text{ yd}}{2} = 22.5$ yd

11. $d = 3.8$ cm
    Radius $= \dfrac{d}{2} = \dfrac{3.8 \text{ cm}}{2} = 1.9$ cm

13. $d = 24$ cm
    Circumference $= \pi d$
    $= 3.14 \times 24$ cm $= 75.36$ cm

15. $r = 11$ in.
    Circumference $= 2\pi r$
    $= 2 \times 3.14 \times 11$ in. ≈ 69.1 in.

17. $d = 26$ in.
    Circumference $= \pi d$
    $\approx 3.14 \times (26 \text{ in.}) \approx 81.6$ in.
    Distance ≈ 81.6 in.

19. $d = 32$ in.
    Circumference $= \pi d$
    $\approx 3.14 \times (32 \text{ in.}) \approx 100.48$ in.
    Distance $= 5(100.48 \text{ in.}) \times \dfrac{1 \text{ ft}}{12 \text{ in.}}$
    $= 41.87$ ft

21. $r = 5$ yd
    Area $= \pi r^2 = 3.14 \times (5 \text{ yd})^2 \approx 78.5 \text{ yd}^2$

23. $r = 17$ m
    Area $= \pi r^2 = 3.14 \times (17 \text{ m})^2 \approx 907.5 \text{ m}^2$

25. $d = 32$ cm, so $r = 16$ cm
    Area $= \pi r^2 = 3.14 \times (16 \text{ cm})^2 \approx 803.8 \text{ cm}^2$

27. $r = 8$ ft
    Area $= \pi r^2 = 3.14 \times (7 \text{ ft})^2 \approx 153.9 \text{ ft}^2$

29. $d = 120$ mi, so $r = 60$ mi
    Area $= \pi r^2 = 3.14 \times (60 \text{ mi})^2 = 11,304 \text{ mi}^2$

31. $d = 0.223$ m
    Circumference $= \pi d$
    $= 3.14159 \times 0.223 \approx 0.70057457$ m

33. Area $= \dfrac{1}{2}\pi r^2 = \dfrac{1}{2} \times 3.14 \times (20 \text{ m})^2$
    $\approx 628 \text{ m}^2$

35. $A = \pi r_0^2 - \pi r_1^2$
    $= 3.14 \times (14 \text{ m})^2 - 3.14 \times (12 \text{ m})^2$
    $= 615.44 \text{ m} - 452.16 \text{ m}$
    $\approx 163.3 \text{ m}^2$

37. $A = \dfrac{1}{2}\pi r^2 + lw$
    $= \dfrac{1}{2} \times 3.14 \times (5 \text{ m})^2 + 15 \text{ m} \times 10 \text{ m}$
    $= 30.25 \text{ m}^2 + 150 \text{ m}^2 \approx 189.3 \text{ m}^2$

39. $A = s^2 = \pi r^2$
    $= 12 \text{ m} \times 12 \text{ m} - 3.14 \times (6 \text{ m})^2$
    $= 144 \text{ m}^2 - 113.04 \text{ m}^2 \approx 31.0 \text{ m}^2$

41. $d = 40$ yd, so $r = 20$ yd
    $l = 120$ yd, $w = 40$ yd
    Total area
    $=$ area of semicircles + area of rectangle
    $= 2\left(\dfrac{\pi r^2}{2}\right) + lw$
    $= 3.14 \times (20 \text{ yd})^2 + 120 \text{ yd} \times 40 \text{ yd}$
    $= 1256 \text{ yd}^2 + 4800 \text{ yd}^2 \approx 6056 \text{ yd}^2$
    Cost $= 6056 \text{ yd}^2 \times \dfrac{\$0.20}{\text{yd}^2} = \$1211.20$

43. Length $=$ Circumference $= \pi d$
    $= 3.14 \times (2 \text{ ft}) = 6.28$ ft

45. Distance $= 35 \times$ Circumference
    $= 35 \times \pi d = 35 \times 3.14 \times 2 \times 14$ in.
    $= 3077.2 \text{ in.} \times \dfrac{1 \text{ ft}}{12 \text{ in.}} \approx 256.43$ ft

47. $r = 16$ in., so $d = 32$ in.
distance = 20,096 in.
$C = 3.14(32)$
$C = 100.48$
$R = 20,096 \div 100.48$
$R = 200$ revolutions

49. $r = \dfrac{d}{2} = \dfrac{64}{2} = 32$ in.
Area $= \pi r^2 = 3.14 \times (32 \text{ in.})^2 \approx 3215.36$

51. $A = 3.14 \times \left(\dfrac{6}{2}\right)^2$
$A = 28.26 \text{ ft}^2$

$28.26 \text{ ft}^2 \times \dfrac{1 \text{ yd}^2}{9 \text{ ft}^2} = 3.14 \text{ yd}^2$

$3.14 \text{ yd}^2 \times \dfrac{\$72}{1 \text{ yd}^2} = \$226.08$

53. Large pizza: $d = 15$ in., so $r = 7.5$ in.
Small pizza: $d = 12$ in., so $r = 6$ in.

  a.   Cost per slice $= \dfrac{\$6.00}{8} = \$0.75$

       Area per slice $= \dfrac{\pi r^2}{8}$

       $= \dfrac{3.14 \times (7.5 \text{ in.})^2}{8} = 22.1 \text{ in.}^2$

  b.   Cost per slice $= \dfrac{\$4.00}{6} = \$0.67$

       Area per slice $= \dfrac{\pi r^2}{6} = \dfrac{3.14 \times (6 \text{ in.})^2}{6}$

       $\approx 18.8 \text{ in.}^2$

  c.   Cost per sq in. of large $= \dfrac{\$6.00}{\pi r^2}$

       $= \dfrac{\$6.00}{3.14 \times (7.5 \text{ in.})^2} = \dfrac{\$0.03}{\text{in.}^2}$

       Cost per slice of small $= \dfrac{\$4.00}{\pi r^2}$

       $= \dfrac{\$4.00}{3.14 \times (6 \text{ in.})^2} \approx \dfrac{\$0.04}{\text{in.}^2}$

       Buy the 15 in. pizza.

Cumulative Review Problems

55. $A = 16\% \times 87 = 0.16 \times 87 = 13.92$

57. $12\% \times b = 720$
$0.12b = 720$
$\dfrac{0.12b}{0.12} = \dfrac{720}{0.12}$
$b = 6000$

7.7 Exercises

  1. $V = lwh$
       box

  3. $V = \dfrac{4\pi r^3}{3}$
       sphere

  5. $V = \dfrac{Bh}{3}$
       pyramid

  7.   Length = 4 m
       Width = 2 m
       Height = 3 m
       Volume $= lwh = 4 \times 2 \times 3 = 24 \text{ m}^3$

  9.   Length = 20 mm
       Width = 14 mm
       Height = 2.5 mm
       Volume $= LWH = 20 \times 14 \times 2.5$
       $= 700 \text{ mm}^3$

11. Radius = 2 m
       Height = 7 m
       Volume $= \pi r^2 h = 3.14 \times 2^2 \times 7 \approx 87.9 \text{ m}^3$

13. Radius = 12 m
       Height = 5 m
       Volume $= \pi r^2 h = 3.14 \times 12^2 \times 5$
       $\approx 2260.8 \text{ m}^3$

15. Radius = 9 yd
       Volume $= \dfrac{4\pi r^3}{3} = \dfrac{4 \times 3.14 \times 9^3}{3}$
       $\approx 3052.1 \text{ yd}^3$

17. Radius = 4 m

$$\text{Volume} = \frac{4\pi r^3}{3} = \frac{4 \times 3.14 \times 4^3}{3}$$
$$\approx 267.9 \text{ m}^3$$

19. Radius = 7 m

$$\text{Volume} = \frac{1}{2} \times \frac{4\pi r^3}{3} = \frac{1}{2} \times \frac{4 \times 3.14 \times 7^3}{3}$$
$$= 718.0 \text{ m}^3$$

21. Radius = 9 cm
Height = 12 cm

$$\text{Volume} = \frac{\pi r^2 h}{3} = \frac{3.14 \times 9^2 \times 2}{3}$$
$$\approx 1017.4 \text{ cm}^3$$

23. Radius = 5 ft
Height = 10 ft

$$\text{Volume} = \frac{\pi r^2 h}{3} = \frac{3.14 \times 5^2 \times 10}{3}$$
$$\approx 261.7 \text{ ft}^3$$

25. Length = 3 m
Height = 7 m

$$\text{Volume} = \frac{Bh}{3} = \frac{3 \times 3 \times 7}{3} = 21 \text{ m}^3$$

27. Length = 12 m
Width = 6 m
Height = 5 m

$$\text{Volume} = \frac{Bh}{3} = \frac{12 \times 6 \times 5}{3} = 120 \text{ m}^3$$

29. Length = 5.88 m
Width = 4.26 m
Height = 6.82 m
Volume = lwh = 5.88 × 4.26 × 6.82
= 170.832816 m^3

31. Radius = 5.21 m

$$\text{Volume} = \frac{4\pi r^3}{3} = \frac{4 \times 3.14159 \times 5.21^3}{3}$$
$$\approx 592.3814 \text{ m}^3$$

33. Length = 6.22 ft
Width = 5.01 ft
Height = 9.212 ft

$$\text{Volume} = \frac{Bh}{3} = \frac{6.22 \times 5.01 \times 9.212}{3}$$
$$= 95.6887288 \text{ ft}^3$$

35. Height = 4 in. $\times \dfrac{1 \text{ yd}}{36 \text{ in.}} = \dfrac{1}{9}$ yd

$$\text{Volume} = LWH = 20 \times 18 \times \frac{1}{9} = 40 \text{ yd}^3$$

37. Outer radius = 5 in.
Inner radius = 3 in.
Height = 20 in.
R = 5 in.
r = 3 in.
h = 20 in.
Unshaded volume
= outer volume − inner volume
= $\pi R^2 h - \pi r^2 h$
= $3.14 \times 5^2 \times 20 - 3.14 \times 3^2 \times 20$
= $1570 - 565.2 = 1004.8$ in.^{3}

39. $\text{Volume} = \dfrac{4\pi r^3}{3} = \dfrac{4 \times 3.14 \times 45,000}{3}$
$\approx 381,510,000,000,000$ mi^3

41. Radius = 5 cm
Height = 9 cm

$$\text{Volume} = \frac{\pi r^2 h}{3} = \frac{3.14 \times 5^2 \times 9}{3}$$
$$\approx 235.5 \text{ cm}^3$$

Cost = cost per cm^3 × volume

$$= \frac{4.00}{1 \text{ cm}^3} \times 235.5 \text{ cm}^3 = \$942$$

43. Length = 130 yd
Width = 87 yd
Height = 70 yd

$$\text{Volume} = \frac{Bh}{3} = \frac{130 \times 87 \times 70}{3}$$
$$= 263,900 \text{ yd}^3$$

Cumulative Review Problems

45. $7\frac{1}{3} + 2\frac{1}{4} = 7\frac{4}{12} + 2\frac{3}{12} = 9\frac{7}{12}$

47. $2\frac{1}{4} \times 3\frac{3}{4} = \frac{9}{4} \times \frac{15}{4} = \frac{135}{16} = 8\frac{7}{16}$

Putting Your Skills to Work

1. $W = PA$

$W = \left(7\,\dfrac{\text{lbs}}{\text{in.}^2}\right)(32\ \text{in}^2)$

$W = 224$ pounds

3. $A = \dfrac{1}{2}h(b_1 + b_2) + bh + \dfrac{1}{2}\pi r^2$

$= \dfrac{1}{2}(3.8)(6+5) + 3.5(3.2) + \dfrac{1}{2}(3.14)(1.6)^2$

$A = 20.9 + 11.2 + 4.0192$

$A \approx 36.1\ \text{in}^2$

$W = PA$

$W = 5.5(36.1)$

$W = 198.7$ pounds

5. Answers will vary.

7.8 Exercises

1. size, shape

3. sides

5. Because the triangles are similar.

$\dfrac{n}{2} = \dfrac{12}{3}$

$3n = 2(12)$

$\dfrac{3n}{3} = \dfrac{2(12)}{3}$

$n = 8$ m

7. The triangles are similar, so

$\dfrac{n}{7} = \dfrac{5}{2}$

$2n = 7(5)$

$2n = 35$

$\dfrac{2n}{2} = \dfrac{35}{2}$

$n = 17.5$ cm

9. The triangles are similar, so

$\dfrac{18}{5} = \dfrac{7}{n}$

$18n = 7(5)$

$18n = 35$

$\dfrac{18n}{18} = \dfrac{35}{18}$

$n = 1.9$ yd

11. Rotate triangle *abc* to match *fde*. The triangles are similar, so

a corresponds to *f*

b corresponds to *e*

c corresponds to *d*

13. Rotate the smaller triangle. The triangles are similar, so

$\dfrac{18}{8} = \dfrac{5}{n}$

$18n = 8(5)$

$18n = 40$

$\dfrac{18n}{18} = \dfrac{40}{18}$

$n = 2.2$ in.

15. The triangles are similar, so

$\dfrac{n}{10.5} = \dfrac{8}{25}$

$25n = 10.5(8)$

$\dfrac{25n}{25} = \dfrac{84}{25}$

$n = 3.36$ m

17. The rectangles are similar, so

$\dfrac{n}{3.5} = \dfrac{3}{5}$

$5n = 3.5(3)$

$\dfrac{5n}{5} = \dfrac{10.5}{5}$

$n = 2.1$ ft

19. The triangles are similar, so

$\dfrac{n}{6} = \dfrac{24}{4}$

$4n = 144$

$\dfrac{4n}{4} = \dfrac{144}{4}$

$n = 36$ ft

21. The triangles are similar, so

$$\frac{n}{96} = \frac{5.5}{6.5}$$

$$6.5n = 5.5(96)$$

$$\frac{6.5n}{6.5} = \frac{528}{6.5}$$

$$n \approx 81.2 \text{ ft}$$

23. The rectangles are similar, so

$$\frac{29}{3} = \frac{14}{n}$$

$$29n = 3(14)$$

$$29n = 42$$

$$\frac{29n}{29} = \frac{42}{29}$$

$$n \approx 1.4 \text{ km}$$

25. The trapezoids are similar, so

$$\frac{n}{7} = \frac{28}{12}$$

$$12n = 28(7)$$

$$12n = 196$$

$$\frac{12n}{21} = \frac{196}{12}$$

$$n \approx 16.3 \text{ cm}$$

27. Perimeter = 100 m for the larger figure. The parallelograms are similar, so

$$\frac{P}{100} = \frac{4}{12}$$

$$12P = 4(100)$$

$$12P = 400$$

$$\frac{12P}{12} = \frac{400}{12}$$

$$P = 33.\overline{3}$$

The perimeter of the small figure ≈ 33.3 m.

29. The figures are similar, so

$$\frac{A}{26} = \left(\frac{2}{3}\right)^2$$

$$9A = 4(26)$$

$$9A = 104$$

$$\frac{9A}{9} = \frac{104}{9}$$

$$A = 11.\overline{5}$$

The area of the smaller figure ≈ 11.6 yd^2

31. $2 \times 3^2 + 4 - 2 \times 5 = 2 \times 9 + 4 - 2 \times 5$
$= 18 + 4 - 10 = 12$

33. $(5)(9) - (21 + 3) \div 8 = (5)(9) - (24) \div 8$
$= 45 - 3 = 42$

7.9 Exercises

1. Length of border = Perimeter = $2l + 2w$
$= 2(6.25) + 2(6.75) = 12.5 + 13.5 = 26$ ft

Cost = Length of border $\times \dfrac{\text{cost}}{\text{ft}}$

$= 25 \text{ ft} \times \dfrac{\$0.85}{\text{ft}} = \$22.10$

3. a. Distance through Suffolk = $13 + 17$
$= 30$ km

Average speed $= \dfrac{\text{distance}}{\text{time}} = \dfrac{30 \text{ km}}{0.4 \text{ hr}}$

$= \dfrac{75 \text{ km}}{\text{hr}}$

b. Distance = $12 + 15 + 11 = 38$ km

Average speed $= \dfrac{38 \text{ km}}{0.5 \text{ hr}} = \dfrac{76 \text{ km}}{\text{hr}}$

c. Average speed is greater through Woodville and Palermo.

5. Area to paint = Total area of walls
$= (7 \times 16) + (7 \times 14) + (7 \times 12) + (7 \times 12)$
$= 112 + 98 + 84 + 84 = 378$ ft^2
Time to paint = area $\div$ rate

$= 378 \text{ ft}^2 \div \dfrac{80 \text{ ft}^2}{25 \text{ min}} = 378 \text{ ft}^2 \times \dfrac{25 \text{ min}}{80 \text{ ft}^2}$

$= 118$ min or 1 hr, 58 min

7. Area carpeted
= Rectangular area − triangular area

$= lw - \dfrac{bh}{2} = (21)(15) - \dfrac{(3)(6)}{2}$

$= 315 - 9 = 306$ ft^2
Cost = Area $\times$ rate

$= 306 \text{ ft}^2 \times \dfrac{\$15}{\text{yd}^2}$

$= 306 \text{ ft}^2 \times \dfrac{1 \text{ yd}^2}{9 \text{ ft}^2} \times \dfrac{\$15}{\text{yd}^2} = \$510.00$

9. Volume $= \pi r^2 h = 3.14 \times (1.5)^2 \times 9$
$= 63.585 \text{ ft}^3$

Gasoline volume $= 63.585 \text{ ft}^3 \times \dfrac{7.5 \text{ gal}}{1 \text{ ft}^3} \times 2$

$= 953.8$ gallons

11. Radius of hole $= \dfrac{2 \text{ m}}{2} = 1 \text{ m}$

Volume of concrete
= volume of box – volume of hole
$= lwh - \pi r^2 h$
$= 7 \times 3 \times 4 - 3.14 \times 1^2 \times 7 = 84 - 21.98$
$= 62.02 \text{ m}^3$

Cost of concrete
= volume of concrete $\times$ rate
$= 62.02 \text{ m}^3 \times \dfrac{\$1.20}{\text{m}^3} = \$74.42$

13. a. Length of one orbit = Circumference
$= \pi d = 3.14 \times 2 \times 6500 = 40{,}820 \text{ km}$

b. Speed $= \dfrac{\text{distance}}{\text{time}} = \dfrac{40{,}820 \text{ km}}{2 \text{ hr}}$

$= \dfrac{20{,}410 \text{ km}}{\text{hr}}$

15. Amount of fence = Perimeter
$= 2l + 2w = 2(456) + 2(625)$
$= 912 + 1250 = 2162 \text{ ft}$

Cost of fence = amount of fence $\times \dfrac{\text{cost}}{\text{ft}}$

$= 2162 \text{ ft} \times \dfrac{\$4.58}{\text{ft}} = \$9880.34$

Cumulative Review Problems

17.
$$
\begin{array}{r}
128 \\
16\overline{)2048} \\
\underline{16} \\
44 \\
\underline{32} \\
128 \\
\underline{128} \\
0
\end{array}
$$

19.
$$
\begin{array}{r}
0.25 \\
1.3\overline{)0.325} \\
\underline{26} \\
65 \\
\underline{65} \\
0
\end{array}
$$

Chapter 7 Review Problems

1. $l = 8.3 \text{ m}, w = 1.6 \text{ m}$
Perimeter $= 2l + 2w = 2 \times 8.3 + 2 \times 1.6$
$= 16.6 + 3.2 = 19.8 \text{ m}$

3. $l = w = 5.8 \text{ yd}$
Perimeter $= 4l = 4(5.8) = 23.2 \text{ yd}$

5. $l = 5.9 \text{ cm}, w = 2.8 \text{ cm}$
Area $= lw = 5.9 \times 2.8 \approx 16.5 \text{ cm}^2$

7. $l = w = 4.3 \text{ in.}$
Area $= l^2 = 4.3^2 \approx 18.5 \text{ in}^2$

9. Perimeter $= 2 + 8 + 8 + 8 + 2 + 3 + 4 + 3$
$= 38 \text{ ft}$

11. Shaded area
= Area rectangle – area two squares
$= lw - 2s^2 = 14 \times 5 - 2 \times 1^2 = 70 - 2$
$= 68 \text{ m}^2$

13. Sides 43 m and 7.2 m
Perimeter $= 2 \times 43 + 2 \times 7.2$
$= 86 + 14.4 = 100.4 \text{ m}$

15. Sides: 22 in., 13 in., 32 in., 13 in.
Perimeter $= 22 + 13 + 32 + 13 = 80 \text{ in.}$

17. $b = 90 \text{ m}, h = 30 \text{ m}$
Area $= bh = 90 \times 30 = 2700 \text{ m}^2$

19. $B = 28 \text{ yd}, b = 20 \text{ yd}, h = 14 \text{ yd}$
Area $= \dfrac{h(b + B)}{2} = \dfrac{14(20 + 28)}{2} = 336 \text{ yd}^2$

21. Total area $= \text{area}_1 + \text{area}_2$
$= \dfrac{h(b_1 + B_1)}{2} + \dfrac{h(b_2 + B_2)}{2}$
$= \dfrac{8(13 + 20)}{2} + \dfrac{20(9 + 20)}{2} = 132 + 290$
$= 422 \text{ cm}^2$

23. Sides: 10 ft, 5 ft, 7 ft
Perimeter = 10 + 5 + 7 = 22 ft

25. Known angles: 15°, 12°
Third angle = x
$15 + 12 + x = 180$
$27 + x = 180$
$x = 153°$

27. $b = 9.6$ m, $h = 5.1$ m
Area $= \dfrac{bh}{2} = \dfrac{9.6 \times 5.1}{2} \approx 24.5$ m^2

29. $b = 12$ cm, $h = 7.6$ cm
Area $= \dfrac{bh}{2} = \dfrac{12 \times 7.6}{2} = 45.6$ cm^2

31. Total area
= area of rectangle + area of triangle
$= lw + \dfrac{bh}{2} = 22 \times 18 + \dfrac{18 \times 6}{2} = 396 + 54$
$= 450$ m^2

33. $\sqrt{81} = 9$

35. $\sqrt{100} = 10$

37. $\sqrt{144} = 12$

39. $\sqrt{36} + \sqrt{0} = 6 + 0 = 6$

41. $\sqrt{9} + \sqrt{4} = 3 + 2 = 5$

43. $\sqrt{35} \approx 5.916$

45. $\sqrt{88} \approx 9.381$

47. $\sqrt{171} \approx 13.077$

49. Hypotenuse $= \sqrt{(\text{leg})^2 + (\text{leg})^2}$
$= \sqrt{(3)^2 + (4)^2} = \sqrt{9 + 16} = \sqrt{25}$
$= 5$ m

51. Leg $= \sqrt{(\text{Hypotenuse})^2 - (\text{leg})^2}$
$= \sqrt{(18)^2 - (16)^2} = \sqrt{324 - 256} = \sqrt{68}$
$= 8.25$ cm

53. Hypotenuse $= \sqrt{(\text{leg})^2 + (\text{leg})^2}$
$= \sqrt{(4)^2 + (5)^2} = \sqrt{16 + 25} = \sqrt{41}$
$= 6.4$ cm

55. Leg $= \sqrt{(\text{Hypotenuse})^2 - (\text{leg})^2}$
$= \sqrt{(11)^2 - (9)^2} = \sqrt{121 - 81} = \sqrt{40}$
$= 6.3$ ft

57. $r = 53$ cm
Diameter $= 2r = 2 \times 53 = 106$ cm

59. $D = 12$ in.
$C = 3.14 \times 12 = 37.7$ in.

61. $r = 6$ m
Area $= \pi r^2 = 3.14 \times 6^2 \approx 113.0$ m^2

63. $d = 16$ ft, so $r = 8$ ft
Area $= \pi r^2 = 3.14 \times 8^2 \approx 201.0$ ft^2

65. Large $r = 11$ in.
Small $r = 7$ in.
Shaded area
= area of large circle – area of small circle
$= \pi r_L^2 - \pi r_S^2 = 3.14 \times 11^2 - 3.14 \times 7^2$
$= 379.94 - 153.86 \approx 226.1$ in^2

67. $l = 24$ ft
$w = 10$ ft
$r = 5$ ft
Total area
= area of rectangle + area of semi-circles
$= lw + 2\left(\dfrac{\pi r^2}{2}\right) = 24 \times 10 + 3.14 \times 5^2$
$= 240 + 78.5 \approx 318.5$ ft^2

69. $b = 12$ ft
$h = 10$ ft
$r = 2$ ft
Shaded area
= area of parallelogram – area of circle
$= bh - \pi r^2 = 12 \times 10 - 3.14 \times 2^2$
$= 120 - 12.56 \approx 107.4$ ft^2

71. $l = 69$ ft, $w = 3$ ft, $h = 2.5$ ft
Volume $= lwh = 6 \times 3 \times 2.5 = 45$ ft^3

73. $r = 15$ ft
Volume $= \dfrac{4\pi r^3}{3} = \dfrac{4 \times 3.14 \times 15^3}{3}$
$\approx 14{,}130$ ft^3

75. $h = 2$ m, $r = 7$ m
Volume $= \pi r^2 h = 3.14 \times 7^2 \times 2 \approx 307.7$ m^3

77. $h = 18$ m, $l = 18$ m, $w = 16$ m
Volume $= \dfrac{lwh}{3} = \dfrac{18 \times 16 \times 18}{3} = 1728$ m^3

79. $h = 9$ ft, $r = 20$ ft
Volume $= \dfrac{\pi r^2 h}{3} = \dfrac{3.14 \times 20^2 \times 9}{3}$
≈ 3768 ft^3

81. The triangles are similar, so
$\dfrac{n}{2} = \dfrac{45}{3}$
$3n = 2 \times 45$
$\dfrac{3n}{3} = \dfrac{90}{3}$
$n = 30$ m

83. Rotate the larger triangle to match the smaller triangle.
$\dfrac{n}{18} = \dfrac{30}{16}$
$16n = 18 \times 30$
$\dfrac{16n}{16} = \dfrac{540}{16}$
$n \approx 33.8$ cm

85. Perimeter of smaller trapezoid
$= 5 + 18 + 5 + 26 = 54$ cm
The trapezoids are similar, so
$\dfrac{P}{54} = \dfrac{108}{18}$
$18P = 54 \times 108$
$\dfrac{18P}{18} = \dfrac{5832}{18}$
$P = 324$ cm

87. $l = 14$ ft, $w = 8$ ft
Length of fencing = perimeter $= 2l + 2w$
$= 2 \times 14 + 2 \times 8 = 28 + 16 = 44$ ft
Cost $= 44$ ft $\times \dfrac{\$2.10}{\text{ft}} = \$92.40$

89. Shaded area
= area of large rectangle
– area of small rectangle
$= l_1 w_1 - l_2 w_2 = 14 \times 8 - 5 \times 4 = 112 - 20$
$= 92$ yd^2
Cost $= 92$ yd$^2 \times \dfrac{\$8.00}{\text{yd}^2} = \$736.00$

91. a. Volume
= Volume of cylinder
+ volume of hemisphere
$= \pi r^2 h + \dfrac{1}{2} \times \dfrac{4\pi r^3}{3}$
$= 3.14 \times 9^2 \times 80 + \dfrac{4 \times 3.14 \times 9^3}{6}$
$= 20{,}347.2 + 1{,}526.04 \approx 21{,}873.2$ ft^3

b. # bushels $= 21{,}873.2$ ft$^3 \times \dfrac{0.8}{\text{ft}^3}$
$= 17{,}498.6$ bushels

Chapter 7 Test

1. $P = 2(9) + 2(11) = 18 + 22 = 40$ yd

3. $P = 2(6.5) + 2(3.5) = 13 + 7 = 20$ m

5. $P = 4.4 + 10.8 + 9.6 = 24.8$ m

7. $A = (10.2)^2 = 104.0$ m^2

9. $A = \dfrac{9(7+25)}{2} = 144 \text{ m}^2$

11. $A = \dfrac{1}{2}(15)(7) = 52.5 \text{ m}^2$

13. $\sqrt{64} = \sqrt{8^2} = 8$

15. $\sqrt{0} + \sqrt{49} = 0 + 7 = 7$

17. $\sqrt{120} \approx 10.954$

19. $h = \sqrt{6^2 + 7^2} = \sqrt{36 + 49} = \sqrt{85} \approx 9.220$

21. $h = \sqrt{5^2 + 3^2} = \sqrt{25 + 9} = \sqrt{34}$
　　$\approx 5.831 \text{ cm}$

23. $C = 2\pi r = 2(3.14)(6) = 37.7 \text{ in.}$

25. $A = (15)(8) - (3.14)(2)^2 = 120 - 12.56$
　　$= 107.4 \text{ in}^2$

27. $V = wlh = (7)(12)(10) = 840 \text{ m}^3$

29. $V = \dfrac{4\pi r^3}{3} = \dfrac{4(3.14)(2)^3}{3} = 33.5 \text{ m}^3$

31. $V = \dfrac{Bh}{3} = \dfrac{(4)(3)(14)}{3} = 56 \text{ m}^3$

33. $\dfrac{n}{7} = \dfrac{60}{9}$
　　$9n = (7)(60)$
　　$9n = 420$
　　$\dfrac{9n}{9} = \dfrac{420}{9}$
　　$n = 46.7 \text{ ft}$

Chapters 1–7 Cumulative Test

1. $\begin{array}{r} 126,350 \\ 278,120 \\ +\ 531,290 \\ \hline 935,760 \end{array}$

3. $\begin{array}{r} \dfrac{17}{18} \\ -\dfrac{11}{30} \end{array} \begin{array}{l} \dfrac{85}{90} \\ = -\dfrac{33}{90} \\ \hline \dfrac{52}{90} = \dfrac{26}{45} \end{array}$

5. $56.1279 \approx 56.13$

7. $0.021\overline{)1.743}$
　　$\underline{1\ 68}$
　　63
　　$\underline{63}$
　　0

9. $\dfrac{7}{100} = \dfrac{56}{n}$
　　$7 \times n = 100 \times 56$
　　$\dfrac{7 \times n}{7} = \dfrac{5600}{7}$
　　$n = 800 \text{ students}$

11. 0.8% of what number is 16?
　　$0.8\% \times n = 16$
　　$\dfrac{0.008 \times n}{0.008} = \dfrac{16}{0.008}$
　　$n = 2000$

13. $586 \text{ cm} \times \dfrac{1 \text{ m}}{100 \text{ cm}} = 5.86 \text{ cm}$

15. $88 \text{ km} \times \dfrac{0.62 \text{ mi}}{1 \text{ km}} = 54.56 \text{ mi}$

17. $P = 86 + 13 + 96 + 13 = 208 \text{ cm}$

19. $A = \dfrac{bh}{2} = \dfrac{1.2 \times 2.4}{2} = 1.4 \text{ cm}^2$

21. Total area = $\text{Area}_1 + \text{Area}_2$
　　$= s^2 + \dfrac{h(B+b)}{2} = (12)^2 + \dfrac{4(12+12)}{2}$
　　$= 144 + 48 = 192 \text{ m}^2$

23. $A = \pi r^2 = 3.14 \times (4)^2 \approx 50.2 \text{ m}^2$

25. $V = \dfrac{4\pi r^3}{3} = \dfrac{4 \times 3.14 \times (9)^3}{3} \approx 3052.1 \text{ cm}^3$

27. $V = \dfrac{\pi r^2 h}{3} = \dfrac{3.14 \times (12)^2 \times 18}{3} \approx 2713.0 \text{ m}^3$

29. $\dfrac{11}{n} = \dfrac{4}{1.5}$

$11 \times 1.5 = n \times 4$

$\dfrac{16.5}{4} = \dfrac{n \times 4}{4}$

$n = 4.1 \text{ ft}$

31. $\sqrt{36} + \sqrt{25} = 6 + 5 = 11$

33. $\text{Hypotenuse} = \sqrt{(\text{leg})^2 + (\text{leg})^2}$

$= \sqrt{(10)^2 + (3)^2} = \sqrt{100 + 9} = \sqrt{109}$

$\approx 10.440 \text{ in.}$

35. $\text{Hypotenuse} = \sqrt{(\text{leg})^2 + (\text{leg})^2}$

Chapter 8

Pretest Chapter 8

1. Under age 18

3. What percent of the students are 25 or older?
Age 25–27 + Over age 27 = 10% + 7%
= 17%

5. How many students are over age 27?
$5000 \times 7\% = 5000 \times 0.07 = 350$ students

7. 600 people

9. 4th quarter of 1993

11. $450 - 350 = 100$ more people

13. December

15. 20,000 sets

17. 55,000 cars

19. $20,000 + 5,000 = 25,000$ cars

21. $\dfrac{40 + 42 + 44 + 27 + 32}{5} = 37$ pages per day

8.1 Exercises

1. Rent takes the largest amount of the budget.

3. $200 is allotted each month for contributions.

5.
$$\begin{array}{r} 350 \\ + \ 150 \\ \hline 500 \end{array}$$
$500 for utilities and transportation

7. $\dfrac{\$500}{\$350} = \dfrac{10}{7}$

9. $\dfrac{\text{Rent}}{\text{Mo. Budget}} = \dfrac{\$600}{\$2000} = \dfrac{3}{10}$

11. Hit batters is the category with the least number of pitches.

13. 294 pitches were balls.

15. 85 hits
294 balls
379 pitches

17. $\dfrac{\text{Strikes}}{\text{Pitches}} = \dfrac{144}{650} = \dfrac{72}{325}$

19. $\dfrac{\text{Balls}}{\text{Strikes}} = \dfrac{294}{144} = \dfrac{49}{24}$

21. 15% of women physicians are between the ages of 45 and 54.

23. $34\% + 38\% = 72\%$

25. Between 35 and 44 = 38% of 118,000
$= 0.38 \times 118,000 = 44,840$

27. Christians = 37% of 5,000,000,000
$= 0.37 \times 5,000,000,000$
$= 1,850,000,000$ people

29. $19\% + 18\% = 37\%$

31.
$$\begin{array}{r} 100\% \ \text{Total} \\ - \ 19\% \ \text{Moslem} \\ \hline 81\% \ \text{not Moslem} \end{array}$$

33. $5,000,000,000 \times n = 75,000,000$
$$\dfrac{5,000,000,000 \times n}{5,000,000,000} = \dfrac{75,000,000}{5,000,000,000}$$
$n = 0.015 = 1.5\%$

Cumulative Review Problems

35. Area $= \dfrac{bh}{2} = \dfrac{6 \times 14}{2} = 42$ in.^{2}

37. Total area $= l_1 w_1 + l_2 w_2 + l_3 w_3 + l_4 w_4$
$= 7(12) + 7(12) + 7(20) + 7(20)$
$= 84 + 84 + 140 + 140$
$= 448$ square yards
448 sq yd $\times \dfrac{1 \text{ gallon}}{28 \text{ sq yd}} = 16$ gallons

8.2 Exercises

1. 10 million people lived in Texas in 1960.

3. 14 million people lived in Texas in 1980.

5. The smallest increase in the population of Texas was from 1960 to 1970.

7. 5 ten thousands = 50,000 women

9. In 1990 more women were enrolled than were men.

11.   50,000 in 1950
   – 25,000 in 1930
    25,000 more enrolled in 1950

13. The greatest increase in the number of women was from 1930–1950.

15. 3.5 million dollars was the profit in 1993.

17. The lowest profit was in 1992.

19.   4.5 million dollars profit in 1991
   – 3.5 million dollars profit in 1990
    1.0 million dollars more in 1991

21. 2.5 inches of rainfall in September 1993.

23. The rainfall in October, November, and December was less than the rainfall of 1992.

25.   4 inches in November 1992
   – 2.5 inches in October 1992
    1.5 inches more in November

27.

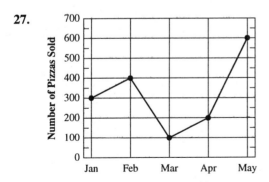

Cumulative Review Problems

29. $7 \times 6 + 3 - 5 \times 2 = 42 + 3 - 10 = 35$

Putting Your Skills to Work

1. 1989; the line representing 9–11 years old is above that of the line representing 6–8 years old.

3. $8.6 - 7.9 = 0.7$
$$\frac{0.7}{7.9} \approx 0.0886$$
The mean age of the trucks increased by about 8.86%. Assume that the percentage increase in the number of trucks is also 8.86%.
$0.0886 \times 52.8 \approx 4.7$
$4.7 + 52.8 = 57.5$
57.5 million trucks would be expected in 1993.

8.3 Exercises

1. 10 cars achieve between 28 and 30.9 mi per gallon

3. 35 cars achieve between 25 and 27.9 mi per gallon.

5. $35 + 10 = 45$ cars

7.   50 cars between 19 and 21.9
   60 cars between 22 and 24.9
   35 cars between 25 and 27.9
   145 cars achieve between 19 and 27.9 mpg.

9. 12 days, emissions were between 13 and 16.9 tons

11. 3 days, emissions were between 25 and 28.9 tons.

13. $5 + 12 + 16 + 9 = 42$ days

15.   12 days for 13–16.9 tons
   16 days for 17–20.9 tons
   + 9 days for 21–24.9 tons
   37 days, emissions were between 13 and 24.9 tons.

17. 16 days for 17–20.9
9 days for 21–24.9
3 days for 25–28.9
+ 2 days for 29–32.9
30 days for 17 or more
What percent of 47 is 30? 63.8%
$R\%$ of $47 = 30$

$$\frac{R}{100} \times 47 = 30$$

$$R = \frac{30 \times 100}{47}$$

$$R \approx 63.8$$

Temperature Class Interval	Tally	Frequency
19. $12° - 16°$	III	3
21. $22° - 26°$	IIIIII	6
23. $32° - 36°$	III	3
25. $42° - 46°$	II	2

27.

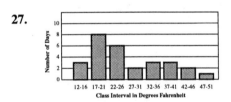

Purchase Price Class Interval	Tally	Frequency
29. $10.00–$15.99	III	3
31. $22.00–$27.99	II	2
33. $34.00–$39.99	I	1
35. $46.00–$51.99	II	2

Cumulative Review Exercises

37. $\dfrac{126}{n} = \dfrac{36}{17}$

$125 \times 17 = n \times 36$

$2142 = n \times 36$

$\dfrac{2142}{36} = \dfrac{n \times 36}{36}$

$59.5 = n$

39. $\dfrac{3}{5} = \dfrac{n}{20}$

$3 \times 20 = 5 \times n$

$\dfrac{60}{5} = \dfrac{5 \times n}{5}$

$n = 12$ pounds

8.4 Exercises

1. Mean $= \dfrac{89 + 92 + 83 + 96 + 99}{5} = \dfrac{459}{5}$
$= 91.8$

3. Mean $= \dfrac{23 + 45 + 63 + 34 + 21 + 42}{6} = \dfrac{228}{6}$
$= 38$

5. Mean $= \dfrac{\begin{array}{c}\$89,000 + \$93,000 + \$62,000 \\ + \$102,000 + \$89,000\end{array}}{5}$

$= \dfrac{\$435,000}{5} = \$87,000$

7. Mean $= \dfrac{8 + 3 + 2 + 5 + 6.5 + 7.5 + 3}{7} = 5$

9. Mean $= \dfrac{\begin{array}{c}67,000 + 86,000 + 107,000 \\ + 134,000\end{array}}{4}$

$= \dfrac{394,000}{4} = 98,500$

11. Batting Average $= \dfrac{\text{\# Hits}}{\text{\# At Bats}}$

$= \dfrac{0 + 2 + 3 + 2 + 2}{5 + 4 + 6 + 5 + 4} = \dfrac{9}{24} = 0.375$

13. Avg miles/gallon $= \dfrac{\text{Miles driven}}{\text{Gallons used}}$

$= \dfrac{276 + 350 + 391 + 336}{12 + 14 + 17 + 14} = \dfrac{1353}{57}$
$= 23.7$ miles per gallon

15. 22, 36, 45, 47, 48, 50, 58
Median $= 47$

17. 865, 968, $\underbrace{999, \; 1023}$, 1052, 1152

Median $= \dfrac{999 + 1023}{2} = 1011$

19. 0.34, 0.52, 0.58, 0.69, 0.71

Median = 0.58

21. Median = $20,250

23. 12, 24, 31, 40, 62, 108

Median = $\dfrac{31+40}{2}=35.5$ minutes

25. 97, 109, 185, 207, 218, 330, 420

Median = $207

27. 22, 36, 36, 37, 44, 48, 53, 60, 64, 71

Median = $\dfrac{44+48}{2}=46$ actors

29. $\quad$ \$ 30,000

$\quad\quad$ 74,500

$\quad\quad$ 47,890

$\quad\quad$ 89,000

$\quad\quad$ 57,645

$\quad\quad$ 78,090

$\quad\quad$ 110,370

$\quad$ + 65,800

$\quad$ \$553,295.00

Mean = $\dfrac{\$553,295.00}{8}=\$69,161.88$

31. 1987, 2576, 3700, 4700, 5000,

7200, 8764, 9365

Median = $\dfrac{4700+5000}{2}=4850$

33. a. Mean

$= \dfrac{2151+2110+2220+2578+2643}{5}$

$= \dfrac{11,707}{5}=2340.4$

2,340,400 barrels of oil

b. $42(2340.4)=98296.8$

98,296,800,000 gallons of oil per year

35. a. Mean = 1500 + 1700 + 1650 + 1300

+ 1440 + 1580 + 1820 + 1380

$= \dfrac{2900+6300}{10}=\dfrac{21,570}{10}=\$2157$

b. 1300, 1380, 1440, 1500, 1580, 1650,

1700, 1820, 2900, 6300

Median = $\dfrac{1580+1650}{2}=\$1615$

37. The mode is 60 since this occurs twice.

39. The modes are 121 and 150 which both occur twice.

41. The mode is $249 which occurs twice.

Chapter 8 Review Problems

1. IBM manufactured 36 computers

3. 11 Compaq + 9 Leading Edge

= 20 Leading Edge or Compaq

5. $\dfrac{36 \text{ by IBM}}{9 \text{ by Leading Edge}}=\dfrac{4}{1}$

7. What *percent* of 120 is manufactured by Leading Edge? 7.5%

$R\% \times 120 = 9$

$\dfrac{R}{100}\times\dfrac{120}{1}=9$

$1.2R = 9$

$R = 7.5$

9. 15% is allotted for transportation.

11. 27% for food + 30% for rent

= 57% is allotted for food and rent.

13. Amount for utilities is 8% of $2400.

Amount = $\dfrac{8}{100}\times 2400 = \$192$

15. 30% for rent + 4% for savings = 34%

Amount for rent and savings

= 34% of $2400

$= \dfrac{34}{100}\times 2400 = \$816$

17. 6000 came in the second quarter of 1993.

19. The greatest number came in the fourth quarter of 1994.

21. 5000 1st quarter 1994 – 4000 1st quarter 1993 = 1000 customer increase.

23. Yes, the third quarter was the lowest quarter each year. This might be due to the construction going on at that time.

25. 400 graduated in 1993.

27. 650 graduated in 1992.

29. 300 in 1990 – 200 in 1989 = 100 more in 1990.

31. 400 in 1993 – 500 in 1992 = –100 drop from 1992 to 1993.

33. 45,000 cones were purchased in July 1992.

35. 20,000 in May 1991 – 10,000 in May 1992 = 10,000 more cones

37. 55,000 in July 1991 – 30,000 in June 1992 = 25,000 more cones

39. The cooler the temperature the fewer cones sold.

41. 50 bridges between 40 and 59 years of age.

43. The greatest number of bridges are between 20 and 39 years old.

45. 70 between 0 and 19 years old + 80 between 20 and 39 years old = 150 bridges.

Number of Defects

Class Interval	Tally	Frequency
47. 0–3	IIIII IIIII	10
49. 8–11	III	3
51. 16–19	II	2

53. 10 had 0 – 3 defects + 8 had 4 – 7 defects = 18 had 0 – 7 defects.

55. Mean $= \dfrac{87 + 105 + 89 + 120 + 139 + 160 + 98}{7}$

$= \dfrac{798}{7} = \$114$

57. Mean $= \dfrac{151 + 140 + 148 + 156 + 183 + 201 + 205 + 228 + 231 + 237}{10}$

$= \dfrac{1880}{10} = 188$ women

59. Mean $= \dfrac{882 + 913 + 1017 + 1592 + 1778 + 1936}{6}$

$= \dfrac{8118}{6} = 1353$ employees

61. 58, 77, 79, 81, 83, 87, 88, 91, 104

Median = 83 students

63. 98,000, 120,000, 126,000, 135,000, 139,000, 144,000, 150,000, 154,000, 156,000, 170,000

Median $= \dfrac{139,000 + 144,000}{2} = \$141,500$

65. 0, 3, 9, 13, 14, 15, 16, <u>18, 19</u>, 21, 24, 25, 26, 28, 31, 36

Median $= \dfrac{18 + 19}{2} = 18.5$ deliveries

67. The median is a better measure of the usual sales because of the one very high data item, 39.

Chapter 8 Test

1. 37% of the automobiles passed inspection.

3. 6% had 3 violations + 2% had 4 violations + 4% had more than 4 violations = 12% had more than 2 violations

5. 21% had 2 violations + 6% had 3 violations = 27% had 2 or 3 violations.
27% of 300,000 $= 0.27 \times 300,000$ = 81,000 automobiles had 2 or 3 violations

7. 500 cars sold in the third quarter of 1993.

9. More cars were sold in 1992 than 1993 during the first quarter.

11. 450 cars in 3rd quarter of 1992 – 300 cars in 4th quarter of 1992
= 150 more cars sold during the 3rd than the 4th quarter of 1993.

13. A 55-year old non-smoker is expected to live 26 more years.

15. The greatest difference in life expectancy is at age 35.

17. 60,000 television sets lasted 6–8 years.

19. 15,000 lasted 12–14 years + 5,000 lasted 15–17 years = 20,000 televisions lasted more than 11 years.

21. Mean
$$= \frac{19+16+15+12+18+17+14+10}{8}$$
$$= \frac{121}{8} = 15.125$$

Chapters 1–8 Cumulative Test

1.
$$\begin{array}{r} 1\ 376 \\ 2\ 804 \\ 9\ 003 \\ +\ 7\ 642 \\ \hline 20{,}825 \end{array}$$

3. $7\frac{1}{5} \qquad 6\frac{48}{40}$
$\underline{-3\frac{3}{8}} \qquad \underline{-3\frac{15}{40}}$
$\qquad\qquad 3\frac{33}{40}$

5. $2864.3719 \approx 2864.37$

7.
$$\begin{array}{r} 72.23 \\ 0.72\overline{)52.0056} \\ \underline{504} \\ 160 \\ \underline{144} \\ 165 \\ \underline{144} \\ 216 \\ \underline{216} \\ 0 \end{array}$$

9. $\dfrac{n}{26{,}390} = \dfrac{3 \text{ defects}}{2030 \text{ cars}}$
$2030n = 3 \times 26{,}390$
$n = \dfrac{79{,}170}{2030}$
$n = 39$ defects

11. 72% of what number if 252?
$72\% \times n = 252$
$\dfrac{0.72 \times n}{0.72} = \dfrac{252}{0.72}$
$n = 350$

13. $18 \text{ yd} \times \dfrac{3 \text{ ft}}{1 \text{ yd}} = 54 \text{ ft}$

15. $P = 4s = 4 \times 17 = 68$ in.

17. Number of Freshmen
$= 32\% \times 12{,}000$
$= 0.32 \times 12{,}000 = 3840$

19. 7,000,000 profit in 2nd quarter 1994
$\underline{-\ 6{,}000{,}000}$ profit in 2nd quarter 1993
$1{,}000{,}000 more profit in 2nd quarter 1994

21. In 1950 and 1960 the annual rainfall in Weston was greater than Dixville.

23. 4 students ages 17–19
7 students ages 20–22
$\underline{+\ 5 \text{ students ages } 23\text{–}25}$
16 students less than 26 years of age

25. $3.95, $4.50, $4.90, $5.00, $7.00, $13.65
Median $= \dfrac{4.90 + 5.00}{2} = \$4.95$

Chapter 9

Pretest Chapter 9

1. $-7 + (-12) = -19$

3. $7.6 + (-3.1) = 4.5$

5. $\dfrac{5}{12} + \left(-\dfrac{3}{4}\right) = \dfrac{5}{12} + \left(-\dfrac{9}{12}\right) = -\dfrac{4}{12} = -\dfrac{1}{3}$

7. $-2.8 + (-4.2) = -7$

9. $13 - 21 = -8$

11. $\dfrac{5}{17} - \left(-\dfrac{9}{17}\right) = \dfrac{5}{17} + \dfrac{9}{17} = \dfrac{14}{17}$

13. $-4.9 - (-6.3) = -4.9 + 6.3 = 1.4$

15. $21 - (-21) = 21 + 21 = 42$

17. $(-3)(-8) = 24$

19. $-72 \div 9 = -8$

21. $\dfrac{72}{-3} = -24$

23. $(-8)(-2)(-4) = -64$

25. $24 \div (-4) + 28 \div (-7) = -6 + (-4) = -10$

27. $7 + (-9) + 2(-5) = 7 + (-9) + (-10) = -12$

29. $5 - (-6) + 18 \div (-3) = 5 + 6 + (-6) = 5$

31. $\dfrac{12 + 8 - 4}{(-4)(3)(4)} = \dfrac{12 + 8 + (-4)}{-48} = \dfrac{16}{-48} = -\dfrac{1}{3}$

33. $80,000 = 8 \times 10^4$

35. $6.7 \times 10^{-3} = 0.0067$

9.1 Exercises

1. $9 + 15 = 24$

3. $6 + (-11) = -17$

5. $-4.9 + (-2.1) = -7$

7. $8.9 + 7.6 = 16.5$

9. $\dfrac{1}{5} + \dfrac{2}{7} = \dfrac{7}{35} + \dfrac{10}{35} = \dfrac{17}{35}$

11. $-\dfrac{1}{12} + \left(-\dfrac{5}{6}\right) = -\dfrac{1}{12} + \left(-\dfrac{10}{12}\right) = -\dfrac{11}{12}$

13. $14 + (-5) = 9$

15. $-16 + 9 = -7$

17. $-17 + 12 = -5$

19. $-36 + 58 = 22$

21. $-9.3 + 6.5 = -2.8$

23. $\dfrac{1}{12} + \left(-\dfrac{3}{4}\right) = \dfrac{1}{12} + \left(-\dfrac{9}{12}\right) = -\dfrac{8}{12} = -\dfrac{2}{3}$

25. $\dfrac{7}{9} + \left(-\dfrac{2}{9}\right) = \dfrac{5}{9}$

27. $-18 + (-4) = -22$

29. $1.5 + (-2.2) = -0.7$

31. $\dfrac{3}{14} + \dfrac{2}{7} = \dfrac{3}{14} + \dfrac{4}{14} = \dfrac{7}{14} = \dfrac{1}{2}$

33. $-15 + (-23) = -38$

35. $-5.5 + (-2.1) = -7.6$

37. $13 + (-9) = 4$

39. $\dfrac{1}{2} + \left(-\dfrac{2}{3}\right) = \dfrac{3}{6} + \left(-\dfrac{4}{6}\right) = -\dfrac{1}{6}$

41. $8.6 + 9.5 = 18.1$

43. $-5 + \left(-\dfrac{1}{2}\right) = -5\dfrac{1}{2}$

45. $6 + (-14) + 4 = -8 + 4 = -4$

47. $-6 + 3 + (-12) + 4 = -18 + 7 = -11$

49. $-7 + 6 + (-2) + 5 + (-3) + (-5)$
$\quad = -17 + 11 = -6$

51. $5 + (-8) + 7 + 20 + (-8) + (-6)$
$\quad = 32 + (-22) = 10$

53. $-\dfrac{45}{225} + \left(-\dfrac{150}{225}\right) + \dfrac{36}{225} + \left(-\dfrac{25}{225}\right)$
$\quad = -\dfrac{45}{225} + \left(-\dfrac{150}{225}\right) + \dfrac{36}{225} + \left(-\dfrac{25}{225}\right)$
$\quad = -\dfrac{184}{225}$

55. $-\$43{,}000 + (-\$51{,}000) = \$-94{,}000$

57. $\$28{,}000 + (-19{,}000) = \$9000$

59. $-\$35{,}000 + (-\$20{,}000) + \$17{,}000$
$\quad = \$-55{,}000 + \$17{,}000 = -\$38{,}000$

61. $-1° + (-17)° = -18°\text{F}$

63. $-5° + 4° = -1°\text{F}$

Cumulative Review Problems

65. $V = \dfrac{4\pi r^3}{3} = \dfrac{4(3.14)(6)^3}{3} = \dfrac{4(3.14)(216)}{3}$
$\quad = 904.3 \text{ ft}^3$

9.2 Exercises

1. $3 - 9 = 3 + (-9) = -6$

3. $-5 - 9 = -5 + (-9) = -14$

5. $-12 - (-10) = -12 + 10 = -2$

7. $3 - (-21) = 3 + 21 = 24$

9. $12 - 30 = 12 + (-30) = -18$

11. $-12 - (-15) = -12 + 15 = 3$

13. $150 - 210 = 150 + (-210) = -60$

15. $300 - (-256) = 300 + 256 = 556$

17. $-58 - 32 = -58 + (-32) = -90$

19. $-45 - (-85) = -45 + 85 = 40$

21. $-2.5 - 4.2 = (-2.5) + (-4.2) = -6.7$

23. $10.6 - 3.5 = 10.6 + (-3.5) = 7.1$

25. $-10.9 - (-2.3) = -10.9 + 2.3 = -8.6$

27. $4.8 - (-2.1) = 4.8 + 2.1 = 6.9$

29. $\dfrac{1}{4} - \left(-\dfrac{3}{4}\right) = \dfrac{1}{4} + \dfrac{3}{4} = \dfrac{4}{4} = 1$

31. $-\dfrac{5}{6} - \dfrac{1}{3} = -\dfrac{5}{6} + \left(-\dfrac{2}{6}\right) = -\dfrac{7}{6} = -1\dfrac{1}{6}$

33. $-\dfrac{5}{12} - \left(-\dfrac{1}{4}\right) = -\dfrac{5}{12} + \dfrac{3}{12} = -\dfrac{2}{12} = -\dfrac{1}{6}$

35. $\dfrac{7}{11} - \dfrac{1}{2} = \dfrac{14}{22} + \left(-\dfrac{11}{22}\right) = \dfrac{3}{22}$

37. $2 - (-8) + 5 = 2 + 8 + 5 = 15$

39. $-5 - 6 - (-11) = -5 + (-6) + 11 = 0$

41. $7 - (-2) - (-8) = 7 + 2 + 8 = 17$

43. $-16 - (-2) - 4 = -16 + 2 + (-4) = -18$

45. $9 - 3 - 2 - 6 = 9 + (-3) + (-2) + (-6) = -2$

47. $-16 + 9 - (-2) - 8 = (-16) + 9 + 2 + (-8)$
$= -13$

49. $\dfrac{1}{4} + \left(-\dfrac{1}{12}\right) - \left(-\dfrac{2}{3}\right) - \dfrac{5}{6} - \dfrac{1}{2}$

$= \dfrac{3}{12} + \left(-\dfrac{1}{12}\right) + \dfrac{8}{12} + \left(-\dfrac{10}{12}\right) + \left(-\dfrac{6}{12}\right)$

$= \dfrac{11}{12} + \left(-\dfrac{17}{12}\right) = -\dfrac{6}{12} = -\dfrac{1}{2}$

51. $5277 - (-844) = 5277 + 844 = 6121$ ft

53. $23° - (-19°) = 23° + 19° = 42°F$

55. $-32,800 - (-6300) = -32,800 + 6300$
$= -26,500$

57. $18,700 - (-6300) = 18,700 + 6300 = 25,000$

59. If the bank wishes to remove an erroneous debit of $80 from a customer's account having a balance of $50, then it would add
Balance $50.00
Credit $80.00
New Balance $130.00

Cumulative Review Problems

61. $20 \times 2 \div 10 + 4 - 3 = 40 \div 10 + 4 - 3$
$= 4 + 4 + (-3) = 5$

9.3 Exercises

1. $9(-3) = -27$

3. $(-6)(-4) = 24$

5. $(-7)(9) = -63$

7. $(3)(9) = 27$

9. $(-20)(-3) = 60$

11. $(-20)(8) = -160$

13. $(2.5)(-0.6) = -1.5$

15. $(-1.5)(-2.5) = 3.75$

17. $\left(-\dfrac{2}{5}\right)\left(\dfrac{3}{7}\right) = -\dfrac{6}{35}$

19. $\left(-\dfrac{4}{12}\right)\left(-\dfrac{3}{23}\right) = \left(-\dfrac{1}{1}\right)\left(-\dfrac{1}{23}\right) = \dfrac{1}{23}$

21. $60 \div (-6) = -10$

23. $121 \div 11 = 11$

25. $-70 \div (-5) = 14$

27. $-16 \div 8 = -2$

29. $\dfrac{48}{-6} = -8$

31. $\dfrac{-72}{-8} = 9$

33. $\dfrac{1}{2} \div \left(-\dfrac{3}{5}\right) = \dfrac{1}{2} \times \left(-\dfrac{5}{3}\right) = -\dfrac{5}{6}$

35. $\dfrac{-\frac{4}{5}}{-\frac{7}{10}} = -\dfrac{4}{5} \times \left(-\dfrac{10}{7}\right) = -\dfrac{4}{1} \times \left(-\dfrac{2}{7}\right)$

$= \dfrac{8}{7} = 1\dfrac{1}{7}$

37. $49.2 \div (-6) = -8.2$

39. $\dfrac{-55.8}{-9} = 6.2$

41. $3(-6)(-4) = -18(-4) = 72$

43. $-8(4)(-6) = (-32)(-6) = 192$

45. $2(-8)(3)\left(-\dfrac{1}{3}\right) = (-16)(3)\left(-\dfrac{1}{3}\right)$

$= (-48)\left(-\dfrac{1}{3}\right) = 16$

47. $(-5)(2)(-1)(-3) = (-10)(-1)(-3) = 10(-3)$
$= -30$

49. $8(-3)(-5)(0)(-2) = (-24)(-5)(0)(-2)$
$= 120(0)(-2) = 0(-2) = 0$

51. $\left(-\dfrac{2}{3}\right)\left(-\dfrac{3}{4}\right)\left(-\dfrac{5}{6}\right)\left(-\dfrac{7}{8}\right)\left(-\dfrac{9}{10}\right)$

$=\left(-\dfrac{1}{1}\right)\left(-\dfrac{1}{2}\right)\left(-\dfrac{1}{2}\right)\left(-\dfrac{7}{8}\right)\left(-\dfrac{3}{2}\right)$

$=-\dfrac{21}{64}$

53. $(2.76)(-3.21)(1.09) = -9.656964$

55. $(-3288) \div (-0.213) = 15{,}436.61972$

57. $17(2) = 34$

59. $4(1) + 2(-1) = 4 + (-2) = 2$

61. $5(2) + 6(-2) + 12(3) = 10 + (-12) + 36 = 34$

63. $8(1) = 8;\ +8$

65. $(-12)(0) = 0$　The mystery number is 0.

67. $(-)(b)(-) = (-)$
$(-b)(-) = (-)$
$b = (-)$
b is negative.

Cumulative Review Problems

69. $A = bh = (15)(6) = 90$ in.^{2}

9.4 Exercises

1. $8 + (-3) + (-6) = -1$

3. $6 + 5(-4) = 6 + (-20) = -14$

5. $16 + 32 \div (-4) = 16 + (-8) = 8$

7. $24 \div (-3) + 16 \div (-4) = -8 + (-4) = -12$

9. $3(-4) + 5(-2) - (-3) = -12 + (-10) + 3$
　　$= -22 + 3 = -19$

11. $-18 \div 2 + 9 = -9 + 9 = 0$

13. $5 - 30 \div 3 = 5 - 10 = -5$

15. $36 \div 12(-2) = 3(-2) = -6$

17. $5(5) - 5 = 25 - 5 = 20$

19. $3(-4) + 6(-2) - 3 = -12 + (-12) + (-3)$
　　$= -24 + (-3) = -27$

21. $8(-7) - 2(-3) = -56 - (-6) = -56 + 6 = -50$

23. $16 - 4(8) + 18 \div (-9) = 16 - 32 + (-2)$
　　$= 16 + (-32) + (-2) = (-16) + (-2) = -18$

25. $16 \div (-2)(3) + 5 - 6 = (-8)(3) + 5 - 6$
　　$= -24 + 5 + (-6) = -19 + (-6) = -25$

27. $\dfrac{8 + 6 - 12}{3 - 6 + 5} = \dfrac{2}{2} = 1$

29. $\dfrac{6(-2) + 4}{5 - 3 - 5} = \dfrac{-12 + 4}{3 + (-5)} = \dfrac{-8}{-2} = 4$

31. $\dfrac{-16 \div (-2)}{3(-4) - 4} = \dfrac{8}{-12 + (-4)} = \dfrac{8}{-16} = -\dfrac{1}{2}$

33. $\dfrac{4 - (-3) - 5}{20 \div (-10)} = \dfrac{4 + 3 + (-5)}{-2} = \dfrac{2}{-2} = -1$

35. $\dfrac{7 - (-1)}{9 - 9 \div (-3)} = \dfrac{7 + 1}{9 - (-3)} = \dfrac{8}{12} = \dfrac{2}{3}$

37. $\dfrac{1}{2} \div \left(-\dfrac{2}{3}\right)\left(-\dfrac{3}{7}\right) + \left(-\dfrac{5}{14}\right)$

$= \dfrac{1}{2}\left(-\dfrac{3}{2}\right)\left(-\dfrac{3}{7}\right) + \left(-\dfrac{5}{14}\right)$

$= \left(-\dfrac{3}{4}\right)\left(-\dfrac{3}{7}\right) + \left(-\dfrac{5}{14}\right)$

$= \dfrac{9}{28} + \left(-\dfrac{5}{14}\right) = \dfrac{9}{28} + \left(-\dfrac{10}{28}\right) = -\dfrac{1}{28}$

39. Average $= \dfrac{-13 + (-14) + (-20)}{3} = \dfrac{-47}{3}$
　　$= -15.7°\text{F}$

41. Average
$= \dfrac{14 + (-1) + (-13) + (-14) + (-20) + (-16)}{6}$

$= \dfrac{-50}{6} = -8.3°\,\text{F}$

43. Total
$$= \frac{\begin{array}{c}(-14)+(-20)+(-16)+(-2)+19+33 \\ +39+38+31+14+(-1)+(-13)\end{array}}{12}$$
$$= \frac{108}{12} = 9°\,\text{F (Average)}$$

Cumulative Review Problems

45. $3840 = 3.84$ km

47. $A = \dfrac{1}{2}h(b_1 + b_2)$
$A = \dfrac{1}{2}(14)(23+37)$
$A = 7(60)$
$A = 420$
420 in.^{2}

Putting Your Skills to Work

1. $1 + 9 = 10$
10 P.M.

3. $6 + (-8) + 3 = 1$
1 A.M.

5. $7.5 + (-7) + 2 + 6 = 8.5$
8:30 A.M. in Bucharest

7. $11 + 3.5 + 4 = 18.5$
$18.5 - 12 = 6.5$
No; it is 6:30 A.M.
$9 + (-6.5) = 2.5$
You have to wait $2\dfrac{1}{2}$ hours.

9.5 Exercises

1. $35 = 3.5 \times 10^1$

3. $137 = 1.37 \times 10^2$

5. $2148 = 2.148 \times 10^3$

7. $120 = 1.20 \times 10^2$

9. $500 = 5 \times 10^2$

11. $26,300 = 2.63 \times 10^4$

13. $288,000 = 2.88 \times 10^5$

15. $4,632,000 = 4.632 \times 10^6$

17. $12,000,000 = 1.2 \times 10^7$

19. $0.67 = 6.7 \times 10^{-1}$

21. $0.398 = 3.98 \times 10^{-1}$

23. $0.00279 = 2.79 \times 10^{-3}$

25. $0.4 = 4 \times 10^{-1}$

27. $0.0015 = 1.5 \times 10^{-3}$

29. $0.000016 = 1.6 \times 10^{-5}$

31. $0.00000531 = 5.31 \times 10^{-6}$

33. $0.0007 = 7 \times 10^{-4}$

35. $0.0000001 = 1 \times 10^{-7}$

37. $1.6 \times 10^1 = 16$

39. $5.36 \times 10^4 = 53,600$

41. $6.2 \times 10^{-2} = 0.062$

43. $5.6 \times 10^{-5} = 0.000056$

45. $6.3 \times 10^{-4} = 0.00063$

47. $9 \times 10^{11} = 900,000,000,000$

49. $3 \times 10^{-7} = 0.0000003$

51. $3.862 \times 10^{-8} = 0.00000003862$

53. $4.6 \times 10^{12} = 4,600,000,000,000$

55. $6.721 \times 10^{10} = 67,210,000,000$

57. $5,878,000,000,000 = 5.878 \times 10^{12}$ mi

59. $0.00000059 = 5.9 \times 10^{-7}$ meter

61. $264,000,000 = 2.64 \times 10^{8}$ people

63. $1.25 \times 10^{13} = 12,500,000,000,000$ insects

65. $7.5 \times 10^{-5} = 0.000075$ centimeter

67. $1.4 \times 10^{10} = 14,000,000,000$ tons

69. $3.38 \times 10^{7} + 5.63 \times 10^{7}$
$= (3.38 + 5.63) \times 10^{7}$
$= 9.01 \times 10^{7}$ dollars

71. $4.52 \times 10^{9} + 3.41 \times 10^{9}$
$= (4.52 + 3.41) \times 10^{9}$
$= 7.93 \times 10^{9}$ dollars

73. $7.18 \times 10^{15} - 2.79 \times 10^{15}$
$= (7.18 - 2.79) \times 10^{15}$
$= 4.39 \times 10^{15}$ miles

75. $4 \times 10^{8} - 3.76 \times 10^{7}$
$= (40 - 3.76) \times 10^{7}$
$= 36.24 \times 10^{7}$
$= 3.624 \times 10^{8}$ feet

Cumulative Review Problems

77. $7.63 \times 2.18 = 16.6334$

79. $0.53 \overline{)0.13674}$ with quotient 0.258

Chapter 9 Review Problems

1. $21 + (-7) = 14$

3. $-15 + (-7) = -22$

5. $-20 + 5 = -15$

7. $-3.6 + (-5.2) = -8.8$

9. $-\dfrac{1}{5} + \left(-\dfrac{1}{3}\right) = -\dfrac{3}{15} + \left(-\dfrac{5}{15}\right) = -\dfrac{8}{15}$

11. $20 + (-14) = 6$

13. $7 + (-2) + 9 + (-3) = 16 + (-5) = 11$

15. $8 + (-7) + (-6) + 3 + (-2) + 8$
$= 19 + (-15) = 4$

17. $12 - 16 = 12 + (-16) = -4$

19. $-2 - 7 = -2 + (-7) = -9$

21. $-36 - (-21) = -36 + 21 = -15$

23. $12 - (-7) = 12 + 7 = 19$

25. $1.6 - 3.2 = 1.6 + (-3.2) = -1.6$

27. $-\dfrac{2}{5} - \left(-\dfrac{1}{3}\right) = -\dfrac{6}{15} + \dfrac{5}{15} = -\dfrac{1}{15}$

29. $5 - (-2) - (-6) = 5 + 2 + 6 = 7 + 6 = 13$

31. $9 - 8 - 6 - 4 = 9 + (-8) + (-6) + (-4)$
$= 1 + (-6) + (-4) = -5 + (-4) = -9$

33. $7(-2) = -14$

35. $(-10)(-5) = 50$

37. $\left(-\dfrac{2}{7}\right)\left(-\dfrac{1}{5}\right) = \dfrac{2}{35}$

39. $(5.2)(-1.5) = -7.8$

41. $-60 \div (-20) = 3$

43. $\dfrac{-36}{4} = -9$

45. $\dfrac{-13.2}{-2.2} = 6$

47. $\dfrac{-\frac{2}{5}}{\frac{4}{7}} = \left(-\dfrac{2}{5}\right)\left(\dfrac{7}{4}\right) = \left(-\dfrac{1}{5}\right)\left(\dfrac{7}{2}\right) = -\dfrac{7}{10}$

49. $3(-5)(-2) = (-15)(-2) = 30$

51. $4(-7)(-8)\left(-\dfrac{1}{2}\right) = (-28)(-8)\left(-\dfrac{1}{2}\right)$

$\quad = 224\left(-\dfrac{1}{2}\right) = -112$

53. $8(-5) - (-6) = -40 + 6 = -34$

55. $7 - 7(-1) = 7 - (-7) = 7 + 7 = 14$

57. $8 - (-30) \div 6 = 8 - (-5) = 8 + 5 = 13$

59. $2(-6) + 3(-4) - (-13) = -12 + (-12) + 13$
$\quad = -11$

61. $36 \div (-12) + 50 \div (-25) = -3 + -2 = -5$

63. $50 \div 25(-4) = 2(-4) = -8$

65. $9(-9) + 9 = -81 + 9 = -72$

67. $\dfrac{4(-6) + 8 - 2}{15 - 7 + 2} = \dfrac{-24 + 8 - 2}{15 - 7 + 2} = \dfrac{-18}{10} = -\dfrac{9}{5}$
$\quad = -1\dfrac{4}{5}$

69. $\dfrac{6 - (-3) - 2}{5 - 2 \div (-1)} = \dfrac{6 + 3 - 2}{5 + 2} = \dfrac{7}{7} = 1$

71. $3,700,000 = 3.7 \times 10^6$

73. $47,320,000,000 = 4.732 \times 10^{10}$

75. $0.007 = 7 \times 10^{-3}$

77. $0.00000763 = 7.63 \times 10^{-6}$

79. $0.02173 = 2.173 \times 10^{-2}$

81. $7 \times 10^5 = 700,000$

83. $3.76 \times 10^3 = 3760$

85. $6.61 \times 10^{-3} = 0.00661$

87. $8 \times 10^{-8} = 0.00000008$

89. $1.98 \times 10^{-5} = 0.0000198$

91. $7.79 \times 10^{15} + 1.93 \times 10^{15}$
$\quad = (7.79 + 1.93) \times 10^{15}$
$\quad = 9.72 \times 10^{15}$

93. $5.04 \times 10^{26} + 9.39 \times 10^{26}$
$\quad = (5.04 + 9.39) \times 10^{26} = 14.43 \times 10^{26}$
$\quad = 1.443 \times 10^{27}$

95. $1.76 \times 10^{26} - 1.08 \times 10^{26}$
$\quad = (1.76 - 1.08) \times 10^{26} = 0.68 \times 10^{26}$
$\quad = 6.8 \times 10^{25}$

Chapter 9 Test

1. $-13 + 8 = -5$

3. $6.7 + (-2.9) = 3.8$

5. $10 + (-7) + 3 + (-9) = 3 + 3 + (-9)$
$\quad = 6 + (-9) = -3$

7. $-32 - 6 = -32 + (-6) = -38$

9. $\dfrac{4}{5} - \left(-\dfrac{1}{3}\right) = \dfrac{4}{5} + \dfrac{1}{3} = \dfrac{12}{15} + \dfrac{5}{15}$
$\quad = \dfrac{17}{15} \text{ or } 1\dfrac{2}{15}$

11. $-2.5 - (-6.5) = -2.5 + 6.5 = 4$

13. $\dfrac{1}{12} - \left(-\dfrac{5}{6}\right) = \dfrac{1}{12} + \dfrac{5}{6} = \dfrac{1}{12} + \dfrac{10}{12} = \dfrac{11}{12}$

15. $(-20)(-6) = 120$

17. $-40 \div (-4) = 10$

19. $\dfrac{-39}{-13} = 3$

21. $(-7)(-2)(4) = (14)(4) = 56$

23. $7 - 2(-5) = 7 + 10 = 17$

25. $18 \div (-3) + 24 \div (-12) = -6 + (-2) = -8$

27. $3 - 9 - (-4) + 6(-5) = 3 + (-9) + 4 + (-30)$
$\quad = -6 + 4 + (-30) = -2 + (-30) = -32$

29. $\dfrac{3+8-5}{(-4)(6)+(-6)(3)} = \dfrac{3+8+(-5)}{-24+(-18)} = \dfrac{6}{-42}$

$= -\dfrac{1}{7}$

31. $80,540 = 8.0540 \times 10^4 = 8.054 \times 10^4$

33. $9.36 \times 10^{-5} = 00009.36 \times 10^{-5}$
$= 0.0000936$

Chapters 1–9 Cumulative Test

1.
$$\begin{array}{r} 28,981 \\ -\ 16,598 \\ \hline 12,383 \end{array}$$

3. $\quad 3\dfrac{1}{4} \qquad\quad 3\dfrac{3}{12}$

$\quad +\ 8\dfrac{2}{3} \qquad +\ 8\dfrac{8}{12}$

$\qquad\qquad\qquad\qquad \dfrac{143}{12}$

$\dfrac{143}{12} = 11\dfrac{11}{12}$

5. $9.812456 \approx 9.812$

7.
$$\begin{array}{r} 12.89 \\ \times\ \ 5.12 \\ \hline 2578 \\ 1\ 289\ \ \\ 64\ 45\ \ \ \ \\ \hline 65.9968 \end{array}$$

9. $\dfrac{n \text{ defects}}{2808 \text{ parts}} = \dfrac{7 \text{ defects}}{156 \text{ parts}}$

$156 \times n = 7 \times 2808$

$\dfrac{156 \times n}{156} = \dfrac{19,656}{156}$

$n = 126 \text{ defects}$

11. 12% of what number is 480?
$12\% \times n = 480$

$\dfrac{0.12 \times n}{0.12} = \dfrac{480}{0.12}$

$n = 4000$

13. $180 \text{ in.} \times \dfrac{1 \text{ yd}}{36 \text{ in.}} = 5 \text{ yd}$

15. a. 300 students age 23–25

b. 500 students age 20–22
300 students age 23–25
<u>200 students age 29–31</u>
1100 students over age 19

17. $-1.2 + (-3.5) = -4.7$

19. $7 - 18 = 7 + (-18) = -11$

21. $5(-3)(-1)(-2)(2) = -60$

23. $6 - 3(-4) = 6 - (-12) = 6 + 12 = 18$

25. $\dfrac{(-2)(-1)+(-4)(-3)}{1+(-4)(2)} = \dfrac{2+12}{1+(-8)} = \dfrac{14}{-7} = -2$

27. $579,863 = 5.79863 \times 10^5$

29. $3.85 \times 10^7 = 38,500,000$

Chapter 10

Pretest Chapter 10

1. $9x - 15x = -6x$

3. $6a - 5b - 9a + 7b = -3a + 2b$

5. $7x - 14 + 5y + 8 - 7y + 9x = 16x - 2y - 6$

7. $6(7x - 3y) = 6(7x) - 6(3y) = 42x - 18y$

9. $-2(1.5a + 3b - 6c - 5)$
$= -2(1.5a) + (-2)(3b) - (-2)(6c) - (-2)(5)$
$= -3a - 6b + 12c + 10$

11. $5 + x = 42$
$5 + x + (-5) = 42 + (-5)$
$x = 37$

13. $x - \dfrac{3}{4} = \dfrac{1}{2}$

$x + \left(-\dfrac{3}{4}\right) + \dfrac{3}{4} = \dfrac{1}{2} + \dfrac{3}{4}$

$x = \dfrac{1}{2} + \dfrac{3}{4}$

$x = \dfrac{5}{4} = 1\dfrac{1}{4}$

15. $5.4x = 27$
$\dfrac{5.4x}{5.4} = \dfrac{27}{5.4}$
$x = 5$

17. $5x - 9 = 26$
$5x + (-9) + 9 = 26 + 9$
$\dfrac{5x}{5} = \dfrac{35}{5}$
$x = 7$

19. $5(x - 1) = 7 - 3(x - 4)$
$5x - 5 = 7 - 3x + 12$
$5x + 3x + (-5) + 5 = -3x + 19 + 5 + 3x$
$\dfrac{8x}{8} = \dfrac{24}{8}$
$x = 3$

21. Let c = weight of computer and p = weight of printer.
$c = p + 9$

23. Let a = height of Mt. Ararat and $a - 1758$ = height of Mt. Hood.

25. Let x = length of one piece and $x + 2.5$ = length of other piece.
$x + x + 2.5 = 18$
$2x + 2.5 = 18$
$2x + 2.5 + (-2.5) = 18 + (-2.5)$
$2x = 15.5$
$\dfrac{2x}{2} = \dfrac{15.5}{2}$
$x = 7.75$ feet
$x + 2.5 = 10.25$ feet

10.1 Exercises

1. $G = 5xy$: The variables are G, x, and y.

3. $S = 4\pi r^2$: The variables are S, r.

5. $p = \dfrac{4ab}{3}$: The variables are p, a, b.

7. $p = 4 \times s^2$
$p = 4s^2$

9. $A = \dfrac{b \times h}{2}$

$A = \dfrac{bh}{2}$

11. $V = \dfrac{4 \times \pi \times r^3}{3}$

$V = \dfrac{4\pi r^3}{3}$

13. $H = 2 \times a - 3 \times b$
$H = 2a - 3b$

15. $9x + 8x = 17x$

17. $-16x + 26x = 10x$

19. $2x - 8x + 5x = -x$

21. $6x - 12x - 15x = -21x$

23. $x + 3x + 8 - 7 = 4x + 1$

25. $1.3x + 10 - 2.4x - 3.6 = -1.1x + 6.4$

27. $-8.2x + 6.1x + 4 - 5.3 = -2.1x - 1.3$

29. $-13x + 7 - 19x - 10 = -13x - 19x + 7 - 10$
      $= -32x - 3$

31. $4x + 3y - 8 - 2x - 6y + 4$
    $= 4x - 2x + 3y - 6y - 8 + 4$
    $= 2x - 3y - 4$

33. $5a - 3b - c + 8a - 2b - 6c$
    $= 5a + 8a - 3b - 2b - c - 6c$
    $= 13a - 5b - 7c$

35. $-7s - 2r + 3 - s - r - 8$
    $= -7s - s - 2r - r + 3 - 8$
    $= -3r - 8s - 5$

37. $8n - 12p + q + 3q - 8p - 9p$
    $= 8n - 12p - 8p - 9p + 1q + 3q$
    $= 8n - 29p + 4q$

39. $7x - 9.5x + 3.6 - 12x - 14x - 8$
    $= -28.5x - 4.4$

41. $7x - 8y + 3 + 8y - 3 - 7x$
    $= 7x - 7x - 8y + 8y + 3 - 3 = 0$

43. $5.2x - 3.4y + 6.8 - 7.2x - 9.5y$
    $= 5.2x - 7.2x - 3.4y - 9.5y + 6.8$
    $= -2x - 12.9y + 6.8$

Cumulative Review Problems

45. $\dfrac{n}{6} = \dfrac{12}{15}$
    $n \times 15 = 6 \times 12$
    $\dfrac{n \times 15}{15} = \dfrac{72}{15}$
    $n = 4.8$

47. $6n = 18$
    $\dfrac{6n}{6} = \dfrac{18}{6}$
    $n = 3$

10.2 Exercises

1. variable

3. $3x$ and x, $2y$ and $-3y$

5. $(5)(x + 7) = 5x + 5(7) = 5x + 35$

7. $4(2x + 7) = 4(2x) + 4(7) = 8x + 28$

9. $(-2)(x + y) = -2x + (-2)y = -2x - 2y$

11. $(-7)(1.5x - 3y) = (-7)(1.5x) - (-7)(3y)$
     $= -10.5x + 21y$

13. $(-3x + 7y)(-10) = (-3x)(-10) + (7y)(-10)$
     $= 30x - 70y$

15. $(2)(x + 3y - 5) = 2(x) + 2(3y) - (2)(5)$
     $= 2x + 6y - 10$

17. $(-3)(a + b + 4c) = (-3)a + (-3)b + (-3)(4c)$
     $= -3a - 3b - 12c$

19. $(2a - 5b + c)(-8)$
     $= (2a)(-8) - (5b)(-8) + (c)(-8)$
     $= -16a + 40b - 8c$

21. $(15)(-12a + 2.2b + 6.7)$
     $= (15)(-12a) + (15)(2.2b) + (15)(6.7)$
     $= -180a + 33b + 100.5$

23. $(4)(a - 3b + 5c + 7)$
     $= 4a - (4)(3b) + (4)(5c) + (4)(7)$
     $= 4a - 12b + 20c + 28$

25. $(-2)(1.3x - 8.5y - 5z + 12)$
     $= (-2)(1.3x) - (-2)(8.5y) - (-2)(5z)$
                    $+ (-2)(12)$
     $= -2.6x + 17y + 10z - 24$

27. $\dfrac{1}{2}\left(2x - 3y + 4z - \dfrac{1}{2}\right)$

$= \dfrac{1}{2}(2x) - \dfrac{1}{2}(3y) + \dfrac{1}{2}(4z) - \dfrac{1}{2}\left(\dfrac{1}{2}\right)$

$= x - \dfrac{3}{2}y + 2z - \dfrac{1}{4}$

29. $A = \dfrac{h(B + b)}{2}$

$A = \dfrac{hB + hb}{2}$

31. $(3)(2x + y) + (2)(x - y)$
$= 6x + 3y + 2x - 2y = 8x + y$

33. $4(5x - 1) + 7(x - 5) = 20x - 4 + 7x - 35$
$= 27x - 39$

35. $(-2)(a - 3b) + (3)(-a + 4b)$
$= -2a + 6b - 3a + 12b$
$= -5a + 18b$

37. $(6)(3x + 2y) - (4)(x + 7)$
$= 18x + 12y - 4x - 28$
$= 14x + 12y - 28$

39. $(1.5)(x + 2.2y) + (3)(2.2x + 1.6y)$
$= 1.5x + 3.3y + 6.6x + 4.8y = 8.1x + 8.1y$

41. $(3)(a + b + 2c) - (4)(3a - b + 2c)$
$= 3a + 3b + 6c - 12a + 4b - 8c$
$= -9a + 7b - 2c$

43.

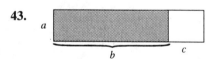

$A = ab + ac$
$A = a(b + c)$

Cumulative Review Problems

45. $C = \pi d = (3.14)(12) \approx 37.68$ in.

47. $A = \dfrac{h(b + B)}{2} = \dfrac{7(9 + 13)}{2} = 77$ cm^2

10.3 Exercises

1. equation

3. opposite

5. $y - 5 = 9$
$y + (-5) + 5 = 9 + 5$
$y = 14$

7. $x + 6 = 15$
$x + 6 + (-6) = 15 + (-6)$
$x = 9$

9. $x + 16 = -2$
$x + 16 + (-16) = -2 + (-16)$
$x = -18$

11. $x - 3 = -11$
$x + (-3) + 3 = -11 + 3$
$x = -8$

13. $4 + x = 13$
$4 + (-4) + x = 13 + (-4)$
$x = 9$

15. $-12 + x = 7$
$-12 + 12 + x = 7 + 12$
$x = 19$

17. $x + 2.4 = 5.6$
$x + 2.4 + (-2.4) = 5.6 + (-2.4)$
$x = 3.2$

19. $x - 4.6 = 5.2$
$x - 4.6 + 4.6 = 5.2 + 4.6$
$x = 9.8$

21. $x + 3.7 = -5$
$x + 3.7 + (-3.7) = -5 + (-3.7)$
$x = -8.7$

23. $x - 7.6 = -8$
$x + (-7.6) + 7.6 = -8 + 7.6$
$x = -0.4$

25. $x + \dfrac{1}{4} = \dfrac{3}{4}$

$x + \dfrac{1}{4} + \left(-\dfrac{1}{4}\right) = \dfrac{3}{4} + \left(-\dfrac{1}{4}\right)$

$x = \dfrac{2}{4} = \dfrac{1}{2}$

27. $x - \dfrac{3}{5} = \dfrac{2}{5}$

$x + \left(-\dfrac{3}{5}\right) + \dfrac{3}{5} = \dfrac{2}{5} + \dfrac{3}{5}$

$x = \dfrac{5}{5} = 1$

29. $x + \dfrac{2}{3} = -\dfrac{5}{6}$

$x + \dfrac{2}{3} + \left(-\dfrac{2}{3}\right) = -\dfrac{5}{6} + \left(-\dfrac{2}{3}\right)$

$x = -\dfrac{9}{6} = -1\dfrac{1}{2}$

31. $x - \dfrac{2}{5} = -\dfrac{3}{4}$

$x + \left(-\dfrac{2}{5}\right) + \dfrac{2}{5} = -\dfrac{3}{4} + \dfrac{2}{5}$

$x = -\dfrac{7}{20}$

33. $3x - 5 = 2x + 9$

$3x + (-2x) + (-5) + 5 = 2x + (-2x) + 9 + 5$

$x = 14$

35. $2x - 7 = x - 19$

$2x + (-x) + (-7) + 7 = x + (-x) - 19 + 7$

$x = -12$

37. $7x - 9 = 6x - 7$

$7x + (-6x) + (-9) + 9 = 6x + (-6x) - 7 + 9$

$x = 2$

39. $5x + 15 = 4x + 8$

$5x + (-4x) + 15 + (-15)$

$= 4x + (-4x) + 8 + (-15)$

$x = -7$

41. $y - \dfrac{1}{2} = 6$

$y + \left(-\dfrac{1}{2}\right) + \dfrac{1}{2} = 6 + \dfrac{1}{2}$

$y = 6\dfrac{1}{2}$

43. $z + 13 = 5$

$z + 13 + (-13) = 5 + (-13)$

$z = -8$

45. $5.9 + y = -5$

$5.9 + (-5.9) + y = -5 + (-5.9)$

$y = -10.9$

47. $2x - 1 = x + 5$

$2x + (-x) + (-1) + 1 = x + (-x) + 5 + 1$

$x = 6$

49. To solve the equation $3x = 12$, divide both sides of the equation by 3 so that x stands alone.

Cumulative Review Problems

51. $2a - 3b + 4a - b = 6a - 4b$

53. $7(2x + 3y) - 3(5x - 1)$
$= 7(2x) + 7(3y) + (-3)(5x) + (-3)(-1)$
$= 14x + 21y - 15x + 3$
$= -x + 21y + 3$

10.4 Exercises

1. Answers may vary. To maintain the balance, whatever you do to one side of the scale, you need to do the same thing to the other side of the scale.

3. $\dfrac{4}{3}$

5. $4x = 36$

$\dfrac{4x}{4} = \dfrac{36}{4}$

$x = 9$

7. $7y = -28$

$$\frac{7y}{7} = \frac{-28}{7}$$

$$y = -4$$

9. $-9x = 18$

$$\frac{-9x}{-9} = \frac{18}{-9}$$

$$x = -2$$

11. $-5x = -40$

$$\frac{-5x}{-5} = \frac{-40}{-5}$$

$$x = 8$$

13. $72 = 8n$

$$\frac{72}{8} = \frac{8n}{8}$$

$$n = 9$$

15. $27 = -3m$

$$\frac{27}{-3} = \frac{-3m}{-3}$$

$$m = -9$$

17. $1.5x = 9$

$$\frac{1.5x}{1.5} = \frac{9}{1.5}$$

$$x = 6$$

19. $0.6x = 6$

$$\frac{0.6x}{0.6} = \frac{6}{0.6}$$

$$x = 10$$

21. $5.5z = 9.9$

$$\frac{5.5z}{5.5} = \frac{9.9}{5.5}$$

$$z = 1.8$$

23. $-0.6x = 2.7$

$$\frac{-0.6x}{-0.6} = \frac{2.7}{-0.6}$$

$$x = -4.5$$

25. $\frac{2}{3}x = 6$

$$\frac{3}{2} \cdot \frac{2}{3}x = 6 \cdot \frac{3}{2}$$

$$x = 9$$

27. $\frac{2}{5}y = 4$

$$\frac{5}{2} \cdot \frac{2}{5}y = 4 \cdot \frac{5}{2}$$

$$y = 10$$

29. $\frac{3}{5}n = \frac{3}{4}$

$$\frac{5}{3} \cdot \frac{3}{5}n = \frac{3}{4} \cdot \frac{5}{3}$$

$$n = \frac{5}{4} = 1\frac{1}{4}$$

31. $\frac{3}{10}x = \frac{1}{5}$

$$\frac{10}{3} \cdot \frac{3}{10}x = \frac{1}{5} \cdot \frac{10}{3}$$

$$x = \frac{2}{3}$$

33. $\frac{1}{2}x = 1\frac{1}{3}$

$$\frac{2}{1} \cdot \frac{1}{2}x = \frac{4}{3} \cdot \frac{2}{1}$$

$$x = \frac{8}{3} = 2\frac{2}{3}$$

35. $1\frac{1}{4}z = 10$

$$\frac{4}{5} \cdot \frac{5}{4}z = \frac{10}{1} \cdot \frac{4}{5}$$

$$z = 8$$

37. First, undo the multiplication.
$4.5 \div 0.5 = 9$
Now divide.
$9 \div 0.5 = 18$
18 is the correct answer.

Cumulative Review Problems

39. $5(-2) + 3(-6) + 8 = -10 + (-18) + 8$
$= -20$

41. $6 - 3x + 5y + 7x - 12y = 4x - 7y + 6$

43. $130.90 - 26.10 = 104.8$
$$\frac{104.8}{26.10} = 4.015$$
401.5%

10.5 Exercises

1. $-4 - 8(-1) \overset{?}{=} -2 - 6(-1)$
$-4 + 8 \overset{?}{=} -2 + 6$
$4 = 4$
Yes

3. $3 - 4(2) \overset{?}{=} 5 - 3(2)$
$3 - 8 \overset{?}{=} 5 - 6$
$-5 \neq -1$
No

5. $4x + 9 = 5$
$4x + 9 + (-9) = 5 + (-9)$
$4x = -4$
$$\frac{4x}{4} = \frac{-4}{4}$$
$x = -1$

7. $12x - 30 = 6$
$12x + (-30) + 30 = 6 + 30$
$12x = 36$
$$\frac{12x}{12} = \frac{36}{12}$$
$x = 3$

9. $9x - 3 = -7$
$9x + (-3) + 3 = -7 + 3$
$9x = -4$
$$\frac{9x}{9} = \frac{-4}{9}$$
$$x = -\frac{4}{9}$$

11. $2x = 7x + 25$
$2x + (-7x) = 7x + (-7x) + 25$
$-5x = 25$
$$\frac{-5x}{-5} = \frac{25}{-5}$$
$x = -5$

13. $-9x = 3x - 10$
$-9x + (-3x) = 3x + (-3x) - 10$
$-12x = -10$
$$\frac{-12x}{-12} = \frac{-10}{-12}$$
$$x = \frac{5}{6}$$

15. $18 - 2x = 4x + 6$
$18 + (-18) + (-4x) - 2x$
$= 4x + (-4x) + 6 + (-18)$
$-6x = -12$
$$\frac{-6x}{-6} = \frac{-12}{-6}$$
$x = 2$

17. $8 + x = 3x - 6$
$8 + (-8) + x + (-3x) = 3x + (-3x) - 6 + (-8)$
$-2x = -14$
$$\frac{-2x}{-2} = \frac{-14}{-2}$$
$x = 7$

19. $7 + 3x = 6x - 8$
$7 + (-7) + 3x + (-6x) = 6x + (-6x) - 8 + (-7)$
$-3x = -15$
$$\frac{-3x}{-3} = \frac{-15}{-3}$$
$x = 5$

21. $5 + 2y = 7 + 5y$
$5 + (-5) + 2y + (-5y) = 7 + (-5) + 5y + (-5y)$
$-3y = 2$
$$\frac{-3y}{-3} = \frac{2}{-3}$$
$$y = -\frac{2}{3}$$

23. $4y + 5 = 2y - 9$
$4y + (-2y) + 5 + (-5) = 2y + (-2y) - 9 + (-5)$
$2y = -14$
$\dfrac{2y}{2} = \dfrac{-14}{2}$
$y = -7$

25. $-10 + 6y + 2 = 3y - 26$
$-8 + 6y = 3y - 26$
$-8 + 8 + 6y + (-3y) = 3y + (-3y) - 26 + 8$
$3y = -18$
$\dfrac{3y}{3} = \dfrac{-18}{3}$
$y = -6$

27. $12 + 4y - 7 = 6y - 9$
$4y + 5 = 6y - 9$
$4y + (-6y) + 5 + (-5) = 6y + (-6y) - 9 + (-5)$
$\dfrac{-2y}{-2} = \dfrac{-14}{-2}$
$y = 7$

29. $5z + 7 - 3z = 17 - 9z + 12$
$2z + 7 = -9z + 29$
$2z + 9z + 7 + (-7) = -9z + 9z + 29 + (-7)$
$\dfrac{11z}{11} = \dfrac{22}{11}$
$z = 2$

31. $9 - 3y + 12 = 7y - 15 + 2y$
$-3y + 21 = 9y - 15$
$-3y + (-9y) + 21 + (-21)$
$= 9y + (-9y) - 15 + (-21)$
$\dfrac{-12y}{-12} = \dfrac{-36}{-12}$
$y = 3$

33. $5(x + 4) = 4x + 15$
$5x + 20 = 4x + 15$
$5x + (-4x) + 20 + (-20)$
$= 4x + (-4x) + 15 + (-20)$
$x = -5$

35. $3(x + 4) + 2x = 7$
$3x + 3(4) + 2x = 7$
$5x + 12 = 7$
$5x + 12 + (-12) = 7 + (-12)$
$\dfrac{5x}{5} = \dfrac{-5}{5}$
$x = -1$

37. $9 + 6(x - 3) = 3x$
$9 + 6x - 18 = 3x$
$6x - 9 = 3x$
$6x + (-3x) + (-9) + 9 = 3x + (-3x) + 9$
$\dfrac{3x}{3} = \dfrac{9}{3}$
$x = 3$

39. $2(y + 3) = 4(y + 5) - 7$
$2y + 6 = 4y + 20 - 7$
$2y + 6 = 4y + 13$
$2y + (-4y) + 6 + (-6)$
$= 4y + (-4y) + 13 + (-6)$
$\dfrac{-2y}{-2} = \dfrac{7}{-2}$
$y = \dfrac{-7}{2} = -3\dfrac{1}{2}$

41. $3(x - 6) = 4(x - 2) - 10$
$3x - 18 = 4x - 18$
$3x + (-4x) - 18 + 18 = 4x + (-4x) - 18 + 18$
$-x = 0$
$x = 0$

43. $(3)(x + 0.2) - (2)(x + 0.25)$
$= (2)(x + 0.3) - 0.5$
$3x + 0.6 - 2x - 0.5 = 2x + 0.6 - 0.5$
$x + 0.1 = 2x + 0.1$
$x + (-2x) + 0.1 + (-0.1)$
$= 2x + (-2x) + 0.1 + (-0.1)$
$-x = 0$
$x = 0$

45. a. $7 + 3x = 6x - 8$
$7 + (-7) + 3x + (-6x)$
$= 6x + (-6x) - 8 + (-7)$
$-3x = -15$
$\dfrac{-3x}{-3} = \dfrac{-15}{-3}$
$x = 5$

b. $7 + 3x = 6x - 8$
$7 + 8 + 3x + (-3x)$
$= 6x + (-3x) + (-8) + 8$
$15 = 3x$
$\dfrac{15}{3} = \dfrac{3x}{3}$
$5 = x$

c. Method (b) is easier because the coefficient of x is positive.

Cumulative Review Problems

47. $V = \dfrac{4\pi r^3}{3} = \dfrac{4(3.14)(46)^3}{3}$

$= \dfrac{4(3.14)(97,336)}{3} = 407,513.4 \text{ cm}^3$

Putting Your Skills to Work

1. $N = PC$
$P = \dfrac{370.0}{265.3} \approx 1.395$
$N = 1.395C$

3. $N = PC$
$P = \dfrac{271.2}{265.3} \approx 1.022$
$N = 1.022C$

5. Higher, maximum
$P = \dfrac{458.4}{265.3} = 1.728$
$N = 1.728(12,680) = 21,911$
Lower, minimum
$P = \dfrac{287.7}{265.3} \approx 1.084$
$N = 1.084(12,680) = 13,745$

10.6 Exercises

1. $e = 7 + m$

3. $h = 42 + f$

5. $b = n - 107$

7. $f = s - 111$

9. $d = e - 5$

11. $l = 2w + 7$

13. $s = 3f - 2$

15. $n = 3000 + 3s$

17. $j + s = 26$

19. $ht = 500$

21. Let c = Charlie's salary
$c + 600$ = Jim's salary

23. Let j = Julie's mileage
$j + 386$ = Barbara's mileage

25. Let b = measure of angle B
$b - 46°$ = measure of angle A

27. Let w = height of Mount Whitney
$w + 4430$ = height of Mount Everest

29. Let e = Ernesto's classes
$2e$ = Wally's classes

31. Let x = width
$3x + 12$ = length

33. Let x = measure of first angle
$2x$ = measure of second angle
$x - 14$ = measure of third angle

Cumulative Review Problems

35. $-6 - (-7)(2) = -6 - (-14)$
$= -6 + 14 = 8$

37. $5 - 5 + 8 - (-4) + 2 - 15$
$= 0 + 8 + 4 + 2 + (-15)$
$= 12 + 2 + (-15) = 14 + (-15) = -1$

10.7 Exercises

1. Let x = length of shorter piece
$x + 5.5$ = length of longer piece
$x + x + 5.5 = 16$
$2x = 10.5$
$\dfrac{2x}{2} = \dfrac{10.5}{2}$
$x = 5.25$
$x + 5.5 = 10.75$
Length of shorter piece = 5.25 feet
Length of longer piece = 10.75 feet

3. Let x = distance the second day
   $x + 97$ = distance the first day
   $x + x + 97 = 560$
   $2x + 97 = 560$
   $2x + 97 + (-97) = 560 + (-97)$
   $2x = 463$
   $\dfrac{2x}{2} = \dfrac{463}{2}$
   $x = 231.5$
   $x + 97 = 328.5$
   Distance the second day = 231.5 miles
   Distance the first day = 328.5 miles

5. Let x = Jack
   $x - 140$ = Jodie
   $x + x - 140 = 670$
   $2x - 140 = 670$
   $\dfrac{2x}{2} = \dfrac{810}{2}$
   $x = 405$
   $x - 140 = 265$
   Jack can leg-press 405 lbs.
   Jodie can leg-press 265 lbs.

7. x = November
   $x + 84$ = May
   $x - 43$ = July
   $x + x + 84 + x - 43 = 398$
   $3x + 41 = 398$
   $\dfrac{3x}{3} = \dfrac{357}{3}$
   $x = 119$
   $x + 84 = 203$
   $x - 43 = 76$
   119 cars washed in November;
   203 cars washed in May;
   76 cars washed in July.

9. x = longer piece
   $x - 4.7$ = shorter piece
   $x + x - 4.7 = 12$
   $2x - 4.7 = 12$
   $\dfrac{2x}{2} = \dfrac{16.7}{2}$
   $x = 8.35$
   $x - 4.7 = 3.65$
   longer piece = 8.35 ft
   shorter piece = 3.65 ft

11. Let x = width of rectangle
    $3x - 2$ = length of rectangle
    $2(x) + 2(3x - 2) = 52$
    $2x + 6x - 4 = 52$
    $8x - 4 = 52$
    $8x + (-4) + 4 = 52 + 4$
    $8x = 56$
    $\dfrac{8x}{8} = \dfrac{56}{8}$
    $x = 7$
    $3x - 2 = 19$
    Width = 7 cm
    Length = 19 cm

13. first side = x
    second side = $2x$
    third side = $x + 12$
    $x + 2x + x + 12 = 44$
    $4x + 12 = 44$
    $\dfrac{4x}{4} = \dfrac{32}{4}$
    $x = 8$
    $2x = 16$
    $x + 12 = 20$
    first side = 8 cm
    second side = 16 cm
    third side = 20 cm

15. first side = x
    second side = $x + 20$
    third side = $x - 4$
    $x + x + 20 + x - 4 = 199$
    $3x + 16 = 199$
    $\dfrac{3x}{3} = \dfrac{183}{3}$
    $x = 61$
    $x + 20 = 81$
    $x - 4 = 77$
    first side = 61 mm
    second side = 81 mm
    third side = 57 mm

17. Let x = no. of degrees in angle A
    $3x$ = no. of degrees in angle B
    $x + 40$ = no. of degrees in angle C
    $x + 3x + x + 40 = 180$
    $5x + 40 = 180$
    $5x + 40 + (-40) = 180 + (-40)$
    $5x = 140$

$$\frac{5x}{5} = \frac{140}{5}$$
$$x = 28$$
$$3x = 84$$
$$x + 40 = 68$$
Angle $A = 28°$, Angle $B = 84°$,
Angle $C = 68°$

19. Let x = total sales
$$2000 + 0.02x = 2800$$
$$2000 + (-2000) + 0.02x = 2800 + (-2000)$$
$$0.02x = 800$$
$$\frac{0.02x}{0.02} = \frac{800}{0.02}$$
$$x = 40{,}000$$
Total sales = \$40,000

21. Let x = yearly rent.
$$100 + 0.12x = 820$$
$$100 + (-100) + 0.12x = 820 + (-100)$$
$$0.12x = 720$$
$$\frac{0.12x}{0.12} = \frac{720}{0.12}$$
$$x = 6000$$
Yearly rent = \$6000

23. $1.02p = 2{,}895{,}300$
$$p = \frac{2{,}895{,}300}{1.02}$$
$$p = 2{,}838{,}529.412$$
$$p = 2{,}838{,}500 \text{ (rounded)}$$

25. Let w = width
Length = $2w + 8.2066$
$$2w + 2(2w + 8.2066) = 2876.39$$
$$2w + 4w + 16.4132 = 2876.39$$
$$6w + 16.4132 = 2876.398$$
$$6w + 16.4132 + (-16.4132)$$
$$= 2876.39 + (-16.4132)$$
$$6w = 2859.9768$$
$$\frac{6w}{6} = \frac{2859.9768}{6}$$
$$w = 476.6628$$
$$2w + 8.2066 = 961.5322$$
Width = 476.6628 yd
Length = 961.5322 yd

27. 1st program = x
2nd program = $2x - 20$
3rd program = $17 + 3(2x - 20)$
$$x + 2x - 20 + 17 + 3(2x - 20) = 570.33$$
$$3x - 3 + 6x - 60 = 570.33$$
$$9x - 63 = 570.33$$
$$9x = 633.33$$
$$x = 70.37$$
$$2x - 20 = \$120.74$$
$$17 + 3(2x - 20) = \$379.22$$
1st program = \$70.37
2nd program = \$120.74
3rd program = \$379.22

Cumulative Review Problems

29. What is 16.5% of 350?
$$a = 0.165 \times 350 = 57.75$$

31. 38% of what number is 190?
$$0.38b = 190$$
$$\frac{0.38b}{0.38} = \frac{190}{0.38}$$
$$b = 500$$

Chapter 10 Review Problems

1. $x + 2y - 6x = -5x + 2y$

3. $a + 8 - 2a + 4 = -a + 12$

5. $5x + 2y - 7x - 9y = 5x - 7x + 2y - 9y$
$$= -2x - 7y$$

7. $5x - 9y - 12 - 6x - 3y + 18$
$$= 5x - 6x - 9y - 3y - 12 + 18$$
$$= -x - 12y + 6$$

9. $1.2a + 5.6b - 3 - 4a - 2.2b + 1$
$$= 1.2a - 4a + 5.6b - 2.2b - 3 + 1$$
$$= -2.8a + 3.4b - 2$$

11. $(-3)(5x + y) = (-3)(5x) + (-3)(y) = -15x - 3y$

13. $(2)(x - 3y + 4) = 2x - (2)(3y) + (2)(4)$
$$= 2x - 6y + 8$$

15. $(-8)(3a - 5b - c)$
$$= (-8)(3a) - (-8)(5b) - (-8)(c)$$
$$= -24a + 40b + 8c$$

17. $(5)(1.2x + 3y - 5.5)$
$= (5)(1.2x) + (5)(3y) - (5)(5.5)$
$= 6x + 15y - 27.5$

19. $(2)(x + 3y) - (4)(x - 2y)$
$= 2x + 6y - 4x + 8y$
$= -2x + 14y$

21. $(-2)(a + b) - (3)(2a + 8)$
$= -2a + (-2b) - 6a - 24$
$= -8a - 2b - 24$

23. $x - 3 = 9$
$x + (-3) + 3 = 9 + 3$
$x = 12$

25. $-8 = x - 12$
$-8 + 12 = x + (-12) + 12$
$x = 4$

27. $x + 8.3 = 20$
$x + 8.3 + (-8.3) = 20 + (-8.3)$
$x = 11.7$

29. $3.1 + x = -9$
$3.1 + (-3.1) + x = -9 + (-3.1)$
$x = -12.1$

31. $x - \dfrac{3}{4} = 2$
$x + \left(-\dfrac{3}{4}\right) = \dfrac{3}{4} = 2 + \dfrac{3}{4}$
$x = \dfrac{11}{4} = 2\dfrac{3}{4}$

33. $x + \dfrac{3}{8} = \dfrac{1}{2}$
$x + \dfrac{3}{8} + \left(-\dfrac{3}{8}\right) = \dfrac{1}{2} + \left(-\dfrac{3}{8}\right)$
$x = \dfrac{1}{8}$

35. $2x - 5 = x + 1$
$2x + (-x) + (-5) + 5 = x + (-x) + 1 + 5$
$x = 6$

37. $2x + 20 = 25 + x$
$2x + (-x) + 20 + (-20)$
$= 25 + (-20) + x + (-x)$
$x = 5$

39. $7x = 56$
$\dfrac{7x}{7} = \dfrac{56}{7}$
$x = 8$

41. $8x = -96$
$\dfrac{8x}{8} = \dfrac{-96}{8}$
$x = -12$

43. $1.5x = 9$
$\dfrac{1.5x}{1.5} = \dfrac{9}{1.5}$
$x = 6$

45. $-7.2x = 36$
$\dfrac{-7.2x}{-7.2} = \dfrac{36}{-7.2}$
$x = -5$

47. $\dfrac{3}{4}x = 6$
$\dfrac{4}{3} \cdot \dfrac{3}{4}x = \dfrac{4}{3} \cdot 6$
$x = 8$

49. $\dfrac{1}{8}x = 2\dfrac{5}{8}$
$\dfrac{8}{1} \cdot \dfrac{1}{8} = \dfrac{21}{8} \cdot \dfrac{8}{1}$
$x = 21$

51. $7x + 8 = 43$
$7 + 8 + (-8) = 43 + (-8)$
$7x = 35$
$\dfrac{7x}{7} = \dfrac{35}{7}$
$x = 5$

53. $3 - 2x = 9 - 8x$
$3 + (-3) - 2x + 8x = 9 + (-3) - 8x + 8x$
$6x = 6$
$$\frac{6x}{6} = \frac{6}{6}$$
$x = 1$

55. $10 + x = 3x - 6$
$10 + (-10) + x + (-3x)$
$= 3x + (-3x) - 6 + (-10)$
$-2x = -16$
$$\frac{-2x}{-2} = \frac{-16}{-2}$$
$x = 8$

57. $9x - 3x + 18 = 36$
$6x + 18 = 36$
$6x + 18 + (-18) = 36 + (-18)$
$6x = 18$
$$\frac{6x}{6} = \frac{18}{6}$$
$x = 3$

59. $5x - 2 = 27$
$5x + (-2) + 2 = 27 + 2$
$5x = 29$
$$\frac{5x}{5} = \frac{29}{5}$$
$$x = \frac{29}{5}$$

61. $2x - 3 - 5x = 13 + (2)(2x - 1)$
$-3x - 3 = 13 + 4x - 2$
$-3x - 3 = 11 + 4x$
$-3x + (-4x) + (-3) + 3 = 11 + 3 + 4x + (-4x)$
$-7x = 14$
$$\frac{-7x}{-7} = \frac{14}{-7}$$
$x = -2$

63. $5 + 2y + (5)(y - 3) = (6)(y + 1)$
$5 + 2y + 5y - 15 = 6y + 6$
$7y - 10 = 6y + 6$
$7y + (-6y) + (-10) + 10$
$= 6y + (-6y) + 6 + 10$
$y = 16$

65. w = weight of the truck
c = weight of the car
$w = c + 3000$

67. A = measure of angle A
B = measure of angle B
$A = 3B$

69. r = Roberto's salary
$r + 2050$ = Michael's salary

71. c = number of Connie's courses
$c - 6$ = number of Nancy's courses

73. x = length of one piece
$x + 6.5$ = length of other piece
$x + x + 6.5 = 60$
$2x + 6.5 = 60$
$2x + 6.5 + (-6.5) = 60 + (-6.5)$
$2x = 53.5$
$$\frac{2x}{2} = \frac{53.5}{2}$$
$x = 26.75$ feet
$x + 6.5 = 33.25$ feet

75. x = # customers in February
$2x$ = # customers in March
$x + 3000$ = # customers in April
$x + 2x + x + 3000 = 45,200$
$4x + 3000 = 45,200$
$4x + 3000 + (-3000) = 45,200 + (-3000)$
$4x = 42,200$
$$\frac{4x}{4} = \frac{42,200}{4}$$
$x = 10,550$ in February
$2x = 21,100$ in March
$x + 3000 = 13,550$ in April

77. w = width
$2w - 3$ = length
$p = 2w + 2l$
$72 = 2w + 2(2w - 3)$
$72 = 2w + 4w - 6$
$72 = 6w - 6$
$72 + 6 = 6w + (-6) + 6$
$78 = 6w$
$$\frac{78}{6} = \frac{6w}{6}$$
$w = 13$ in.
$l = 2w - 3 = 23$ in.

79. x = length of 1st side
$x + 7$ = length of 2nd side
$x - 4$ = length of 3rd side
p = total length
$99 = x + x + 7 + x - 4$
$99 = 3x + 3$
$99 + (-3) = 3x + 3 + (-3)$
$96 = 3x$
$\dfrac{96}{3} = \dfrac{3x}{3}$
$x = 32$ m
$x + 7 = 39$ m
$x - 4 = 28$ m

Chapter 10 Test

1. $5a - 11a = -6a$

3. $-3x + 7y - 8x - 5y = -3x - 8x + 7y - 5y$
$= -11x + 2y$

5. $7x - 8y + 2z - 9z + 8y$
$= 7x - 8y + 8y + 2z - 9z = 7x - 7z$

7. $(5)(12x - 5y) = 5(12x) + 5(-5y) = 60x - 25y$

9. $(-1.5)(3a - 2b + c - 8)$
$= (-1.5)(3a) + (-1.5)(-2b)$
$\qquad\qquad + (-1.5)(c) + (-1.5)(-8)$
$= -4.5a + 3b - 1.5c + 12$

11. $-5 - 3x = 19$
$5 + (-5) - 3x = 5 + 19$
$-3x = 24$
$\dfrac{-3x}{-3} = \dfrac{24}{-3}$
$x = -8$

13. $-5x + 9 = -4x - 6$
$-5x + 5x + 9 = -4x + 5x - 6$
$9 = x - 6$
$9 + 6 = x - 6 + 6$
$15 = x$

15. $2x - 5 + 7x = 4x - 1 + x$
$9x - 5 = 5x - 1$
$9x + (-5x) - 5 = 5x + (-5x) - 1$
$4x - 5 = -1$
$4x - 5 + 5 = -1 + 5$
$4x = 4$

$\dfrac{4x}{4} = \dfrac{4}{4}$
$x = 1$

17. $s = f + 15$

19. 1st angle: $\dfrac{1}{2}s$
2nd angle: s
3rd angle: $2s$

21. acres in Prentice farm: x
acres in Smithfield farm: $3x$
$x + 3x = 348$
$4x = 348$
$\dfrac{4x}{4} = \dfrac{348}{4}$
$x = 87$
$3x = 3(87) = 261$
Prentice farm: 87 acres;
Smithfield farm: 261 acres

23. miles on Monday: x
miles on Tuesday: $x + 56$
miles on Wednesday: $x - 14$
$x + x + 56 + x - 14 = 975$
$3x + 42 = 975$
$3x + 42 + (-42) = 975 + (-42)$
$3x = 933$
$\dfrac{3x}{3} = \dfrac{933}{3}$
$x = 311$
$x + 56 = 311 + 56 = 367$
$x - 14 = 311 - 14 = 297$
Monday: 311 mi; Tuesday: 367 mi;
Wednesday: 297 mi

Chapters 1–10 Cumulative Test

1.
$$\begin{array}{r} 456 \\ 89 \\ 123 \\ +\ 79 \\ \hline 747 \end{array}$$

3. $45{,}678{,}934 \approx 45{,}678{,}900$

5. $3\dfrac{1}{4} \times 2\dfrac{1}{2} = \dfrac{13}{4} \times \dfrac{5}{2} = \dfrac{65}{8} = 8\dfrac{1}{8}$

7.
$$\begin{array}{r} 34,007.090 \\ -\ 3,456.789 \\ \hline 30,550.301 \end{array}$$

9. What is 28.5% of $5600?
$28.5\% \times 5600 = n$
$0.285 \times 5600 = n$
$n = \$1596$

11. 345 mm = 0.345 m

13. $c = \pi d = 3.14(12) = 37.7$ yd

15. $4 - 8 + 12 - 32 - 7 = -31$

17. $3a - 5b - 12a - 6b = -9a - 11b$

19. $(-7)(-3x + y - 8)$
$= (-7)(-3x) + (-7)(y) + (-7)(-8)$
$= 21x - 7y + 56$

21. $5x - 5 = 7x - 13$
$5x + (-7x) + (-5) + 5 = 7x + (-7x) + 5 - 13$
$-2x = -8$
$\dfrac{-2x}{-2} = \dfrac{-8}{-2}$
$x = 4$

23. $x - 2 + 5x + 3 = 183 - x$
$6x + 1 = 183 - x$
$6x + x + 1 + (-1) = 183 + (-x) + x + (-1)$
$7x = 182$
$\dfrac{7x}{7} = \dfrac{182}{7}$
$x = 26$

25. p = weight of printer
$p + 322$ = weight of computer

27. x = miles driven on Thursday
$x + 48$ = miles driven on Friday
$x - 95$ = miles driven on Saturday
$x + x + 48 + x - 95 = 1081$
$3x - 47 = 1081$
$3x + (-437) + 47 = 1081 + 47$
$3x = 1128$
$\dfrac{3x}{3} = \dfrac{1128}{3}$
$x = 376$ miles on Thursday
$x + 48 = 424$ miles on Friday
$x - 95 = 281$ miles on Saturday

Practice Final Examination

1. 82,367 = Eighty-two thousand, three hundred sixty-seven

3. $19 + 23 + 16 + 45 + 70 = 173$

5.
$$\begin{array}{r} 78 \\ \times\ 54 \\ \hline 312 \\ 390 \\ \hline 4212 \end{array}$$

7.
$$\begin{array}{r} 158 \\ 7\overline{)1106} \\ \underline{7} \\ 40 \\ \underline{35} \\ 56 \\ \underline{56} \\ 0 \end{array}$$

9. $3^4 + 20 \div 4 \times 2 + 5^2 = 81 + 10 + 25 = 116$

11. $\dfrac{14}{30} = \dfrac{14 \div 2}{30 \div 2} = \dfrac{7}{15}$

13. $\dfrac{1}{10} + \dfrac{3}{4} + \dfrac{4}{5} = \dfrac{1}{10} \times \dfrac{2}{2} + \dfrac{3}{4} \times \dfrac{5}{5} + \dfrac{4}{5} \times \dfrac{4}{4}$
$= \dfrac{2}{20} + \dfrac{15}{20} + \dfrac{16}{20} = \dfrac{33}{20} = 1\dfrac{13}{20}$

15.
$$\begin{array}{cc} 4\dfrac{5}{7} & 4\dfrac{10}{14} \\ -2\dfrac{1}{2} & -2\dfrac{7}{14} \\ \hline & 2\dfrac{3}{14} \end{array}$$

17. $\dfrac{7}{9} \div \dfrac{5}{18} = \dfrac{7}{9} \times \dfrac{18}{5} = \dfrac{14}{5} = 2\dfrac{4}{5}$

19. $1\dfrac{1}{2} + 3\dfrac{1}{4} + 2\dfrac{1}{10} = \dfrac{3}{2} + \dfrac{13}{4} + \dfrac{21}{10}$
$= \dfrac{30}{20} + \dfrac{65}{20} + \dfrac{42}{20} = \dfrac{137}{20} = 6\dfrac{17}{20}$ miles

21. $\dfrac{719}{1000} = 0.719$

23. $0.315 > 0.309$

25. $9.6 + 3.82 + 1.05 + 7.3 = 21.77$

27.
$$\begin{array}{r} 1.23 \\ \times\ 0.4 \\ \hline 0.492 \end{array}$$

29.
$$\begin{array}{r} 0.8125 \\ 16\overline{)13.0000} \\ 12\ 8 \\ \hline 20 \\ 16 \\ \hline 40 \\ 32 \\ \hline 80 \\ 80 \\ \hline 0 \end{array}$$

$$\frac{13}{16} = 0.8125$$

31. $\dfrac{7000}{215} = \dfrac{7000 \div 5}{215 \div 5} = \dfrac{1400 \text{ students}}{43 \text{ faculty}}$

33. $\dfrac{5}{9} = \dfrac{n}{17}$
$5 \times 17 = 9 \times n$
$\dfrac{85}{9} = \dfrac{9 \times n}{9}$
$n \approx 9.4$

35. $\dfrac{n}{12} = \dfrac{5}{4}$
$n \times 4 = 12 \times 5$
$\dfrac{n \times 4}{4} = \dfrac{60}{4}$
$n = 15$

37. $\dfrac{2000}{3} = \dfrac{n}{5}$
$2000 \times 5 = 3 \times n$
$\dfrac{10,000}{3} = \dfrac{3 \times n}{3}$
$n = \$3333.33$

39. $\dfrac{68}{5} = \dfrac{4000}{n}$
$68 \times n = 5 \times 4000$
$\dfrac{68 \times n}{68} = \dfrac{20,000}{68}$
$n = \$294.12$ withheld

41. $0.0063 = 0.63\%$

43. $164\% = 1.64$

45. 6.3% of 4800
$6.3\% \times 4800 = n$
$0.063 \times 4800 = n$
$n = 302.4$

47. 126% of 3400
$126\% \times 3400 = n$
$1.26 \times 3400 = n$
$n = 4284$

49. $28\% \times n = 1260$
$\dfrac{0.28 \times n}{0.28} = \dfrac{1260}{0.28}$
$n = 4500$ students

51. $17 \text{ qt} \times \dfrac{1 \text{ gallon}}{4 \text{ quarts}} = 4.25 \text{ gal}$

53. $16 \text{ ft} \times \dfrac{12 \text{ in.}}{1 \text{ foot}} = 192 \text{ in.}$

55. $6.98 \text{ g} = 0.0698 \text{ kg}$

57. $12 \text{ mi} \times \dfrac{1.61 \text{ km}}{1 \text{ mi}} = 19.32 \text{ km}$

59. $126,400,000,000 = 1.264 \times 10^{11}$

61. $P = 2l + 2w = 2(6) + 2(1.2) = 12 + 2.4$
$= 14.4 \text{ m}$

63. $A = \dfrac{bh}{2} = \dfrac{6(1.8)}{2} = 5.4 \text{ sq ft}$

65. $A = \pi r^2 = 3.14 \times (6)^2 \approx 113.04 \text{ sq m}$

67. $V = \dfrac{\pi r^2 h}{3} = \dfrac{\pi (4)^2 \cdot 10}{3} \approx 167.47$ cu cm

69. Total area
= Area of square + Area of triangle
$= s^2 + \dfrac{bh}{2} = (5)^2 + \dfrac{3(5)}{2} = 32.5$ sq m

71. 8 million dollars in profit

73. 50°F

75. 600 students are between 17–22 years old.

77. Mean $= \dfrac{8 + 12 + 16 + 17 + 20 + 22}{6} \approx 15.83$

Median $= \dfrac{16 + 17}{2} = 16.5$

79. $\sqrt{123} = 11.091$

81. $-8 + (-2) + (-3) = -13$

83. $9 - 12 = 9 + (-12) = -3$

85. $2(-3)(4)(-1) = 24$

87. $(-16) \div (-2) + (-4) = 8 + (-4) = 4$

89. $7 - (-3) + 12 \div (-6) = 7 + 3 + (-2) = 8$

91. $5x - 3y - 8x - 4y = -3x - 7y$

93. $-2(x - 3y - 5) = -2x + 6y + 10$

95. $5 - 4x = -3$
$5 + (-5) - 4x = -3 + (-5)$
$\dfrac{-4x}{-4} = \dfrac{-8}{-4}$
$x = 2$

97. $7 - 2x = 10 + 4x$
$7 + (-7) - 2x + (-4x)$
$= 10 + (-7) + 4x + (-4x)$
$\dfrac{-6x}{-6} = \dfrac{3}{-6}$
$x = -\dfrac{1}{2}$

99. $x =$ # of students taking math
$x + 12 =$ # of students taking history
$2x =$ # of students taking psychology
$x + (x + 12) + 2x = 452$
$4x + 12 = 452$
$4x + 12 + (-12) = 452 + (-12)$
$4x = 440$
$x = 110$
$x + 12 = 122$
$2x = 220$
110 students are taking math.
122 students are taking history.